ABERDEEN ROYAL INFIRMARY

ABERDEEN ROYAL INFIRMARY

THE PEOPLE'S HOSPITAL OF THE NORTH-EAST

Edited by

Iain D. Levack, TD, MD, FFARCS

Department of Anaesthetics
Aberdeen Royal Infirmary
Foresterhill
Aberdeen

and

H. A. F. Dudley, CBE, ChM, FRCS(Eng.), FRCS(Ed.), FRACS

Emeritus Professor of Surgery
University of London;
Formerly Professor of Surgery
St Mary's Hospital Medical School
London

BAILLIERE TINDALL

LONDON   PHILADELPHIA   TORONTO   SYDNEY   TOKYO

Baillière Tindall

24–28 Oval Road
London NW1 7DX

The Curtis Center,
Independence Square West,
Philadelphia, PA 19106–3399, USA

55 Homer Avenue
Toronto, Ontario M8Z 4X6, Canada

Harcourt Brace Jovanovich Group
(Australia) Pty Ltd.,
30–52 Smidmore St,
Marrickville, NSW 2204, Australia

Harcourt Brace Jovanovich (Japan) Inc.,
Ichibancho Central Building,
22–1 Ichibancho
Chiyoda-ku, Tokyo 102, Japan

This book is printed on acid-free paper

ISBN 0–7020–1666–7

A catalogue record for this book is available from The British Library

Typeset by Columns Design and Production Services Ltd,
Reading, England.
Printed in Spain

Contents

I am delighted to offer my greetings and very sincere good wishes to all those associated with the Aberdeen Royal Infirmary on the 250th Anniversary of its foundation.

I have for long felt a very warm regard for the Infirmary, having accompanied The Duke of York when the Foresterhill buildings were opened by His Royal Highness in 1936.

Since then my own connection with the Infirmary has led me to have an unqualified admiration for its splendid achievements, and I hope from my heart that it will continue to flourish and prosper in the years ahead.

Elizabeth R

May 1990

Contributors

Alexander Adam	Consultant orthopaedic surgeon (1983)*
Eileen A. Bailey	Paramedical services manager
N. Bruce Bennet	Honorary consultant physician – haematology, reader in medicine
Elizabeth K. Brand	Unit physiotherapist
Graeme R.D. Catto	Honorary consultant physician – nephrology, professor of medicine and therapeutics, clinical services co-ordinator
Charles Cockburn, TD	Consultant ophthalmologist (1973)
H. Margaret Crompton, OBE	Chief area nursing officer (1981)
Ronald P. Cumming	Consultant surgeon to the Shetland Isles (1985)
Allan W. Downie	Honorary consultant physician – neurology (1987), senior lecturer in medicine
James K. Finlayson	Consultant physician (1985)
James S. Finnie	Associate specialist in venereology (1989)
Andrew V. Foote	Consultant cardiothoracic surgeon (1992)
Robert J.A. Fraser	Consultant neurosurgeon (1982)
Samuel C. Frazer	Professor of chemical pathology (1983)
William R. Gauld, TD	Consultant physician (1977)
W.N. Bruce George	Trew, Dunn Architects (1984)
Lewis A. Gillanders	Consultant radiologist (1988), clinical professor of radiology
F.J. Sambrook Gowar, VRD	Consultant thoracic surgeon (1975)
W.D. Buff Hardie	Secretary to Grampian Health Board (1983)
Margaret I.W. Hay (née Thomson)	Matron to Morningfield Hospital and Glenburn Wing (resigned 1969). Formerly sister in neurosurgery
George Innes	Reader in community medicine
Peter F. Jones	Consultant surgeon (1985), clinical professor of surgery
Charles W. King	General administrator to Grampian Health Board (1984)
Zygmunt H. Krukowski	Consultant surgeon
Joseph S. Legge	Consultant physician in thoracic medicine
H. Brodie M. Lewis	Director Aberdeen and NE Scotland Blood Transfusion Service (1983)
John McConachie	General medical practitioner Lossiemouth (1981)
Wilma I. MacPherson	Director of nursing services (resigned 1991)
John R. Mallard	Professor of bio-medical physics and bio-engineering (1992)
Norman A. Matheson	Consultant surgeon (1992)

W. Malcolm Millar, CBE	Honorary consultant psychiatrist (1977), professor of mental health
George P. Milne	Consultant obstetrician and gynaecologist (1976)
J. Kenneth W. Morrice	Consultant psychiatrist (1985)
Ian F.K. Muir, MBE, VRD	Consultant plastic surgeon (1986)
J. Nelson Norman	Honorary consultant surgeon, reader in surgery (resigned 1976), professor of environmental and offshore medicine, medical director, The Robert Gordon Institute of Technology
James F. Philip	Consultant surgeon (1976), professor of clinical oncology
Ian A. Porter	Consultant bacteriologist (1982)
David M. Proctor, OBE, CStJ, DL	Consultant in accident and emergency (1981)
Alfred W. Raffan, TD	Consultant anaesthetist (1977)
Alexander M. Rennie, TD	Consultant orthopaedic surgeon (1976), clinical professor of orthopaedic surgery
Avril Scott	Speech and language therapy manager
Geoffrey B. Scott	Senior lecturer in pathology
David S. Short	Consultant physician (1983), clinical professor of medicine – cardiology
George Smith, MBE	Honorary consultant surgeon (1982), Regius professor of surgery
Kenneth B. Stewart	Chief administrative pharmaceutical officer (1981)
John Steyn, CStJ	Consultant surgeon – urology
David Suttar	Senior social worker
Garden H. Swapp	Consultant obstetrician and gynaecologist
Kenneth A. Webster	Senior nursing tutor
Charles D. Weir, MC	Consultant otolaryngologist (1977)
Roy D. Weir, OBE	Professor of community medicine (1991)
Michael J. Williams	Consultant physician
Hazel A. Witte (née Coubrough)	Adviser in dietetics

* denotes year of retiral.

Introduction

To construct a history of a great institution which has been in existence for 250 years is to attempt to weave together many strands of human activity – ambitions for the care of the sick, the resources and state of technology available to those with such aims, changing patterns of society and the lives of individuals whose contributions must never be underestimated. Though history is a seamless bale of cloth coming continuously off the loom of life, inevitably any historical garment must be stylized by the tailor of the day. As the garment makers we have had to reach towards an account which is both readable and, we hope, largely accurate and to choose time periods which we believe contain significant and easily interpretable changes. To do this it has been necessary to blend our contributors' manuscripts into what we see as a coherent whole.

The Royal Infirmary was initially the outcome of charitable intent but its 250 years have embraced large changes in both the content and the delivery of medical care as well as in our society, changes marked both by watersheds in the application of knowledge to treatment and cataclysmic events such as the World Wars. Though future historians will inevitably place these in a different perspective, we see the Infirmary as straddling four periods. First, its early years from 1739 to approximately 1800 during which the old hospice ('spital' in local dialect) concept – in the sense of care and shelter, albeit with the aim of returning inmates to a useful life in the community – was dominant. Second, the 19th century and the period before World War I in the 20th – roughly the Victorian–Edwardian era – during which there were two notable watersheds: the development of professional nursing as an outcome of the Crimean war; and the introduction of antisepsis–asepsis after 1869. Also at this time there were the first real signs of the emergence of medical specialities as we now know them. Third, the years between the two World Wars when we see that last trend gaining momentum against a background of social change which would ultimately result in the National Health Service (NHS). Fourth, from the end of World War II to the present day – a time of both the inception of the NHS and many 'revolutions' in medical care. It is the last about which we have the best documentary evidence supplemented by the memories and writings of those still alive. We have therefore organized the book loosely around these periods though the complexity of the woof and warp of history makes this impossible to do in a truly rigorous or tidy way.

Four other matters. We are enduringly grateful to our contributors. We have tried to acknowledge their contributions within the final text and if anyone sees phrases that he or she is certain they wrote but have not been attributed we hope we shall be forgiven. Secondly, though we concur in part with Carlyle's view that history is 'but the lives of great men' (and were he writing today he would have also to say 'women'), we have, for a considerable number of the individuals mentioned in this account, felt that the flow of description should not be interrupted by too much biographical detail. In consequence we have assigned the biographies of most individuals to notes which we believe will be of interest to all and the starting point for some who wish to pursue in more detail the careers of those Aberdonians, other North-Easterners and Sassenachs who have contributed to the Aberdeen Royal Infirmary as we know it today. For obvious reasons we have limited entries to people who, as we write, are no longer with us. Doubtless we have not included some that our critics would deem important. If so we apologise but we have worked chiefly from the names included in the manuscripts of our contributors.

Thirdly, throughout the text there are frequent references to costs. As all who live in the 1990s know, the vagaries of economics make comparison from one time to another extremely difficult though the trend always seems to be to reduce the 'real' value of what one holds. Our expert adviser tells us that the period from 1800 to 1913 was in fact one of deflation so that the value of the pound, initially at about £175 in present day terms fell to about £106. Between the beginning of World War I and 1965 inflation dominated and by the second date £100 had become £556.

Fourthly, though it will appear unnecessary to local readers, we have given in the chapter notes for the benefit of those whose inheritance does not include a knowledge of the Scots vernacular, brief definitions of some words. These are taken from *The Concise Scots Dictionary* (Aberdeen University Press, 1985) and *The Scots Thesaurus* (Aberdeen University Press, 1990). The colophons which appear on pages ii and 54 are the armorial bearings of the Corporation of the Royal Infirmary and Lunatic Asylum of Aberdeen 1887; the current arms of Aberdeen Royal Infirmary 1988 and the nurses' badge of Grampian Foresterhill College.

Lastly it is both a duty and a pleasure to acknowledge the gracious note from Her Majesty the Queen Mother which forms a front paper to this account. Her Majesty has, amongst her many other activities, played a notable part in the encouragement of hospitals throughout the United Kingdom. On behalf of the Medico-Chirurgical Society, the patients and past and present staff of the Royal Infirmary we would wish her to know that her greetings and good wishes are both appreciated and reciprocated.

Acknowledgements

The initiative for this history came from the Aberdeen Medico-Chirurgical Society during its bicentennial year when the then President James Kyle, CBE suggested that the Society should promote a definitive history of Aberdeen Royal Infirmary. The proposal was unanimously approved and publication during the 250th anniversary year of the Hospital was deemed appropriate. Those who have contributed manuscripts (and often also additional information) are listed on pp. ix and x. Many others – too numerous to acknowledge individually – have helped us with information and advice, though the onus for checking on and deciding whether or not to include material remains with the editors. We thank Mr Alexander Adam, Librarian, Aberdeen Medico-Chirurgical Society; Miss Isabella Deans and staff, Local Studies, Aberdeen Central Library; Mr Keith Duguid and staff, Medical Illustration, University of Aberdeen; Captain Colin A. Farquharson, Lord Lieutenant of Aberdeenshire; Dr W.R. Gauld, Editor, *Aberdeen Postgraduate Medical Bulletin*; Mr A.A. Gunn, Librarian, Royal College of Surgeons of Edinburgh and his staff; Emeritus Professor Malcolm MacLeod; Dr N.C. Sharp of Keith; two secretaries: Mrs Pamela Smith, Aberdeen Medico-Chirurgical Society and Mrs Kathleen Middleton, Ward 37, Aberdeen Royal Infirmary; the Staff, Special Collections, University of Aberdeen; Miss Fiona Watson, Archivist, Grampian Health Board; Dr Marion White, Aberdeen Royal Infirmary. We are indebted to Mr Philip Ziegler and Harper Collins Publishers for permission to quote an extract from his *King Edward the VIII – the Official Biography*. For permission to reproduce illustrations, we acknowledge the following: Aberdeen City Council for Plates 6 and 15; Aberdeen Journals for Plates 1, 3, 4, 16, 18, 19, 22, 23, 40, 41, 42, 43, 48, 49, 51; Aberdeen University Library for Plates 10 and 34; the *British Journal of Anaesthesia* for Plate 47; the *British Journal of Surgery* Society for Plate 24; Camera Press Ltd. London for the official portrait of Her Majesty the Queen Mother; The George Trew and Dunn Partnership for Plates 2, 21 and 25; Parke Davis Medical for Plate 20; Mrs Violet Simpson for Plate 5; Dr F.W. Smith for Plate 50; and SmithKline Beecham for Plate 54.

Generous supporters of our appeal for financial support were: Aberdeen City Council; Bank of Scotland; Boots Pharmaceuticals UK Ltd; British Petroleum; Hall and Tawse Scotland Ltd; *St John Hospital* (whose help was particularly munificent); Grampian Health Board; Grampian Television; Imperial Chemical Industries; Medical and Dental Defence Union of Scotland; Offshore Medical Support; Oil Industry Community Fund; Ohmeda; The Robert Gordon Institute of Technology; Royal Bank of Scotland; and the University of Aberdeen.

Finally we owe a debt of gratitude first to Aberdeen University Press for help in the early stages of preparation for publication and second to Mr Sean Duggan, Editor-in-Chief of Baillière Tindall who, without hesitation, took on the publication of this book at short notice. His staff expedited their publishing routines with care and consideration.

IDL
HAFD

Aberdeen Royal Infirmary

Vantaged now above the steepled town,
windowed towards the Grampians and the sea,
its granite buildings range the fields and woods
that once lay undisturbed on Stockethill.

For Matthew Hay possessed a clear ideal
that grouped the city's hospitals as one,
and found a site on Foresterhill's broad acres
to make the dream reality, the plan fulfilled.

Town and University, Lords and Laity,
gave their support, each 'according to his means'.
Thus the New Infirmary was founded
and modern buildings rose against the sky.

From Woolmanhill Foresterhill was born,
from Workhouse and Bedlam, salves and nostrums,
to anaesthetics, antibiotics, scans and lasers-
challenging the Captains of the Men of death.

So let us praise our famous men –
Elphinstone, Cumyne, Leslie and Gregory,
Chalmers, Lewis, McGrigor and Ogston –
'for their work continueth greater than their knowing'.

Ken Morrice

1

Homage to a Hospital

Norman Matheson writes: The Aberdeen Royal Infirmary (ARI) has served the North-East for all of 250 years. In contrast, the contributors and editors of this book are mere birds of passage. Still, thirty odd years, from fledgling to tattered feathers in the *milieu intérieur* is long enough to absorb the essence of the place and to recognize its maternal influence on a professional lifetime. The sense of community which it has for me and the pride and security in being part of it are of course personal emotions and they are contemporary but with a backward-looking glance at the recent past. Different feelings would be expressed by those who passed through long ago and by those who will come this way in the future. Long enough too to pay a tribute of affection.

What is it that breathes life into these blocks of grey granite? A hospital has an individuality, an ambience, an atmosphere, a personality even, subject with time to subtle or dramatic change, mostly regretted or lamented, difficult to capture or encapsulate and variously experienced. Can the same be said of office blocks, supermarkets or warehouses? Schools? – definitely yes, because they bustle with youth and contain, or used to do, colourful and intelligent personalities. Churches have atmosphere but hospitals pulsate. Hospitals are emotionally charged with the drama of living, surviving, suffering and dying. At least we regard it as a drama and see it in terms of success and failure, ecstasy and agony, despite the complete indifference of nature. A hospital vibrates with the emotions of its temporary inhabitants, patients and staff, both with heightened perception, as well as with the memories of those gone before.

Architecture sets a sense of place. Within the jargon coined by management consultants to clothe insubstantial flesh there is one neologism that falls softly on the ear and brings with it a breath of fresh air: a 'greenfield site'. It sounds good even though the greenfield is presently to be devoured by earthmovers.

When I first set foot in it, the ARI was on a greenfield site *par excellence*: wide acres of uncluttered lawn stretched in unlimited vistas to north, south and west. And to the east – on stepping out of the staff entrance – there lay the sea in the distance. The view is now blocked by storeys of concrete which link the solid granite of the ARI to the architectural confectionery of the medical school. What did it mean at the end of the day to see the distant, sparkling sea? It is a question of aesthetics and to many it means little or nothing.

Plate 1 A Nightingale ward at Foresterhill, circa 1960. 'The sun streams in' and there are flowers on the table. Privacy is however only possible by the use of screens (see right background).

There were other joys and they are still there though those closeted in the unimaginatively named Phase I and II know them not. Take a trip on a sunny afternoon to the old surgical block and walk into one of the Nightingale wards (Plate 1). What will strike you first is sunlight streaming in from all aspects. These wards sparkle with light. It lifted one's spirits each sunny day and surely it had the same effect on patients – the sea can also be seen! If we could step back 30 years and visit what was ward 9 female you would be even more amazed – by flowers. Flowers in profusion, the fruition of the skill and dedication of one remarkable ward sister.

The Nightingale ward had other attractions apart from sunlight and spaciousness. The patients were in the swim together, some of them up to their eyes, a camaraderie developed, mobile patients sat and talked to non-mobile, errands were run, food trolleys pushed, bread buttered, tea poured and, in adversity, new friendships struck. The first bed nearest the door was a precarious place to be in terms of outcome, but it was a comfort for the incumbent to be aware of the constantly passing stream of traffic and to know that a raised hand would instantly summon aid in the form of a nearby nurse or patient to the bedside. The corridors also had their inbuilt attractions. The high windowsills could have been purpose designed for the exchange of confidences. Conveniently placed at elbow level, a windowsill would accommodate two earnest individuals in conversation with an intimacy that does not exist elsewhere. Where do doctors talk to each other and consult their diaries in this way nowadays? Or are there no trysts to be made, sins to be confessed and subterfuges to be hatched? The long

Plate 2 Post-war architecture. South aspect of Phase I, 1966. The 1936 buildings peep over the far aspect.

table outside the porters' office in the main entrance concourse was installed as a focal point, a meeting place for consultants – one of Sandy Michie's few less realistic and unrealized ideas; I have never met another consultant at that table.

The architecture of the more recent additions to ARI is pleasing enough from the exterior although it does not compare with granite, apart from the curious excrescences protruding from the second floor of Phase I (Plate 2). Within, however, there is or was an unremitting sense of grey drabness; and the patients cannot see out of the windows. Still, better a window one cannot see out of than no windows at all. Work areas without windows are now known to be an abomination. You get used to this deprivation in the operating theatres when fully absorbed but it was a pleasure to be aware from time to time of filtered sunlight or falling snow and in some theatres one could even open a window and get a waft of fresh air – that abomination of bacteriologists. The noise in the new theatres is not that of the sough of a November wind or rain on glass but a cacophony of warning devices emitting different refrains according to various presumed hazards – a new and intrusive *musique anaesthésique*. Granted, in terms of patient care there has been progress, enormous and remarkable progress. The first bed in the Nightingale ward, the best we had for relatively low-tech surgery, is no comparison with the dedicated skills of the intensive care unit. How shortsighted it was for some surgeons to oppose this development for years. If I were sick enough I know where I'd rather be though I'd miss the sunlight and the flowers.

Although architecture is an important aspect of it, the ambience of a hospital and that which lives in the memory is largely influenced by the personalities who inhabit it now and in the past. In the past they seemed larger than life and definitely larger than nowadays, but this may depend on the sensibilities of impressionable youth. Perhaps there are still Sir Lancelot Spratt look-alikes stalking the wards and apeing the behaviour of bygone years. Some of these individuals were tyrants (is tyranny always an expression of inadequacy?) and they instilled unjustified terror. They were paid enormous deference. There is something to be said for the use of the word 'Sir' long since deleted from nursing manuals and it was not a wholly distasteful mark of respect for occupants to rise when a consultant came into a staff room, but to be helped don hat (black Homburg usually) and Crombie coat, to be shepherded to the lift and even to one's Bentley by an entourage of sheepish, sycophantic, white-coated in-dividuals from senior registrar down went beyond reason and dignity. There was more time in those days and less self expression amongst the young.

Physicians seemed to be less colourful and subject to less extreme behaviour than surgeons although, by all accounts, A.G. Anderson set an enviable pattern never likely to be followed (Plate 3).

In my lifetime one individual stood out. He had few acolytes and to be approved of was privilege enough to induce the adoration of a puppy. I deny, however, that this is the reason I remember this particular physician with a spreading smile. Was it his visage, his open vilification of certain colleagues, his remarkable coarseness and profanity at times, or the beauty, and I don't exaggerate, of his invective that made him lovable? Shall I name him? Perhaps not, those who knew him will recognize him and those who did not will be undiminished. To hear him, two or more pink gins to the good, round upon the ill-prepared in softly spoken shards of steel at evening Clinico-Pathological Conferences was a delight, perverse perhaps, but keenly anticipated and long savoured. How I remember him with affection and regard.

But there were others who set the character of this place in those simpler days. Petrie, for example, head porter, who stood frock-coated like a Colossus at the main entrance, then at the east end of the building. Woe betide any individual who presumed to set foot in the hospital unauthorized, on the pretext perhaps of visiting a patient outwith the regulation half hour. That is except for those whose origins were in upper Banffshire for whom access was freely granted, and why should these hardy souls not have had the benefit of this small perk?

The hospital appeared to be run, and I think it was, by two individuals, the Medical Superintendent in the form of Sandy Michie aided by the omniscient Bella Thain in the General Office. 'Leave that to me, boy' was the usual response to some administrative problem presented after a knock on Sandy Michie's door. Advice was given and action taken without the need even to make an appointment let alone to refer the matter to an endless series of different

Plate 3 The traditional Christmas dinner. A.G. Anderson fulfils his only surgical role carving the Christmas turkey. The photograph was taken just after the end of World War II; the stack of at least 20 plates testifies to a full ward.

committees in the pretence of democracy. Sandy Michie was not confined to his office. He made forays into the wards and sometimes even risked a diagnosis. Those brilliant diagnostic coups from a distance were usually of some dire infectious disease that had defied elucidation by mere everyday clinicians. At least it may have been so, according to Sandy that is, on one frequently recounted occasion.

La recherche du temps perdu, is the sweet musing symptomatic of the moist and often jaundiced eye of advancing years. Things will never be the same again! Of course not, we move on to new and different pastures that in some ways sustain the constancy of the past and in others represent change and occasionally progress.

One large difference in the hospital over the last 20 years or so, which in some ways is progress and in others not, is its vast increase in size. It does make sense to centralize all the acute services if possible, but the blood supply is attenuated and the organization is undergoing ischaemic necrosis at its centre. And who are the multitude who now traverse the corridors? Time was when one strolled along the main corridor and knew everyone one met – pleasantries were exchanged and all was well in the world. Now I know them not and they know me not.

There are some though whose presence ensures that the earthy flavour of the

North-East persists undiluted. I refer to the porters, amongst whom there are some notable individuals and one in particular whose broad Buchan tongue was recently audible in the corridors and with more immediate pleasure in the lifts. Chairbound patients were engaged in a continual homely dialogue encompassing the rainfall or lack of it, the progress of the tattie crop, the state of the times and were offered homespun philosophy. It must have been a comfort to patients to find themselves shepherded about the hospital in such sturdy, voluble and compassionate hands, and it was fun to eavesdrop.

And the cleaners or whatever their new title is now. We used to have almost permanent fixtures in the form of ward-maids who were an important link in the staffing chain. They also looked after the doctors in the days when doctors were thought to be an invaluable asset to a hospital and not to be regarded at best with suspicion and at worst as a bunch of recalcitrant renegades to be contained at all costs. A cup of coffee or tea was there for the asking and none of this nonsense of everyone going through the motions of 'washing' their own cup. If George Gordon Bruce had been asked to wash his cup he would have been at immediate risk of apoplexy; and the fate of those making the suggestion hardly bears contemplation. Is there any other workplace to match the ARI nowadays for the low standard of hygiene of the cups used by staff? At times a plate of food might be rescued from the remains of the patients' trolley, otherwise destined for the pigs' swill. Not scrounged without principle but a sensible occasional convenience for those who were busy and part of goodwill and right thinking within a unit. These days are gone, but now at 5.00 p.m. and other times the lifts see an influx, a bevy of green-clad women, young and not so young, with a camaraderie of their own, laughing and chattering in the Aberdeen patois. They are no doubt disadvantaged in social terms or they would not be there but together their spirit transcends adversity. They are bright, cheery and colourful – I salute them. And a tribute also to the ward secretaries, these grossly underpaid and undervalued young women who underpin the framework of day to day efficiency. They appear to be keeping their noses above the surface of a deluge of requests from on high for data, data and more data. Will data solve the ills of the NHS?

But if salutes are to be flourished and tributes paid the constancy of a hospital's being are the patients. The ARI is for them, it is their hospital and I think most of them know it with a hint of concealed pride. They deserve that their faith be justified and by and large it is. They have not noticeably changed. There are exceptions of course but as a whole they are worthy, brave, uncomplaining, unquestioning and accepting of their fate. They 'dree their weird',[1] are grateful for small mercies and implicit in their trust. Are we always sufficiently aware of the privilege it is to serve them without the intrusion of financial consideration?

The last five years have seen a transformation of the ARI in terms of visual impact, attributable to what some may see as the frivolity of art (Plate 4). The usual questions expected from the archetypal Aberdonian in the face of art are, 'Fit's it supposed to be then?'[2] and 'Foo muckle did it cost?'[3] and I suppose these questions have been put in front of many of the works displayed.

Plate 4 Lower entrance hall, Phase I, 1987. A part of the large art collection referred
to on p. 6 is on display.

Art is a proper part of architecture long neglected in this country in
comparison with more enlightened lands where it is a requirement to set aside a
percentage of the total budget of new public buildings for contemporary art.
Apart from all the other factors that contribute to ambience, art also gives a sense
of place and community. A hospital, however, should never aspire to being an
art gallery. Did I hear someone say, 'you could have fooled me'. No, definitely
not: in a gallery, morose and threatening, even downright ugly works may be
right and proper but hospital art should be uplifting. I agree, there are one or
two early acquired works on display that might fit better in the first category
than the second but the overall effect has surely been stunning, especially of the
commissioned pieces in the chapel, the linear accelerator room and the main link
corridor. Some modern Scottish art may at first sight be abstruse and puzzling
but not meaningless. Public art, apart from beautifying, should perhaps also
have an instructive, educational or enlightening role; no-one can tell me that the
effect would have been better with an unremitting series of pretty landscapes
with highland cattle tentatively testing the water. This is a new and exciting
injection of culture and interest into this brave place and one that we are told by
visiting professionals is unique in terms of quality. Surely even those whose eye
is not yet in tune with what is on show would not deny that there has been a
great improvement in the look of the corridors. Or have they forgotten the
banded paintwork in the regulation colours of cream, brown and green?

When it comes to sculpture, a veil (or should it be a smokescreen?) should perhaps be drawn across the first faltering efforts of the art project. Sculpture is so much more emotive than other forms of visual art and the first large piece acquired at the behest of the Scottish Arts Council was the butt of much misunderstanding and ridicule. There were those who were not sorry when recurrent vandalism culminated in a conflagration and the work was, in effect, cremated. Like all endings this was not necessarily to be lamented – in a way it was quite fitting. Arsonists will be up against sterner stuff in the future however – several tonnes of sculpted granite will be more durable and I think more in sympathy with the environment of the hospital. When it comes to the 300th anniversary this place, if it still stands, should be a veritable Gulbenkian museum.

What of the future? Now we genuflect (some lower than others) before 'managerial evangelism' and listen to the litany, or at least are aware of the chanting in the background: audit, options appraisal, resource management, plan for action, change agents, opting out, independent trusts, GP budgets. Will all the data spewed out by computers be meaningful, reliable, capable of interpretation and the basis of improved patient care? If so I shall be astonished and shall have to acknowledge that human nature is not what I thought it was. And will this new cult, the god of which is money, or the lack of it, bring the heathens to the altar? Or will it stifle those who work selflessly with dedication, compassion, originality and common sense? Crusades are for crusaders. Others remain agnostic or frankly atheistic, especially when the creed of the high priests is political rather than humanitarian.

Twenty years from now, a hundred years from now, the ARI will still contain a microcosm of humanity, a *mélange* of mediocrity and excellence but with a unique recurrent influx of highly intelligent, eager and untarnished youngsters. Will the necessary ingredients for their professional fulfillment and for medical progress still be there, and will there still be a detectable upward-seeking spiral of endeavour fuelled as before by unquenched idealism and academic purpose rather than greed? Or have we known a golden age?

2

Origins

June 14th 1742. Mistress Strachan intimating to the Directors that she was ready to enter upon her charge in the Infirmary, they appointed Mister David Cuthbert their cashier to put the said Mrs Strachan into possession of the house this day . . . . and to give her what money she wanted for subsistence.[1]

So opened the Infirmary. It was part of the Voluntary Hospital movement which began in the early years of the 18th century; after the Reformation the care of the sick poor had passed out of the hands of the Church and it had become evident that it was seriously inadequate. Examples in England, led the College of Physicians in Edinburgh in 1725 to propose that hospitals be established and funds were raised by public subscription. The Edinburgh Infirmary was opened in 1729 and in its first year 35 patients were admitted, including one each from Caithness, Peterhead and the Isle of Mull.[2]

In 1733, the Town's Hospital was opened in Glasgow. Strictly speaking this was not a hospital or infirmary in the modern sense but a workhouse. The establishment of these institutions did not go unnoticed by the Town Council and the citizens of Aberdeen, and they proceeded to make plans for a workhouse and infirmary in the city, this leading to the foundation of Aberdeen Infirmary, the second voluntary hospital in Scotland. On 7 February 1739 the following announcement was made:

The Magistrates and Town Council of Aberdeen, taking to their consideration the great numbers of idle people, strolling beggars and vagabonds, who infest the Burgh and Neighbourhood, with the many poor Residents in this place, who, by reason of old age and poverty are reduced to the greatest extremity of hunger and cold, many of them being necessitate to beg from door to door . . .

The statement goes on to say that a Public House or Infirmary has been found 'in all places' to be the most effective remedy for this problem, and also proposes to provide for the working poor, when they are sick or old, and for those deprived of their reason. It was proposed to buy a large ruinous building on the north side of Castle Street, near to the Town House and to establish in it a workhouse. On this site it was also intended to erect an infirmary for the sick poor 'especially those who were honest and laborious, but rendered unfit by sickness' with a branch for the care of the insane.[1]

On 30 May 1739, the Town Council enacted rules for the appointment of directors for the workhouse and infirmary providing an impetus for its estabishment in a manner that was to be repeated in the development of Foresterhill (see p.45). Each of the four main Societies of the Town (the Town Council, the 'Gild' Court, the Church Session, and the Convener Court of the Trades), were to elect four directors with the Provost as Chairman, and one director from the physicians and surgeons. These directors were to obtain contributions and to be responsible for the buildings. They were duly elected on 18 June. At their first general meeting it is minuted:

> June 25th, In the year of our Lord seventeen hundred and thirty-nine, the Magistrates and principal inhabitants of Aberdeen, taking under their consideration the miserable circumstances that fellow creatures are reduced to by Bodily Distempers and that by want of proper care by Physicians they are rendered altogether useless and consequently troublesome to Society, and they being informed that, to remedy this great evil, Infirmaries have latterly been erected in the cities of Edinburgh and Glasgow by public contributions from the inhabitants . . . into which all proper objects are received and regularly attended by Physicians. Upon the 25th day of June the Magistrates called to the Town House the principal persons belonging to the different Socities (*sic*) within the Burgh and represented to them that having had under their deliberation the Erection of an Infirmary within this place, but having no public funds which can be applied to said purpose, after the example of other towns, they proposed contributions to be raised from all the inhabitants. . . . All which being considered by said General Meeting they unanimously agreed to the overture made by the Magistrates, approved what the Council had done, and immediately each person subscribed on a roll of parchment provided for the purpose the quota he intended to pay and proposed that so many of their number should join the four Baillies and go from house to house in town, and obtain subscriptions for this charitable and good undertaking, and also that each should write to their friends and acquaintances in *all* places, soliciting their contributions and assistance.[1]

Finally the meeting decided that William Chrystal, Wright,[3] late Convener of Trades and 'ane ingenious man' should go to Edinburgh and Glasgow to inspect the Infirmaries there before drawing up a suitable plan for Aberdeen.

A second general meeting was held on 30 November 1739 when the 'different Society's within the town' agreed that the Infirmary should be built on the 'Woman-hill', to the west side of the town because of 'the goodness of the air in that place' (see also p.14). The workhouse was to be on the original site near the Tolbooth. From this time the two institutions developed separately though the Infirmary was bound to accept sick patients from the workhouse when required. At the same meeting William Chrystal submitted his plan for a building, which was approved, the cost to be £480.[4]

The Magistrates and workmen visited the site on 27 December and marked out the ground and on 1 January 1740, 'the Magistrates, Town Council, many of the principal inhabitants, and the entire Freemasons of the town marched in procession up the Woolmanhill to watch the laying of the foundation stone'.[1] On 2 May 1741 it was noted that 'the Infirmary house is finished' (Plate 5) and that the funds appropriate for expenditure on the Infirmary were:

ABERDEEN INFIRMARY 1749.

Plate 5 An interpretation of the likely appearance of the first Infirmary Building by Jackson Simpson (1893–1963). He was a popular Aberdeen watercolourist and was also known for his etchings.

The Bedlam Fund, after deductions as per act of the Council	£307. 6.8 Scots
From Master of Guild Brethren's Hospital the Sick Fund, per act of Council	£129.13.4 Scots
From the Trustees of Anderson's Mortification	£300.00.0 Scots
	£737.—.– Scots

The income from this small sum was insufficient to meet the cost of fitting up the Infirmary and its running expenses and, over succeeding years, many appeals were launched to attract contributions (at 1 October 1742, the sum raised by the original appeal in 1739 totalled £510.9s.71/3d. sterling sufficient to pay for the building but insufficient to pay for the expense of fitting it up[5]).

The funds allocated by the Town Council had their origin in pre-existing 'hospitals' in Aberdeen. These were originally guest houses and were intended for the poor and the aged and not primarily for the treatment of sick persons; the Guild Brethren's Hospital, also known as the Hospital of St Thomas, came under the control of the Town Council at the Reformation. In 1609 the tradesmen were excluded from it because they had not contributed to its upkeep, and in 1633 Dr Guild (a doctor of theology) established the Trades Hospital from property of the Holy Trinity Friars. It was supported by donations from the Trades. In addition there was a leper hospital, the income of which, when leprosy died out, came to be used for the benefit of the insane. Its money came into the possession of the Town Council, and was given to the Infirmary which was to care for the insane, in addition to its function of treating the curable sick poor. The Guild Brethren's Hospital continued until 1771 and the Trades Hospital until 1800, when their medical function was taken over by the Infirmary.[6] On 24 October 1741 Provost Robertson suggested to the directors 'that the doors of the Infirmary should be thrown open to the poor throughout the country' instead of, as originally intended, reserving its benefits for the inhabitants of the city alone; and, at a meeting two days later it was resolved that the Infirmary 'should be as extensive and universally useful as possible, but more particularly, that the same shall be extended to the Counties of Aberdeen, Kincardine, and Banff'.[7]

As the quotation which begins the chapter tells us, Mrs Isobel Strachan, who had been appointed 'Mistress of the House' the previous month, took possession of her charge on the 14 June 1742. On 24 August it was noted that Dr James Gordon of Pitlurg and Straloch (Professor of Medicine at Marischal College)[8] was willing to act as physician and surgeon 'as a tryal' at a fee of 10 guineas plus the cost of drugs 'only the drugs are to be charged at the lowest price at sight of the physicians in the town'. He was unanimously appointed and instructed to keep a book of records of the patients. These books have been preserved, for the most part, though some records up to 1 April 1743 are missing. The first entry in the 'Day Book of Doctor James Gordon, Aberdeen 1743' was made on that date. Initially the entries were very detailed and entered daily but, as the number of patients increased, they became more concise and less frequent, though still complete. It is on record that Gordon returned his fee for the good of the house and went round the hospital at one o'clock daily with the students.

On the same day (24 August 1742) four patients were 'recommended as objects' for the Infirmary, three from Aberdeen and one from the Mearns.[9] It was agreed that they be admitted provided that Gordon found them capable of cure. They are recorded on 2 November 1742 as follows:

> William Davidson, from the workhouse, with a broken arm, cured and to return to the workhouse. Alexander Davidson, 'universal rheumatic pains and a palsie of one of his limbs', judged incurable and 'not a proper object for the Infirmary'. He was transferred to the workhouse. Jean Craig and William Thomson, both 'on a way to cure'.[10]

The first directors or managers of the Infirmary, nine in number, were appointed by the Town Council on 15 October 1742 and held their first meeting on 2 November. William Chalmers, Provost in 1739 when the Infirmary was planned (Plate 6), headed the list, along with Alexander Robertson Provost in 1740–41. The others were: Alexander Rose, physician; Charles Maitland, surgeon; John Burnet, a merchant; John Richart, a major benefactor who left the whole of his estate , valued at £4,172, to the workhouse and the Infirmary; James Ogilvie, Collector of Customs; John Osborn, Principal of Marischal College; and the Rev. John Gordon of St Paul's Chapel. A tenth director, David Cuthbert, was appointed by Lord Pitsligo, who, as a benefactor, had the right to choose a representative. At this first meeting, under the chairmanship of Provost

Plate 6 William Chalmers. Lord Provost of Aberdeen 1738–9 and 1745–6.

Robertson, the directors decided to have a meeting weekly on Tuesdays. At the subsequent meetings, most of the work was carried out by the two ex-Provosts and Dr Rose, three being a quorum. Charles Maitland and John Richart never attended. A general meeting was held annually at which new directors were appointed and the following arrangements were made: snecks[11] were to be supplied for the doors and a hawthorn hedge was to be planted round the house to provide shelter. Mrs Strachan was to have two women servants.

On the 17 November 1742, those present drew up a set of 17 rules for the running of the Infirmary. The physician, or his deputy, was to visit daily, and he was to keep 'proper books on the Edinburgh plan'. Patients were admitted if he considered them after inspection to be 'proper objects' – that is patients in which there was some hope of cure. The person recommending admission was to defray funeral expenses and, after cure or if incurable, was to pay the expense of removal to his own home. Males and females were to be kept in separate rooms, and were not to go in each others' rooms. If a patient did not observe the regimen of diet and medicines recommended by the physician he was to be 'turned out of the house'. The mistress was to attend the physician when he visited patients to receive his orders about diet and to give it to the patients accordingly – no other food whatsoever was to be given. She was to remove patients' clothing on admission and return it cleaned on discharge; the clothes and bedding left after discharge were to be cleaned by her. She was to report any misbehaviour to the directors so that the 'persons guilty may be punished'. No patient was to go outdoors except by permission of the physician. The servants were to give food and drink only as ordered under penalty of dismissal. Total control of admission and discharge was to be with the directors at their weekly meetings on the recommendation of the physician but emergencies could be admitted at the discretion of one or two directors – subsequently ratified by the committee.

Some of the regulations have a strangely current ring. Patients approved for admission were to be admitted at once, and if there was no room, to be put on a waiting list and admitted in turn when a bed was available. The physician had to report weekly to the directors on the progress of his patients, and to justify his prognosis that they were curable – an early example of medical audit. In September 1746 another rule was added; no patient was to be rejected without a second medical opinion. It could be added that the admission of patients only if there was hope of cure is an example of what is now called 'resource allocation'. With the building completed, Mrs Strachan in her charge, the first four patients under treatment, directors having been appointed and rules drawn up for the management of the hospital, the Infirmary was now firmly established.

The site of the Infirmary and the Well of Spa[12]

Woolmanhill was chosen as the site of the new hospital because of the 'goodness of the air in that place'. It had for long been a place of pilgrimage for the sick and suffering of Aberdeen and district. In his 'Description of Aberdeen' in 1661, Parson Gordon of Rothiemay records:[13]

> Upon the west syde of the toune, at a small distance ther is a small, swelling hill to be seen, corruptlie called the Woman-hill, but more properlie the Woollmanhill, because it is affirmed that in old tymes the sellers of Wooll quoho came from the neirest parts about the toune took ther stand ther upon mercat dayes. Under the hill there runs a spring of water . . . .easily distinguished, both by its taste and colour . . .This spring is called the Well of Spaa. – so called I suppose, because it resembles in its taste and colour the waters of Spaa in the bishopric of Liege.

The Well of Spa (Plate 7) is first recorded in a tract dated 1580, attributed to Dr Gilbert Skene 'Ane Breif Description of the Qualities and effects of the Well of Woman-hill beside Aberdene'. The water is said to be of 'medicinall qualitie' – containing Iryn, Brynstane and Brasse[14] and is effective in many diseases of the mouth, stomach, liver, kidneys and bladder. In 1615 Dr William Barclay wrote an account of the well entitled 'Callirhoe, the Nymph of Aberdene Resuscitat'.[15] In 1635 George Jamesone, the distinguished Aberdeen painter, having obtained relief by taking the waters of the well, erected a building over it, with portraits of six apostles on each side. This was destroyed by flood in 1650, but the building was replaced in 1670 by Alexander Skene of Newtyle.[16] It again fell into disrepair and was rebuilt by Dr James Gordon of Pitlurg in 1751. The building was renovated in 1851 and moved to its present site near the Denburn Centre in 1977.

The inscription reads:
RENOVATUM EST OPUS
ANNO
MD CCC LI

Below this are the figures of a rose, a thistle, and a fleur-de-lys and beneath them the motto: 'As Heaven Gives me, so give I thee' – George Jamesone's inscription. Beneath this the figure of the sun, flanked by the inscription of Alexander Skene:

Hoc Fonte Derivata Salus
In Patriain Populumque fluat.
Spada Rediviva 1670

Plate 7 The Well of Spa. The date and artist of this drawing in the Marischal Museum Collection are not known.

The original building

We do not have a detailed description of William Chrystal's building, which was demolished in the 1830s to allow for re-building. From an inventory made by Mistress Strachan in 1746 we learn that there was a pantry and a kitchen, an east and west vault, a doctor's room, an east room and a west room, a south closet and a north closet. The last two rooms were presumably those fitted up on the upper floor in 1744, as warmer rooms for patients under treatment with 'salivations of mercury. . . shaping the west gavel of the House and building four chimneys therein upon the two floors under the roof'.[17]

It appears that it was a plain stone building, with two storeys, an attic and a slated roof. There was accommodation for six patients, with a seventh in emergency. The house was surrounded by a garden and enclosed by a hawthorn hedge. It had cost £484 and £170 was spent on fitting up the interior.

The founders

It is apparent that the Town Council of Aberdeen was chiefly responsible for the foundation of the Infirmary and, through the directors, it maintained control in its early years. The contribution of two individuals is outstanding. William Chalmers (1695–1770), a merchant in Aberdeen and Provost in 1738–39 when the Infirmary was first proposed and again in 1745–46 when it was re-opened after the Jacobite rising. His name heads the subscription list, with the sum of £3. *6s.8d.*

> The Poor's Hospital and Infirmary, the most useful and extensive charity foundations in this place and the North of Scotland, of both of which he was a zealous promoter, will be lasting monuments of his public spirit, and endear his memory to many generations.[18]

In 1741 the Town Council agreed to have his portrait painted at the town's expense, in gratitude for his having provided cheap oatmeal for the poor. John Alexander was the artist and it originally hung in the Town House. In 1756, however, William Chalmers petitioned the Council that the portrait be transferred to the Director's Hall in the Infirmary. His wish was granted and the portrait was still in the possession of the Infirmary in 1897 but was later returned to the Town House where it is to this day.[19]

Alexander Rose was one of the directors of the Infirmary in its early years and was an enthusiastic supporter. He was a regular attender at the weekly meetings and when the appointed physician could not attend he presented the reports on the patients. Like Gordon the first physician, he had been to Leyden, the leading medical centre of the day, and while there may have learned how to operate for cataract. This procedure he carried out with notable success in the Infirmary. He was a leading figure in the Musical Society, a body which raised considerable sums for the Infirmary, eventually holding an annual charity concert for this purpose.

THE FIRST INFIRMARY BUILDING

In the first year 21 patients were admitted. Of these nine were cured, 10 dismissed 'uncured after a long trial' and two died. At the end of the year Dr Gordon resigned. He was replaced by a surgeon, Andrew Skene, at the same 10 guinea annual salary. Skene's admission policy may have differed from that of his predecessor as his success rate was much higher, although fewer patients were admitted. Out of 24 treated in the next two years 18 were cured, four dismissed as incurable and two died.[20]

While he was negotiating with the directors at the end of his second year, the work of the Infirmary was brought to an abrupt stop. A force of Jacobites led by John Hamilton, the Duke of Gordon's factor, entered Aberdeen and prevented the election of magistrates and therefore of new directors to the Infirmary. The soldiers took over the hospital, housing in it their own sick and wounded, and wounded prisoners, mostly McLeods, taken at the Battle of Inverurie in December 1745. In February 1746 the Jacobites retreated and until August 1746 the hospital was in turn occupied by the Duke of Cumberland's army.[21]

When the Infirmary re-opened Mrs Strachan resigned as mistress. This public-spirited lady had taken up her appointment with no mention of salary. This was first discussed with her on 18 October 1743 when she refused wages for the first five months of her tenure of office and also refused more than she had received in her previous employment, £4 per year. She was replaced by Mrs Margaret Fraser.

Andrew Burnet[22] was appointed surgeon and continued on an annual basis until August 1751 when he resigned because of ill health. He remained as surgeon however, while his successor Thomas Livingstone,[23] travelled 'for his further improvement'.[24] Dr Livingstone eventually took up his post in August 1752.

During these years the Infirmary expanded at a steady pace. Although the original intention was to have seven beds only, this number was sometimes exceeded. In May 1743 for instance, eight boys from the Poor's Hospital were admitted and accommodated in a single upper room. They brought their own bedding with them and their expenses were paid by the Poor's House. Two warm rooms were added in May 1744 for 'patients under salivations' but in May 1745 the directors decided that, because of the state of the funds, the numbers should be restricted to six beds with a seventh emergency bed. However, in 1748 five more beds were added and in 1749 two more small rooms for patients under treatment with salivation of mercury were fitted up. In the same year Mr Burnet reported that the Infirmary could provide seven more beds, to a total of 20 in all, and these were immediately installed. Two years later Mrs Fraser was requested to arrange for a builder to construct a brew house and two cellars of stone and lime on the west end of the building; at the same time five more beds were added.

At the annual general meeting on 20 November 1753, a major extension was proposed by the physicians as follows:

First floor or ground flat. A Room for the Managers, Shop & Small Laboratory, Room for a clerk & a Mortuary with a Drug-room.
Second floor. Consisting of a ward with beds on each side fronting one another and two closets at each end with chimneys for mercurial patients.
Third floor. An operation room with a Small closet for holding of Instruments or for the operator to dress or undress in, on each side of which there may be little convenient apartments for accommodating the patients during their recovery after the operations.

To these proposals the meeting added rooms for a girnel[25] and cellars[26]. Thus were laid the foundations of a modern hospital, anticipating Nightingale wards by more than a 100 years, and recovery rooms by 200 years.

On 9 April 1754 the meeting of the managers recommended that the Provost

write a letter to Dr Gordon of Pitlurg, present master of the Mason's Lodge that he and his fraternity may be pleased to give their countenance to the laying of the foundation stone of the new building of the said Infirmary[27]

The laying of the foundation stone was noted in the *Aberdeen Journal*:

The Society of Free and Accepted Masons, whose characteristic it is to promote

Plate 8 The original foundation stone now in the wall of the Porter's lodge of the east Jubilee building at Woolmanhill (see note 29).

every benevolent design, convened last Thursday morning at their Lodge in the Links, and from thence in the most decent and solemn manner walked into Town. In the Castle Street they were joined by the Lord Provost and Magistrates, and the Gentlemen Managers of the Infirmary, who attended the procession thro' the city to the Infirmary, where JAMES GORDON of PITLURG Esq, present Right Worshipful Master, assisted by the Wardens etc made the following speech to the Magistrates and Directors of the Infirmary, and afterwards laid the first stone of the new intended building with the usual solemnity.

The Ceremony being over, the whole Company returned in like good order to the Town House, where they were genteelly entertained by the Magistrates. In the evening, the Masons gave a most elegant ball to the Ladies in Town, and the whole concluded with the greatest harmony and decency.[28]

The foundation stone of the new building, to be known as the 'East Wing', was found in 1893 by workmen excavating the site for the new Medical Block. It had been buried at a depth of three feet. On the direction of the then managers who had more sense of history than some of their successors, the stone was built into the wall of the Porter's Lodge at the entrance to the Infirmary at Woolmanhill, where it can still be seen. The inscription is shown in Plate 8.[29]

Finding money for the Infirmary in its early years caused the directors much concern. The original subscriptions had been insufficient to pay for the building and for fitting it out, and money had to be borrowed. The only annual income available was the interest on the funds in the hands of the Town Council, which apparently amounted to a mere £11 per annum. The first of many appeals to the public was made in May 1745 when 500 copies of the State of the Infirmary were ordered to be printed and distributed. This was repeated in 1752, 650 copies being made, 120 of which were to be sent to 'our countrymen in Jamaica'. In 1748, an appeal was made to the Synod[30] of Aberdeen for church collections. This was later extended to Moray, Ross and Brechin and so began the annual church collections which were an important source of revenue until the inception of the National Health Service in 1948. At times the directors were insistent in their demands, on one occasion proposing that a list of parishes which had not contributed should be published in the local paper, and on another, that no patients from these parishes would be admitted. Also they sought to draw up a list of non-contributors in the City of Aberdeen, so that ways of making them pay could be found.

Many other sources of income are recorded. In February 1743, a box 'for the charity of visitors' later called the Poor's Box was made, which supplied small sums – up to £5.5s. annually. The grass in the garden was cut and sold for hay each year, providing in 1748, £2.3s.10d. Houses on the Bleachfield[31] which had been let to the Infirmary, were leased for rent. In 1750, eight guineas – a fine on a Mr Fraser for an insult to the Sheriff – was paid to the Infirmary and in 1753 the cashier reported that he had got a guinea from Thomas Mosman as a fine for an irregular marriage.[32] All these efforts to raise money were successful. Having, in their own words, conducted their affairs with all possible economy and frugality, the directors were able to report that above the expenses for the year 1753 of £230.8s.2 11/12d. there was a balance of £261.17s.6 1/12d.[33]

The full-time staff of the Infirmary in those early years consisted of the mistress, and two maid servants, increased to three in 1745 and to four in 1748. The duties of one maid included looking after the Infirmary cow. The mistress was responsible for the general management of the hospital. She attended the physician on his daily rounds; carried out his instructions on diet and general regimen of care for the patients; and was instructed to insure that no visitors brought in food for the patients. She was not without her problems. On being asked to find extra milk for the patients, she reported that she had been unable to do so. Once she was 'used in an impertinent manner' by the master of a patient; the directors instructed that thereafter he be banned from admission to the Infirmary. On 5 July 1743 she reported a more alarming incident: disorderly persons from the town had thrown stones at the cell where 'the madwoman was kept', forced open the windows of the kitchen and pantry and threatened to break open the doors 'if they got not out the maidservants'. Again in 1753 it was noted,

> Because of the abuses committed on the Lord's day by strangers coming into the Infirmary the Mistress is appointed to deny access to any such persons without an express order from one of the managers.[34]

Other staff were employed part time. As already mentioned, the physician was expected to visit the hospital daily. The first named nurse was appointed in October 1744. She was Margaret Grubb, and, at a salary of 1s. 6 7/12d. per week plus 'her entertainment in the house during the time she may happen to be employed for the same purpose', she undertook to nurse patients under treatment by salivations of mercury.[35] The Town Sergeant was required to attend the Bedlam patients once weekly, at an annual salary of £1. He was lax in doing so and had to be reminded by the managers. In 1753 he was asked to attend on Sunday for several weeks to put a stop to disorders on that day. Ministers of the town were asked to visit the Infirmary to 'pray and converse with the sick' – it being noted that they did not do so.

Lastly there was the gardener, Alexander Drysdale. He advised the managers on gardening subjects, but it seems that he employed others to carry out the actual work. He was asked for his opinion about a suitable place for a 'physic garden' when the physicians recommended that this be established in 1743. He considered that the hospital garden was too exposed for this purpose, and proposed a more sheltered area known as the Bleachfield, to the north west of the Infirmary. The Town Council let the Bleachfield in 1748 to the Infirmary for 19 years at a nominal rent and it was later sold to the hospital. It was an extensive area, containing several houses which were sublet at an annual rent. However, as a physic garden, it does not appear to have been a success. 'Neglected and waste in 1755, it was let in 1800'.[21]

Some idea of conditions within the Infirmary can be gleaned from the minutes. Male and female patients were strictly segregated and infectious cases, on the rare occasions when they were admitted, were isolated. The diet was frugal, consisting largely of the old Scottish standby of oatmeal, sowens[36] and milk, the last provided by the Infirmary cow. Ale was also provided. Fires were lit in winter. The blankets were of rough cloth and the mattresses were filled with straw. Spitting boxes were provided for the patients.

Of the patients admitted about three quarters were surgical. Many were the victims of accidents some complicated by 'mortification' of the limb. The doctor's room was noted to contain two machines for broken legs. Amputations were carried out for bone and joint infections and for 'mortification'. One patient's discharge was delayed while he awaited the fitting of a wooden leg. Other successful procedures were excisions of cancer of the lip and nose and couching for cataract, several patients returning to have the second eye treated, after a successful operation on the first.

The managers were concerned that no one in Aberdeen could 'cut for stone', patients having to travel to Edinburgh for this procedure. Dr Livingstone, on his return from training, was the first Aberdeen surgeon to carry out this difficult operation, in which stones were removed from the bladder through a perineal incision. In those pre-anaesthetic days the procedure must have been a horrifying ordeal for the patient and it was only carried out when symptoms had become intolerable. Nevertheless it is recorded that of the first 15 patients treated in the Infirmary, 13 made a complete recovery. Similarly, of 20 amputations of the larger extremities, 'there has not one died of the operation'.[20]

The medical treatment of patients was severely limited because of lack of accurate knowledge of the cause of disease, and because few effective drugs were available. Much emphasis was placed on diet, cleanliness, and 'the goodness of the air'. Prominent in the minutes is the treatment known as 'salivations of mercury', for which special warm rooms were provided. In 1750 three patients were admitted for whom mercury was thought to be the only hope of cure. They suffered from, respectively, a bad sore throat, warts and itch and scrophula.[37] Salivations was an unpleasant treatment in which mercury was administered until what we now know to be the symptoms of poisoning occurred. Absorption of the element, applied as an ointment to the skin, was more rapid when the skin was warm, hence the need for heated rooms. Increased secretion of saliva was produced, two to three pints a day being thought to be ideal. This was often accompanied by ulcers on the tongue and mouth, loss of weight, weakness and tremor. It was believed at the time that the evil humours of the disease were excreted in the saliva, and so a cure was achieved. One hundred years later the method was confined to the treatment of syphilis, in which it may have been effective.

A detailed account of the treatment of an insane patient is available. Mr Kay, a 'lunatic schoolteacher from Calder (Cawdor) was recommended to be admitted, in November 1748'. He died in his cell some months later. On 12 June 1750 it was noted that his widow was spreading rumours about his ill-treatment to the people of Moray and it was decided to publish a true account of his treatment in the *Aberdeen Journal* which appeared on 26 June 1750. In this the managers stated that they:

> had admitted Mr Kay unwillingly because of the unlikelihood of a cure but had taken him in out of sympathy for his wife and friends. They had fitted up a room suitable for him and hired a servant, at their own expense, to look after him and to administer the regimen advised by the physician. In spite of all the care provided he became more violent, tearing his clothing and bed clothes to pieces, removing stones from the wall, and taking down the lintel of the door, a very large stone. They again refitted the room which put them to ten pounds sterling and upwards of extraordinary expenditure, and then were obliged to chain him which they did with all the tenderness his terrible condition would admit of.

The account in the *Aberdeen Journal* ended by pointing out that although sent for, Mrs Kay had not visited him in hospital until after his death, and made no arrangement for his funeral, which was carried out at the expense of the magistrates of Aberdeen.[38]

Patients came from far and near to the Infirmary. They are recorded as being admitted from the Parish of Reay in the far north, from Ross and Moray, and from many of the parishes of Aberdeenshire, Banff and Kincardine. Some had already had treatment by persons of which the Infirmary managers clearly disapproved. For example in September 1743, two patients, 'one disjointed in the thigh and with several discharging sores' and a second 'half disjointed at the shoulder with discharging wounds', were admitted. Their condition was considered to be due to the 'violence and mismanagement' of one John Milne a 'pretended bonesetter'. The magistrates were asked to take action against him. On another occasion William Hay of Old Deer had a large hard excrescence on his left hand cut two months before, by 'an itinerant professor of medicine who left him and other patients to their shifts'. His admission was recommended.[39]

In the period to May 1754, a total of 699 patients were admitted; 456 were considered to be cured; 167 dismissed uncured after a long trial; 44 died and 32 remained in the hospital.[20]

Developments

In June 1755, the new building, later to be named the 'East Wing', was finished
and the keys handed to Mrs Fraser the housekeeper. The cost was £495 sterling.
In addition to the ward of 12 beds, 12 more were provided in six small rooms to
make a total of 57 in the Infirmary.

At the Annual General Meeting of the new and old managers in 1758, a further
extension, the 'West Wing', was proposed, for the accommodation of 'poor
distressed lying-in women of the town and country'. A sub-committee was
formed to make plans for the building; to insert an advertisement in 'Aberdeen's
Newspaper'; to print and distribute widely an appeal for funds, pointing out that
'poor women are often in distress in labour, and many of them die for lack of
proper care'; and to open a subscription list. Just over a year later an estimate for
the new building for £477. 17s. 6d. was accepted. To this was added the sum of
£10 to cover the cost of having the west front built in ashlar instead of rubble.[40]
The accommodation in the new building was similar to that in the east wing,
with the exception of the ground floor, which was to contain a waste-house, a
brew-house and cellars. It is noteworthy that the rooms for patients contained
fireplaces but, in the upper storey of this building, two closets 'without fires'
were to be provided 'for nurses or other use'.[41] After several delays due to minor
alterations to the building, the west wing received its first pregnant patient on
5 January 1762. She was duly delivered. She suffered from 'lues venerea'[42] and
was detained in hospital until 17 August when she was dismissed, 'cured'.

With the opening of the west wing, the Infirmary had accommodation for 80
patients. No other major building expansion was to be made until the end of the
century, when the 'Lunatic Asylum' was founded. However, several smaller
projects were completed. The physicians first proposed that a bath-house for hot
and cold baths be built in 1750 and funds for this purpose were collected over the
years. After many delays the bath-house was eventually completed in 1774 and a
bath-keeper was appointed. It contained four baths, dressing rooms and a public
room, of which only one bath was for the use of the Infirmary patients. One bath
and dressing room was reserved for ladies and two for gentlemen, at the cost of
half a guinea for an annual ticket, or sixpence for casual use. It was not a success.
The bath-keeper was suspected of feathering his own nest and there was trouble
both with flooding and encrustation of the lead pipes supplying the water. In
1783 it was decided to let the bath-house and in 1788 it was to be let or sold. No
buyer or lessee could be found until 1821, when it was finally disposed of.[43]

Walls round the garden were built and rebuilt, and the Infirmary building
itself was often repaired, the doors and windows being done with 'red oil paint'.
A large hen house of stone and wood was constructed and a wall was erected
round the dung-hill which was 'removed to the westmost part of the new ground
because it is nauseous to the house'.[44] In 1798 it was noted that the Denburn was
to be covered over and a new road built to Gilcomston. The Infirmary feu'd[45] off

land behind the hospital for building along this road, which was given the name of 'Spa Street'.

Finance

The difficulties of financing the enlarged hospital continued to cause the managers much concern. They appealed repeatedly to 'our countrymen' in Edinburgh, London, Holland and the West Indies as well as to the citizens of Aberdeen and surrounding counties. As in the past (p.19) they were particularly insistent in their requests for church collections, which were eventually held annually throughout the North and North-East of Scotland. Ministers who did not hold collections were reminded that patients from their parishes could not be admitted, a threat which was never carried out. In 1764 the church collections amounted to £521. 19s. 2 1/2d., more than two-fifths of the total running costs of the Infirmary.[46] A feature of these was that up to £30 a year consisted of 'bad copper' which had to be melted down and was sold for about one-fifth of its face value. In 1776 it was decided to charge patients who could afford it 4d. a day and to appeal both to Aberdonians and to people in those parts of the country from which patients came, to give an annual subscription. There was limited success with the latter proposal but the subsistence charge of 4d. a day was discontinued in 1780 because it turned people against the Infirmary.

Contributions to the funds were many and varied. The landed aristocracy such as the Earl of Findlater, and the Duke of Gordon gave large sums. Other generous benefactors were the Musical Society, the County Club and the Shipmasters. Sir Francis Grant transferred one of his 10 shares in Whale Fishing to the Infirmary. Mr Adams, an architect in London, gave 60 bolls[47] of English coals in appreciation of the care taken of workmen injured at the quarry of Nigg. A fine of £2 on James Nicol for mixing English and Scots coal and passing it off as English, was handed over by the Dean of Guild. Fifty pounds, the surplus of a fund raised to ransom William Paterson a slave in Algiers, was received in 1796. Other donations came from grateful patients. Particularly notable is the gift of William Muir, a labourer. In gratitude to the Infirmary he gave all his savings, a total of £155, on condition that the Infirmary paid the interest to himself and his wife during their declining years. This the Infirmary agreed to do and offered to pay double interest on £50 of his donation.[48]

In 1767 negotiations were begun to obtain money from the War Office to pay for soldiers in the Infirmary; it was pointed out that there were usually 15 soldiers under treatment, as there was no military hospital north of Edinburgh. The request was at first refused but later a grant of 5s. a day plus 6d. a day for each soldier in hospital was agreed, this being the same allowance as for soldiers in the Royal Infirmary of Edinburgh. The 6d. daily was later reduced to 4d. to which the managers reluctantly agreed, considering that the 2d. 'was not worth fighting over'.[49] After the death of Thomas Livingstone, General MacKay, Commander-in-Chief of the Army, wrote to say that the 5s. a day allowance must now cease and wished to know if Livingstone had ever paid any of it or kept it to himself. Provost Jopp replied that Livingstone had never taken a penny of the money, that the soldiers ward was in good order and appealed for help for 'this successful charity'.[50] The daily 5s. was continued and in 1787 the sum received from the Army was £91. 5s.[51]

In spite of all efforts, by 1783 the Infirmary had fallen into debt mainly because of 'the advanced Price of Provisions in the last years, the great deficiency of Donations and Collections upon which the support of the House chiefly depends, and a considerable increase of the numbers of patients'.[52] The usual appeal was sent out to individuals, churches and institutions at home and abroad with limited success. Relief came from a group of public-spirited gentlemen, who made an anonymous gift of £500 to pay off the debt and of £1,500 to add to the capital fund of the hospital. However, this was only a temporary respite. At the end of the century, expenditure was once more exceeding income and strict economies, together with suggestions for restricting the number of patients, were instituted.

The Royal Charter

Concern about the management of the funds of the hospital was first expressed in 1754, when the Clerk presented an account of the monies in the hands of the Town Council for the maintenance of the Infirmary and the new building. The Provost was asked to inform the magistrates that they wished to have a copy of the 'stocked money', in the hands of the Master of Hospitals, to be available for inspection by anyone who wished to see it. In 1768 it was noted that the state of funds was very precarious and uncertain in that there was no authentic document thereof lodged with any proper authority. It was proposed that the managers should meet the Town Council and magistrates to discuss this. A few months later the Town Clerk was asked to provide a statement of the hospital funds which was received in 1770 and a proposal was made that an Act of the Town Council should be obtained to transfer these to the Infirmary Treasurer. Legal advice was obtained and on 30 May 1770 we read:

> It is the unanimous opinion of this committee (i.e. the sub-committee appointed to investigate the hospital's funds) that the directors of the Infirmary should resolve to make immediate application for a Royal Charter. . .

A year later a sub-committee was appointed for the purpose of obtaining this charter. The Petition to King George III was signed in 1772 and the Charter, dated at St James's 31 March 1773, was presented at a general meeting of the managers on 13 July 1773. The Charter is written in Latin[53] and its translation into English was to be the cause of some disputation.[54] A translation begins:

> CHARTER, ERECTING THE PRESIDENT AND MANAGERS OF THE INFIRMARY OF ABERDEEN INTO ONE BODY POLITIK, ONE THOUSAND SEVEN HUNDRED AND SEVENTY THREE
> George by the Grace of God, King of Great Britain, France and Ireland, defender of

the faith. To all good men to whom these presents shall come, greeting. Whereas we, considering that the Provost and Magistrates of the City of Aberdeen, and others the Managers of the Hospital built within the said City of Aberdeen under the name of the Infirmary of Aberdeen for the reception and cure of poor persons belonging to the northern counties of Scotland: have represented to us by an humble petition, that in the year one thousand seven hundred and thirty-nine, a voluntary subscription was begun, under regulations established by the magistrates and common council of the City of Aberdeen, for the reception of poor people, who are sick or hurt, belonging to the northern counties of Scotland: And that under those regulations, this charity had subsisted for more than thirty years; during which time they had built and supported a large Infirmary, and had, besides defraying the expenses, made a saving of upwards of five thousand pounds sterling; and that this Infirmary was then in such a flourishing condition, as to admit above eight hundred sick people yearly; And that the said petitioners had been advised, and did believe, that if they and their successors in the management of the said charity were invested with corporate powers, the same would become more extensive, and publicly useful, and the monies would be employed to more advantage and safety; wherefore they prayed that we would grant unto them our royal charter for erecting them and their successors in the management of the said charity, into a body politik and corporate, under the name of the Infirmary of Aberdeen, with a perpetual succession, and all the powers usually granted to bodies of the like kind.

The charter goes on to nominate the Provost, the ex-Provost, four Baillies, the Dean of Guild, the Treasurer, the Convener of the Trades, the Professor of Medicine of Marischal College, the Moderator of the Synod of Aberdeen and certain contributors to the funds of the Infirmary, together with 14 other persons who were to be elected annually, to be called one corporation under the title of the 'President and managers of the Infirmary of Aberdeen', and

that they and their successors shall, forever hereafter, have a perpetual succession, for the better and more effectual managing, directing, ordering, and appointing all things relevant to the Infirmary of Aberdeen . . .

The corporation was empowered to buy land and property of a rental not exceeding £500 yearly but 'it should not be in the power of the President and Managers to spend more than the free yearly produce of the lands and securities belonging to the said Incorporation, and of the current collections, subscriptions, and donations for such year shall produce'.

A general meeting was to be held on the first Monday of December in each year. Fourteen managers were to be selected to serve with those nominated by virtue of their office and those life managers by virtue of their contributions to the Infirmary, as the president and managers of the Infirmary. One of the 14 managers was to be a minister of Aberdeen, one from the Society of Shipmasters and two from the physicians residing in Aberdeen. The Provost of Aberdeen and, in his absence, the magistrate next to him in rank was to be the perpetual president of the corporation.

Four quarterly general courts were to be held, the first on the third Monday in June 1773, with powers to appoint sub-committees for specific purposes and to employ

treasurers, officers, servants, and other persons' as required, and with full authority 'of appointing, framing, and making such and so many by-laws, statutes, rules and ordinances as they or the major part of them shall judge proper and necessary.[55]

Meetings – administration

The first general meeting after the granting of the Charter was held in December 1773. The stipulated 14 managers were elected, making a total of 33 in all. They were divided into six groups, each being responsible for the weekly meetings for two months in the year. Immediate steps were taken to gain control of the money in the hands of the Town Council and in April 1776, after protracted negotiations, the president was able to put a bond for £2,000 into the Infirmary's Charter chest consisting of £1,732 owed to the Infirmary and made up from other funds. In 1774 detailed regulations for the running of the Infirmary were approved.[56] Emergencies requiring immediate surgery were to be admitted at once but others, with their recommendations, were to apply on Tuesdays at 3 p.m. No cases of 'Scrophula, Consumption, or Sivans'[57] were to be admitted. None were to be admitted who could be treated as an out-patient. A waiting list was to be established when there was 'want of room' and patients admitted in turn. Strict rules for patient's behaviour were instituted, under penalty of dismissal if they were broken.

Two directors were to inspect the house regularly and interview separately the housekeeper, the nurses and servants, and the patients. The physician was to visit his patients each day before noon to give his instructions to the housekeeper, who was to be unmarried and to live in the House. The gardener and porter also were to be unmarried and the nurses and servants were to be 'free of the burthen of children and care of family'. The housekeeper was in charge of the day to day running of the hospital and was to oversee the nurses and servants. She was to visit the wards twice a day and to see that patients were given their diets as prescribed by the physicians; lock the doors and gates at night and open them in the morning. Particular emphasis was placed on cleanliness. It is noteworthy that until 1800, only three complaints were made to the directors during their inspections; two were from the soldiers, complaining about the food, and lack of chairs. The third concerned the 'throwing out of nastiness from the windows of the middle ward'. The nurses were instructed to prevent this practice.

The Dispensary

In 1781, the managers considered the desirability of extending medical advice to all those who needed it but who were not suitable for treatment at the Infirmary. They are listed as those suffering from incurable or lingering diseases, those who could not be moved to the hospital, mothers who could not leave their families and those suffering from infectious diseases such as 'fever and smallpox'. It was also noted that children could not be properly cared for in the Infirmary. It was thought that the only additional expense would be the fee of the attending physician and that the Infirmary might benefit because many patients would be treated who might otherwise attend the hospital as out-patients or in-patients. William Livingstone was appointed at a salary of 40 guineas and, as part of his duties, was to inoculate against smallpox such children of the poor as would agree to it. The service was to be confined to the city and suburbs, later reduced to the city and Footdee only. In 1782 Livingstone was succeeded by George French who resigned three years later 'as I find it impracticable to execute the duties expected from me with any material benefit to the Poor patients recommended to my care, or any satisfaction to myself'.[58] He was followed by Alexander Gordon. During his tenure of office he observed an epidemic of puerperal fever, which enabled him to establish for the first time the infectious nature of this disease. His article (published in 1795) entitled 'A treatise on child bed fever which prevailed as an epidemic in Aberdeen from 1789 to 1792' is a medical classic. Unfortunately his ideas were not accepted, and it was not until 50 years later that Semmelweis in Vienna confirmed his findings, which slowly gained recognition by the profession.[59]

The general service, established in 1781, became known as the Dispensary. In 1790 it separated totally from the Infirmary and led to the founding in 1823 of the 'General Dispensary, Vaccine and Lying-in Institution' which gave free medical advice and treatment to all who required it, and included patients at home who were unable to attend. In 1948, the National Health Service made it redundant.

The mentally ill

Another offspring of the Royal Infirmary was the Royal Mental Hospital, now the Royal Cornhill (see p.39). The facilities for the treatment of the mentally ill in the Infirmary had never been satisfactory and the accommodation was insufficient. In 1756 the Bedlam cells were reserved for use by the inhabitants of the City of Aberdeen only because it was said the Bedlam Fund had been established for this purpose. This was illogical as the same applied to the other hospital funds used to support the Infirmary. In 1773 it was noted that patients in the cells were often troublesome and dangerous and a coal cellar was adapted for use as a Bedlam, being fitted up with five small cells. On several occasions these cells were all occupied and patients requiring care could not be admitted. In passing, it should be noted that the Town Council had apparently not contributed anything from the Bedlam Fund to the Infirmary and it was not until 1782 that it reluctantly was persuaded to pass an act allowing £30 a year from the Fund. In 1796 a sub-committee was appointed to look for a site for a Mental Hospital, it being noted that the Montrose Asylum, the first in Scotland and initiated in 1779, was 'an excellent establishment'.[60] An enclosure known as Clerkseat, bounded in the south by the Foresterhill Burn and on the east by the road to Berryden, was chosen. A single storey quadrangular building was built there with 12 cells, eight by eight and a half feet, and accommodation for staff. It was opened in 1800 on part of the site of the present Royal Cornhill Hospital.

Fever

Another idea which was discussed over many years, was the provision of a ward
for infectious diseases. This was first suggested in 1781 and funds were, at
different times, left to the Infirmary for this purpose. In 1791 the physicians were
asked to give proposals for a fever ward, but nothing came of it. It was not until
1820 that the fever ward was finally built (see p.31).

Hospital life

The day to day running of the hospital remained as described on p.13.
Mrs Margaret Fraser resigned in 1763, being no longer fit to continue; she was
then allowed a room in the House, her board, washing, coals and candle during
the pleasure of the directors, who recommended to the Town Council to give her
'such supply as she is entitled to as a Burgess' daughter and a good servant of the
House'.[61] Her successor was Mrs Farquhar at a salary of £5 per annum and she
died in 1794 while still in post, leaving £10 to the Infirmary. In her early years she
was clearly very efficient and received an annual bonus from the directors. Later,
however, she came under suspicion for her handling of the wines and, after
prolonged investigation of her accounts, and those of the physicians, handling of
the wines was removed from her jurisdiction. She was followed by Mrs Warrack.
    Very little is known of the maids and nurses of whom there were three and
five respectively in 1765. Mrs Jean Baird, the first hospital midwife, was paid one
guinea a year from 1763 until 1767 but then her name disappears from the
records. (After 1767, the admission of women in labour was discontinued. No
reason for this is given in the records, but the numbers admitted to the lying-in
ward were small, the largest number in one year being eight.[62]) In 1774,
Mrs Farquhar informed the managers that Margaret Peter, who had been a good
servant for more than 20 years, was no longer fit to work. Like Mrs Fraser,
Margaret Peter was given a room and board in the Infirmary.
    James McEdward , a strong young man, was hired in 1768 to act as gardener,
to oversee the people in Bedlam, to run messages and to act as porter. All these
duties he apparently carried out conscientiously, finding time in addition, to
collect money for the Infirmary. He grew herbs for the physicians and vegetables
for the Infirmary, being able to sell off the excess at times for the Infirmary funds.
In 1780 he had to resign because of ill health and was succeeded by John Smith
who was less successful. By 1800 the garden and adjacent ground was in a very
poor state and did not contribute significantly to the Infirmary. On the same date
it was recommended that a full time porter be appointed 'to guard the door'.[63]
    Physicians were employed part time. Thomas Livingstone, appointed in 1751
at £20 a year, served the Infirmary faithfully for 32 years. On his resignation he
gave his last year's salary of 50 guineas to the Hospital. When rumours were
circulated that he was overcharging for drugs, he insisted that his accounts be
reviewed by his fellow physicians. They found that his charges were, in fact,

very much less than usual. Nevertheless Livingstone refused to supply drugs to the Infirmary thereafter.

A second surgeon, Alexander Robertson, was appointed as an assistant in 1760. He was followed by Dr Stuart and Dr Ligertwood in 1777. In 1783 William Livingstone (1760–1822) succeeded his father, Thomas – and served with Dr Stuart. On the death of Thomas in 1785, George French, who had recently resigned as physician to the Dispensary, succeeded him. William Livingstone was appointed professor of medicine at Marischal College in 1793. Although his own efforts to establish lecture courses failed, he was a strong supporter of the students' Medical Society (see also p.212).

His colleague George French (1765–1833) had given lectures in chemistry since 1784, and became professor of chemistry at Marischal College in 1793. Although convinced of the necessity of lectures in chemistry, he was opposed to systematic medical teaching, and dissuaded apprentices from joining the Medical Society. However, he became reconciled and when he died left a number of volumes of manuscript notes of Dr Cullen's lectures of 1776–80. These give a clear and accurate account of the practice of medicine of the time. French had an apothecary's shop in the Upperkirkgate 'provided with an assortment of the most reputed patent medicines and several perfumery articles'.[64]

For the first 30 years of the Infirmary's existence there appears to have been no special provision made for the spiritual wants of the patients. Evidently their needs did not rest as a heavy burden upon the city ministers' conscience, though on more than one occasion the managers passed resolutions requesting these clergymen to visit the Infirmary at least once a week. Eventually in 1774 the appointment of a chaplain was recommended and in 1775 Mr Anderson of Robert Gordon's Hospital[65] offered his services at a yearly salary of £15. The cashier was instructed to buy a suitable Bible at the first auction sale and at first a daily service was held at 10 a.m. not inappropriately in the operating room. However, shortly after his appointment, a room with an outside stair was fitted up above the Bedlam cells and a bell hung in the middle of the lobby to call the patients to prayer. In 1784 his salary was discontinued because of the financial stringencies of the time, and he served on a voluntary basis for three and a half years. He was then re-engaged, by a majority vote, at a salary of £10 a year.[66]

The small staff of the Infirmary must have been hard-pressed to look after the needs of the many patients under their care. In 1754–55 there were 257 admissions, rising to 855 in 1766. Thereafter the number remained fairly constant, 863 being admitted in 1796. Large numbers of out-patients also attended – there were 2,297 in 1777.[67] The diseases from which these patients suffered were many and varied and in some respects differed from those met with today. Most patients were in the 10 to 40 age group and young children were quite frequently admitted. They suffered from ulcers, diseased bones and joints, rheumatism, abscesses, sore throats and pneumonia, fractures, burns and other injuries. Bladder stone and cataracts were treated by operation. Inflammatory eye diseases were particularly common. Although infectious diseases including scrophula and venereal disease were excluded by the regulations of the Infirmary, in fact large numbers of patients suffering from these diseases were admitted including some cases of smallpox. The admission of several soldiers with inflamed lacerations on the back is a reminder of the harsh military discipline of the day. Another sidelight on the activities of the time is given by the statement, in 1781, 'that some of the men belonging to Privateers of this place' had been recommended for admission. At the next quarterly general meeting, their request was turned down.[68]

Surgical treatment included 'couching' for cataract,[69] amputations, excision of tumours, 'cutting for stone', opening of abscesses, and curetting of infected ulcers and bone. For more than a century it was unusual for more than two operations to be performed in a week so the surgeons generally worked for their living as general practitioners, in midwifery and, after Jenner's demonstration in 1796 of the value of cowpox inoculation, as vaccinators. Medically, patients were dosed with purgatives, diuretics, carminatives, and diaphoretics; peruvian bark (quinine) was used in the treatment of fever and severe pain was controlled by opiates in the preparation laudanum. Wine was frequently prescribed as a tonic. Blistering and cupping were also used. Bleeding, a treatment used widely at the time for many different conditions, was apparently viewed with some suspicion, as it was to be used only in fevers and strangulated hernia and then only in a strictly limited fashion.[70] As early as 1768, an 'electric machine' was installed in the hospital. It was used in the treatment of rheumatism and paralysis. In spite of the limited therapeutic resources available, three-quarters of the patients were regularly discharged cured, or sufficiently improved as to be able to resume their usual occupations.

All patients who were able to do so had to assist in the work of the hospital. They were strictly forbidden to accept any food from visitors in that diet was considered of great importance in the treatment of illness. In 1800 this diet was, for those who did not have a special prescription from the physicians:

Breakfast   When oatmeal is above 15d a peck, Breakfast shall
consist of half a pound of good Wheaten Bread with a pint of milk.
When at or under that price a pint and half of porridge with a pint of
milk or Table Beer.
Dinner   A quart of good broth made with a sufficiency of Potatoes,
Turnips, Carrots, Greens and Onions, with half a pound of Bread. If a
portion of meat be thought necessary for any of the ordinary patients, the Nurse is
to receive orders from the attending Physician to that purpose.
Supper   The same as breakfast, substituting Sowens[71] instead of
Porridge when they can be made.

Soldiers. The same rule of diet to be followed for the soldiers,
half a pound of meat that has been boiled in the broth to be allowed
each for dinner.[72]

Although this diet may seem monotonous and inadequate by modern standards, it did not differ from that of the poorer people of the North-East of Scotland at that time nor for many years afterwards.

3

The 19th Century and Beyond

1801–1850

The beginning of the 19th century saw the Infirmary with a total complement of 80 beds compared to the original six, treating close on 900 patients a year against 21 in its first year and established as the Royal Infirmary by the charter of 1773. The opening of the Royal Asylum at Clerkseat in 1800 allowed the closure of the six Bedlam cells as it was considered to be 'prejudicial to sick persons to have those who were under mental derangement lodged in the same house', but the new hospital retained its administrative links with the Infirmary until 1948 (see also Chapter 10).

In August 1812 a memorandum submitted by the physicians and signed by James Moir[1] and John Charles Ogilvie[2], pointed out that the pressure of admissions necessitated: (1) a rejection of a proportion of these; (2) discharging patients too early; and (3) overcrowding when urgent admissions were necessary. To the late 20th century reader these complaints have a not unfamiliar ring. They went on to say that 'it is on such occasions often found necessary to huddle together two patients in one bed – a thing which is nowadays reprobated in the strongest manner by every medical man conversant with Hospital practice as what ought never to be permitted'. Subsequent to this, a plan was drawn up to increase the bed complement by 35 or 40 but, as so often happened, sufficient resources were not available to defray the estimated cost of £1,160. A less ambitious project was produced, combined with an appeal to the provincial Synod of Aberdeen, the general public, graduates of the school of medicine and wealthy members of the rural and urban communities. It was 1819 before a new ward was completed to accommodate 42 patients. In the previous year a severe outbreak of 'fever' in Aberdeen had required the conversion of a manufacturing house in the Gallowgate to serve as a hospital followed by the take-over of the military ward and barracks to use as a house of recovery.

By the year 1816 what had been an open site at Woolmanhill was being surrounded by the extension of the city so it was decided to pull down the original boundary wall and take in the complete bank to Spa Street. Between 1823 and 1824, £400 was spent on the original building. In 1831 the oil lamps were replaced by gas.

A decision was taken in 1832 to build a new fever department as the first

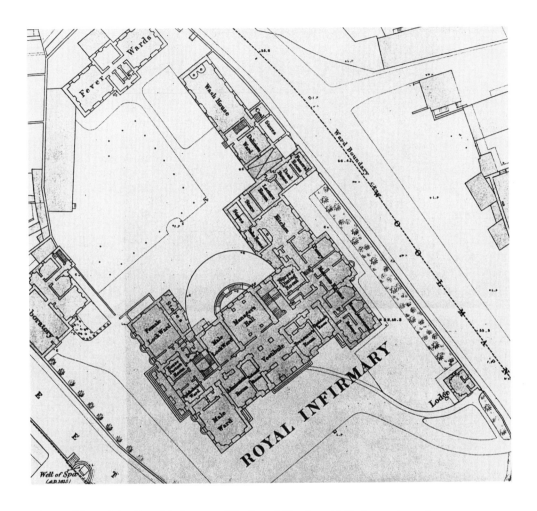

Plate 9 Plan of the Royal Infirmary, Woolmanhill, circa 1840. A number of areas are
mentioned in the text.

phase of a larger hospital to be completed when funds permitted. This wing was
opened in 1833 at a cost of £5,000 and provided 60 beds. The following year,
discussions commenced about the new hospital and in 1835 a meeting of the
managers accepted, on the casting vote of the then Provost James Blaikie of
Craigebuckler,[3] a proposal to build. The main opposition came from Mr Henry
Lumsden who pointed out that the new building which was estimated to cost
£12,000 would add only 18 beds to the existing complement of 182. The design
was produced by the Aberdeen architect Archibald Simpson, then at the height
of his powers and influence.[4] Building began in 1837 and was completed in 1840
at a final cost of £16,700 – closer to the estimate than was possible in the latter
half of the 20th century. Accommodation was now available for 230 patients. The
Simpson building on the south aspect of Woolmanhill survives today (Plates 9

Plate 10 The Simpson Building from the south-east, circa 1885. The driveway shown no longer exists. The dome containing the first operating theatre is clearly seen. (From the George Washington Wilson collection.)

and 10). During construction separate surgical and medical wards were marked off and, as a result of petitions from Dr Cadenhead of the Ophthalmic Institution (see Chapter 9), two wards were set aside for ophthalmic patients. About the same time the managers, in order to get the benefit of the cholera fund which was in the hands of the Aberdeen Board of Health, instituted plans for a new fever house. Building of this began in 1844 and was completed the same year.

As a last word on the physical structure of the Royal Infirmary during the first half of the 19th century, 1849 was notable for a fire that broke out close to the John Forbes ward and resulted in a scenario which bordered on slapstick.[5] The police were notified and three fire appliances arrived, later supplemented by the barrack's engine and a troop of soldiers. The water supply proved completely inadequate so Councillor Sutherland[6] provided bales of cloth to dam the Denburn. One of the magistrates dispatched a man to open the sluices of the Gilcomston dam. Two lines of buckets were instituted passing from the burn near the head of St Andrews Street, one to handle full buckets the other empty ones. Captain Tryon, RN[7] mounted the burning roof and it was reported that 'he rushed about barking his orders as if on board a belligerent three decker – just the sort of voice to frighten the French.' Eventually he fell through the roof but was not badly hurt. The fire was finally put out, the damage – estimated at £402 – being paid by insurance companies. A contract was immediately arranged for restoration at a cost of £364. It is not difficult, given these figures, to see why Aberdeen has a reputation for 'canny' financial dealing.

Organization and staffing

Inevitably, though perhaps not desirably, the growth of the Royal Infirmary led to changes in administration and staffing. By 1816 the managers had moved with the times to introduce a regulation that all candidates for the position of physician and surgeon should undergo examination by the medical managers. There were also comments on the way the institution carried out its task. Pointed criticism (admittedly with a general political background) of the running of the hospital appeared in a pamphlet published in 1830 which incorporated a letter to the managers from a country practitioner.[8] Having commented on the development of academic and clinical services over the years, he suggested that appointment to hospitals funded by public donation had placed physicians in the public eye and had made them more accountable, thus encouraging the establishment of a group of medical men who combined science and practical ability. He put forward the view that Aberdeen should follow the example of other areas by separating physicians from surgeons; in addition the post of 'admission doctor' should be discarded, leaving physicians and surgeons to admit their own patients. He counselled against taking the advice of medical managers as the existing doctors would offer to cover all duties – for 'no one cares to divide his power with another, provided he can keep it all to himself'. The Edinburgh system was, in his opinion, better where a variety of surgeons operated the hospital services in rotation. One of his most interesting points was his contention that the usual doctor's visit at home saw the father disappear to leave the doctor with the wife and children. Wives, therefore, got much greater knowledge of medicine so it would be of advantage if they managed the Infirmary. We shall encounter his views on the hospital and its role in Chapter 19.

Some of these points were re-iterated in a letter from 'A Benevolent Individual and Interested Person' written in 1833.[9] An additional recommendation in this letter was access for the press to all general meetings. The writer's comments on the list of nominees to be managers of the Infirmary bears quotation: 'Is it that one man among you has united for his own gratification, this jumble of relatives, givers of dinners and disappointed aspirants to the office and dignity of councillors?' It is hardly surprising that these comments were dismissed by the managers.

How much these observations and criticisms influenced the managers is unclear from the written record but administration did move on apace. In September 1838 the 'Regulations of the Royal Infirmary of Aberdeen'[10] were issued. The first section dealt with management which was to be entrusted to a committee consisting of the president of the court of managers who would act as convener and 16 other members, to include two magistrates of Aberdeen, two clergymen, two advocates and two physicians or surgeons. This group would meet at least once a month. Four sub-committees would be appointed to examine and warrant accounts, peruse the housekeeper's weekly accounts and the physicians' reports and inspect the wards, inquiring into the treatment of patients and their accommodation. They would check on every article of provision designated in the housekeeper's reports, calling occasionally during the distribution of victuals to patients and servants, ensuring that the strictest economy was observed. The housekeeper would be questioned privately about the behaviour of nurses, patients and servants, whether nurses and servants accepted gratuities from patients or their friends and if any of them were 'quarrelsome or given to swearing or abusive language.' In addition each nurse, servant and patient would be interviewed privately and complaints noted. Other duties would involve inspecting the apothecary's shop and the medicines procured from it, directing the modes of procuring and using provisions and checking quality, inquiring into the general conduct of all persons employed and finally handling disputes. The committees would also examine and insert in the minutes the balance of the treasurer's accounts, receive plans and tenders for proposed buildings and alteration and give directions for and superintend the execution of plans agreed on by the general courts. The main committee would receive the reports of the sub-committees, suggest plans for improvement in every department of management, report to each quarterly court on business transacted in the preceding quarter, prepare the routine business of the quarterly courts and draw up an annual report to be issued to the public. The committee would be subject to revision and control by the general courts of the president and managers who would take responsibility for such matters as the enactment of bye-laws, the election and dismissal of medical officers, house surgeons, apothecary, treasurer, clerk and matron, the borrowing or lending of money and the buying, selling or letting of lands and buildings.

The medical establishment at that time (1838) was two physicians, two surgeons, a house surgeon and an apothecary. Physicians and surgeons had to visit all patients at 12 noon and 'at such other times as they may judge proper'. If unavailable they must arrange for a colleague or the house surgeon to deputize. No patient was to stay longer than six weeks unless the medical officer was of the opinion that he or she was 'in the way of recovery'. The ophthalmic surgeon was to visit every Tuesday, Thursday and Saturday at 1 p.m. The house surgeon had to reside in-house and must not be absent at any time except with leave from the committee or medical officers. He was responsible for all general running of the wards, the supervision of students (in the absence of medical officers), nurses and patients, the care of surgical instruments and the carrying out of minor operations. He had to visit all the wards between 7 and 9 p.m and keep a register of patients for submission weekly to the sub-committee. The apothecary's role was also defined (see p.197).

Admission of patients could be recommended by the 'managers of the hospital, the clergy and elders of the several parishes and also the clergy, elders and managers of all other congregations who contributed annually for the support of the house, and those who individually subscribe for the same purpose'. The person who had recommended admission was bound to remove the patient when discharged by the physician; failing this, the sponsor could be charged with the cost of sending the patient home.[11] Accident and fever cases could be admitted at any hour but other patients had to apply at 12 noon, any day except Sunday. No person suffering from an incurable disease or smallpox could be admitted; if the Infirmary was full, preference was given to persons living at the greatest distance from it.

Patients, if able, had to rise at 7 a.m. in summer and 8 a.m in winter and were allowed to sit up until 9 p.m. from 1 September until 1 April and until 10 p.m. from 1 April to 1 September. No male patient was to enter the female ward and vice versa. Cards, dice and other games were banned as was smoking. Patients had to assist in the work of the hospital if fit to do so; they had to behave 'decently and discreetly' and had to be in the wards when the medical officer visited. Apart from normal discharge when cured, patients could be dismissed for falsifying information about their illness, refusing food or medicine prescribed, immorality, causing a disturbance, disobeying the housekeeper's orders, detaining acquaintances longer than permitted or breaking other rules. If so discharged, they could never again be admitted unless suffering from fever or a severe accident.

There was an establishment for a treasurer and also a clerk and book-keeper but these offices could be combined. The housekeeper must be unmarried, without a family and be able to keep accounts. She would be responsible for hiring and supervising nurses and maidservants, provisions, meals, patient discipline and ward cleanliness. It was decreed that 'the practice of sprinkling sand upon the floors be totally abolished'. She had to go round the wards in the morning and the evening. A basic diet was outlined and is considered in Chapter 18. Not only the housekeeper but also nurses and servants must be 'free from the burden of children and the care of a family'. Nurses were to scour the wards every morning (7 a.m. in summer and 8 a.m. in winter) and to see that 'no dirt, tow or rags be suffered to remain in the wards, or to be thrown out of any window or down the sinks or water closets'. No person employed by the Infirmary if once removed for misconduct, could again be taken into the service of the house.

The house-porter also had to reside in the house and have charge of the brew house with its utensils and make the beer for the institution once a week. He had to look after the lighting, heating, weighing of meat and various aspects of cleaning and had to keep the roof of the building free of snow. He was charged to relieve the gate porter so that the latter could go to church. This individual must be unmarried and constantly in attendance at the gate; he was responsible for admitting visitors and also for keeping patients within the ground unless they had permission to go out. Chair-porters – the old equivalent of ambulancemen and who transported patients from any part of the town for a fee – had to reside near the Infirmary.

In May 1848 a sub-committee reported on the admission of paupers to the Infirmary as parochial boards had been accused of sending in terminal and even moribund patients.[12] Under the reformed Poor Law Act (1845), the boards had become compulsorily responsible for the provision of medicines, medical attendance and advice to the poor on their list though there is much evidence of their relatively feeble performance in this regard.[13] In Scotland more so than in England, the Infirmaries continued to take patients who should have been consigned to 'the Poor Law'[12] and looked after in facilities provided under its rules . These thrifty habits of parochial boards were to persist until the end of the century and the belated development of hospitals not under the voluntary scheme such as Stobhill in Glasgow and the 'regional' hospitals, e.g. Eastern, Western, both in that city and in Edinburgh. It was noted that in Edinburgh and Glasgow a charge was applied by the Infirmary for the treatment of such patients; in Edinburgh the previous year this had been a total of £100 while in Glasgow it was 15 shillings (75 p) per patient. It was therefore recommended that a charge of ten pence per day (£15 per year) be levied for each patient which was the actual cost involved and was also the amount charged for lunatic asylum admissions, military admissions to the Infirmary and for paupers sent from prisons. All admissions should be certified by the parish medical officer and subject to veto by the hospital medical officer. The report came to the quarterly court in September when it was decided to set up a special committee 'for enquiry as to the origin and constitution of the Infirmary and the right of the parochial poor of the City to the free benefit of the Institution'. The committee reported in November, finding no evidence that parochial paupers had a right to free treatment; a general meeting in February 1849 accepted the report, rejecting the motion that compulsory charge might prejudice donations from rural areas.

1851–1921

As with most other cities, the Industrial Revolution which straddled the end of the 18th and first half of the 19th century had seen a steady growth in the population of Aberdeen. In part this was the outcome of a remarkable industrial diversification shared between textiles (wool and cotton), paper, engineering, shipbuilding, granite quarrying and stone dressing, whaling and fishing to mention but a few.[14] The city recorded just over 12,000 inhabitants in 1801 but, by the time of the census of 1841, this had risen to 63,000. It is said to have doubled again by 1861. Not surprisingly this growth was reflected in an increasing pressure on hospital accommodation. From 1830–1840 the average number of patients treated was just under 1,700 but this rose in the next 10 years to 2,155. On the economic side, the building developments in the first half of the century had resulted in financial strain and in 1859 the managers reported that capital had been encroached upon for £5,000. It was pointed out that costs were still cheaper in Aberdeen than in Edinburgh, Glasgow or Dundee though Aberdeen had the lowest mortality. The financial statement of 1861 disclosed a deficit of £860 and reductions in dietary provisions were introduced producing savings of £426 on butcher meat, wine, spirits, porter and small beer. Economies were also effected in fuel, lighting and washing.

The pace of development of the city and the rising numbers of the sick and injured, coupled with the dire financial state of the institution, seem to have had two effects. First continued change in managerial arrangements plus appeals to the public for money and, second, a drive to rebuild the hospital and to hive off parts of its function elsewhere.

A new charter

Application was made in 1851 for a new Royal Charter of Incorporation of the President and Managers of the Infirmary of Aberdeen, extending the powers of the managers and transferring these powers to their successors. A range of organizations wanted to be represented on the management, one section of the town council, led by Dr Christie, suggesting that the whole council should be managers *ex officio* in view of the liberal contributions given to the Infirmary by the council. The parochial boards of Oldmachar and St Nicholas advanced their claim on the grounds that four-fifths of the lunatics in the asylum (still under the administrative control of the Infirmary) were financed by them and the Free Church Synod put forward their case because the Church of Scotland (the established church) was represented. Similarly the senatus of King's College requested a voice because the professoriate of Marischal College were already included (the union of the two colleges was yet to come – see p.215). In the final list, the managers made only limited concessions and compromises, for example, the inclusion of the professor of medicine from King's. It is of interest, though scarcely surprising, that one of the existing managers (William Laing, a physician) was the president of the Aberdeen Medico-Chirurgical Society.

The charter was finally granted on 26 August 1852 establishing an extensive list of managers as 'One Corporation and Body Corporate and Politic, under the Name and Title of "The President and Managers of the Infirmary of Aberdeen" to administer the affairs of the Infirmary and Lunatic Asylum, deal in property, handle funds and promote their collection, have the right to raise and carry actions, to sue and be sued'.[15] The president and managers were to 'have and use a common seal for the public business and affairs' and to renew this seal when required. The funds and property of the Infirmary were to be vested in the corporation. The provost was to be president with the senior magistrate as his deputy. Public bodies or individuals bequeathing £50 could nominate a manager for life. Trustees and executors donating money could nominate one, two or three life managers depending on the amount. There was also provision for appointing 'managers for a year' – persons donating £3 annually, one partner or member nominated by a public joint stock company or public board contributing £10 annually and representatives of congregations in proportion to sums donated. Regulations were laid down regarding the holding of quarterly general courts and other general courts who could appoint committees. The managers were given powers to appoint a treasurer, clerks and other officials and to make 'byelaws, statutes, rules and ordinances'. Expenditure was not to exceed annual income and annual accounts of income and expenditure had to be produced for public inspection. Freedom was granted to apply for further privileges which might render the charter more effective.

Nevertheless financial difficulties persisted and it was perhaps typical of the Victorian era that in 1883 a special committee under the convenorship of Alexander Edmond[16] issued an 'Appeal to the Working Classes' to be distributed through employers in an attempt to increase annual revenue. In this it was pointed out that the annual sum now required to run the Infirmary was £6,600 and emphasized that whereas Edinburgh's public bodies and workers contributed £3,183 a year to their Infirmary, Aberdeen could only manage £506. It was suggested that the current example set by some employers whereby one half to two pence a month was deducted from employees' wages should be copied. It is also perhaps a not unjustified comment on the careful nature of the Aberdonian that there is no hard evidence that the recommendation was widely put into effect.

Reform and change continued to exercise the managers and in 1887 they made application to parliament for an Act to repeal certain charters and provide for the incorporation of the existing managers in a new form, giving them powers to include in a new corporation all hospitals, asylums and dispensaries and in particular the Hospital for the Relief of Incurables (Morningfield), the Ophthalmic Institution, the Dispensary and the Hospital for Sick Children. Apart from the Lunatic Asylum all these were public charities. This Act of Incorporation came into force in July 1887, establishing the Aberdeen Royal Infirmary and Lunatic Asylum Corporation.[17]

Buildings

In the annual report for 1872, it was reported that conferences had taken place about the promotion of a convalescent hospital to be built at some distance from the city and which would require the expenditure of £3,000. The following year Lochhead House (within the curtilage of what is now Royal Cornhill Hospital) and grounds at Newhills (to the west of the city near Bucksburn) were purchased providing accommodation for 14 patients, a number increased to 22 in 1881. The next year it was decided to add two wards for the treatment of consumption but it was also mooted that £2,000 in the trust fund of Mrs Allan of Potterton should be used to build a hospital for the treatment of this condition. However, instead it was decided to establish two wards at Newhills for this purpose and to put Mrs Allan's money towards an extension to the Infirmary.[18] Because of the poor level of public financial support, Lochhead came under threat of closure in 1888 but this was averted, partly by the sale of the hospital to the Royal Asylum Board with an arrangement that it would be leased back to the Infirmary for two years while alternative accommodation was secured, preferably farther from the City. By 1896 a new convalescent hospital was under construction at Pitfodels and in October the following year it was opened. It continued in use until 1964 (it has been the Aberdeen–American school since 1972) when its function was replaced by Glen o' Dee (at Banchory). Lochhead House closed in 1948 and was subsequently used for student accommodation before it was demolished in 1990.

But this is to jump ahead, for major changes centred on Woolmanhill followed the report of a committee of managers and medical experts in 1885 on adding to the buildings there which concluded 'the hospital is opposed to the now universally accepted principles of hospital construction' which 'in several instances violates the primary condition of health'.[19] Though the phrase is reminiscent of Florence Nightingale's statement that the first duty of a hospital is not to do harm, we do not know just what these points of opposition were. As a result the managers resolved that 'the existing house must undergo complete internal reconstruction, and that a large addition must be built'. At the general quarterly court of managers on 13 December 1886, Lord Provost William Henderson[20] moved that a scheme should be instituted for 'the erection upon the present site of an hospital which be at once a credit to the city and a worthy memorial to the 50th aniversary of Her Majesty's reign' (there was no mention of any improvement in the welfare of the patients that it might treat). The cost was estimated at £20,000–24,000, which was considered too high, so architects were asked to prepare plans which retained the existing building and provided accommodation in pavilions. A public appeal raised £23,000 (promised or paid) in six months and this sum had reached £29,000 by the middle of 1888. At the end of the year and of Provost Henderson's term of office it had reached £30,594 from over 21,000 donors by which time the control of the fund had also passed from the finance committee to the board of directors. The new plans based on a design put forward by Mr H. Saxon Snell,[21] who had been retained in 1885 along with the local firm of Smith and Kelly, were adopted by the quarterly court on 13 June 1887 (Plate 11). The main building was preserved for administrative purposes and new pavilions were to be erected on the west, east and north sides. The existing west pavilion, running parallel to Spa Street would retain the structure though not the function of the 'typhus house' which would be converted into special wards. A southward extension of this block was to provide a surgical unit of six wards, an eye department of two wards and one ward for gynaecology. The east pavilion parallel to Woolmanhill, incorporated a medical unit of six wards while the north extension was to house the laundry and a pathology laboratory (see p.185). In the surgical area there were to be two operating theatres at the rear of the basement, one accommodating 200 students and the other 60 (see p.94). The estimated cost was £30,890 but, in spite of this increase from the previous level that had been considered, the scheme was set in motion and the surgical block was completed in 1892. The opening ceremony was performed by Princess Louise, Marchioness of Lorne on the 4 October 1892. A polished granite slab, which recorded the building as the Queen Victoria surgical pavilion and that it had been erected in honour of her jubilee, was placed in the wall at the entrance. In 1991 it has disappeared. Though the 50th jubilee had passed in 1887 and 'sixty glorious years' was not to be completed for a further half decade, we must assume from William Henderson's words that the surgical pavilion commemorates, a little belatedly, 50 years of Victoria on the throne (and his knighthood which was bestowed in 1893).

Plate 11 The overall plan for the extension proposed by Saxon Snell. The domed Simpson building is to the left. Most of this development persists in 1992 though much modified internally. The current entrance is now where the figures stand in the right foreground and the form of the entrance lodge to the right is curved rather than rectangular.

ABERDEEN
ROYAL INFIRMARY
VIEW
SHEWING PROPOSED
NEW PAVILIONS
H. SAXON SNELL & SONS ARCH.
W. J. SMITH

Woolmanhill

Spa St.

The medical pavilion was however on time for the golden jubilee and was opened by the Dowager Countess of Errol in 1897. The following year the first ward for disease of women was inaugurated under the charge of Professor Stephenson (see p. 43). By now and in addition to the medical and surgical pavilions, the Infirmary also provided a dental department where teeth were extracted free of charge except where chloroform was used for which the fee was one shilling. There was an in-patient and out-patient eye department equipped with a powerful magnet for the removal of metallic foreign bodies – a common industrial injury in the days before eye protection became routine. The basement housed an electric department for nerve stimulation, a bath for hydrotherapy and an X-ray department for both diagnosis and the ultraviolet therapy of such diseases as lupus vulgaris (cutaneous tuberculosis). The laundry boasted steam-driven washing and wringing machines and a huge apparatus called a 'decoudon calender' for drying clothes between heated rollers. Heating of the building was by two water tube boilers which consumed 5 tons of coal a day through self-feeding stokers. The electric supply came from two 64 h.p. and one 15 h.p. engines (the general provision of urban electricity in Aberdeen dates from 1894 but presumably the Infirmary's own supply was planned long before this).

By the turn of the century £70,955 had been spent on the project in addition to which the entire furnishings of the surgical pavilion had been paid for by the widow of Alexander Black of Hyde Park Gardens, London[22] and her daughter Mrs Pickering of Kincardine. The Jubilee Extension scheme was finally achieved in 1900, the total cost amounting to £75,296 which left a debt of £24,665. Public subscriptions had largely dried up and there was an accumulation of interest on the loan over the five year period 1896 to 1901 of £3,358. A saviour then appeared in the person of Lord Mount-Stephen[23] (Plate 12). Through Lord Provost John Fleming[24] he presented the managers with £25,000 to clear the outstanding debt and in 1902 he transferred to the Infirmary securities of the nominal value of Canadian $100,000 which at that time would provide an annual income of £1,000. In recognition of this beneficence the new medical block was named the Mount-Stephen Pavilion and the appropriate plaque erected which cannot now be found. The creation of a new casualty department and a stack of operating theatres subsequent to a further donation from Lord Mount-Stephen in 1908 is recounted in Chapters 7 and 9. The completion of the casualty department in 1912 released space for doctors' accommodation and provided offices for the medical superintendent and his staff which were completed by 1915. New ENT wards (see Chapter 9) were opened in 1913.

Staff

It is impossible to detail here all the staff both medical and other who gave dedicated service to the Royal Infirmary during the last half of the 19th century and the first quarter of the 20th. Many of them, such as Alexander Ogston, will be considered elsewhere in this account or are recorded in the biographical notes. Two characters are noteworthy. Miss Rachel Lumsden, honorary

Plate 12 George Stephen, first Baron Mount-Stephen, patient at Woolmanhill and
  generous benefactor.

superintendent from 1885 to 1897,[25] and William Carnie,[26] clerk and treasurer
from 1861 to 1898 , both long-serving members.

The patients and their illnesses

Infectious diseases played a major part in the activities of the Infirmary during
the whole of the 19th century but increased in importance and severity as the
City grew in size. In September 1863 an epidemic of typhus struck Aberdeen
affecting predominantly those who lived in areas of high population density
such as the Gallowgate and Causewayend. The number of cases reached a peak
in December and the disease smouldered on with further peaks in September of
the following year and the spring and autumn of 1865. Patients with the disease
continued to be admitted for the first half of 1866 and the epidemic was not
judged to be over until June of that year. Over the three year period there were
754 male and 977 female victims, the largest number being in the 10–25 age
group. The mortality was 13 per cent. Some idea of the strain on the resources of
the Infirmary can be gained from the largest figure for monthly admissions
which was 133 in December 1863 and from the fact that the average time spent in

hospital by those who survived was 30 days. Five years later there was an outbreak of smallpox which continued for 15 months until July of 1872. The Infirmary could not cope and attempts had to be made to find alternative accommodation. For reasons that seem to lie in the infective nature of the disease these efforts were obstructed first by the city parochial board and then by the board of supervision. Eventually premises were acquired at Mounthooly. In all there were 230 cases with 37 deaths but throughout the city as a whole 163 people died. As we have already seen and in spite of an early determination to isolate infectious patients (see p.28), Aberdeen had lagged behind similar institutions in providing separate accommodation for these, so that patients with highly transmissible diseases continued to be admitted to the general wards. The reason was lack of money though one contemporary suggested that, had it been a question of cattle plague, action would have been prompt enough. Eventually, on the advice of the Medico-Chirugical Society and the university, all infectious fevers were refused admission, the one exception being typhoid. The City Hospital had opened in 1877 and thereafter took all such patients. As we have recorded (p.40) this freed the 'typhus ward' for reallocation. That tuberculosis was a problem is apparent from the decision (p.39) to have wards for its treatment at Newhills. This was the beginning of a long and distinguished association between Aberdeen and the management of this one-time scourge (see p.144).

The emergence of the specialities for the treatment of various diseases is further considered in Chapters 9 and 10. Some idea of the considerable growth of the role of the Infirmary can be gained from the figures for 1903; 2,665 patients were admitted; there were now 31 medical staff, nine sisters and 63 nurses and probationers; 23 domestic staff supplemented by six porters. An average of 25 surgical out-patients were seen daily and 33 operations carried out every week. In 1902, 3,730 patients had been treated in the casualty department and 9,554 had attended the out-patient departments. A contemporary description of the scene is as follows:

> Enter by the waiting room: what a picture! There were all sorts and conditions of people gathered together, in all stages of suffering and convalescence, each awaiting his or her turn to be summoned into the ward. And sometimes even the waiting room is insufficient to accommodate them all, so that they crowd the passages.

Such was the Royal Infirmary as it entered the second quarter of the 20th century.[27]

4

To the Healing Winds of Foresterhill

From the turn of the 19th century the relentless expansion of the city of Aberdeen westward from the sea, hemmed in the site of the Royal Infirmary at Woolmanhill. Moreover the hospital was separated from Marischal College and was not in any physical intimacy with the other institutions such as the Children's and Maternity Hospitals. At the close of World War I it was clear that the existing premises were cramped, out of date and quite inadequate for the growing needs of the people of north-east Scotland. Waiting lists were increasing and more beds were needed. New thinking was required and was provided by Matthew Hay[1] (Plate 13), the professor of medical jurisprudence (forensic medicine) and medical officer of health, who in 1920 produced the Joint Hospitals scheme.

How much of this proposal was truly the brain child of Hay is not clear from the written record but Norman Logie,[2] whose account of the Foresterhill development is the definitive record,[3] maintains that Hay 'used to spend his Sunday mornings tramping the outskirts of Aberdeen looking for a suitable site for his dream child'. Whether or not it was his idea alone or the outcome of discussions with his friends and professional colleagues it was given considerable impetus by Ashley Mackintosh[4] (Plate 14) whose occupancy of the chair of medicine (1912–30) spanned the critical years of the inception and acceptance of the scheme. Prominent also and acting as a focus for debate and action was the Medico-Chirurgical Society which in the 1920s was (and still is) a meeting place for members of all the diverse practitioners of medicine from consultants and academics to general practitioners.

As Logie recounts, the first formal event in this momentous development was a special meeting of the Society in February 1920 at which the scheme to be created on the Foresterhill site was outlined. In its original form – the Infirmary, the Children's Hospital, a tuberculosis hospital, all the university medical departments other than those in the basic sciences, a dental hospital, the Incurables Hospital from Morningfield, the Eye Institute and accommodation for patients with mental illness plus a nurses' home and a hostel for medical students – the concept was nothing less than the establishment of a complete medical centre.[5] As such it was well ahead of its time in the United Kingdom and even today it is doubtful if such a concentration, modified but still adhering to the original idea, has been achieved elsewhere.

Plate 13 Matthew Hay.

The outcome of this meeting was a decision to bring together representatives of the Society, the Town Council, the Infirmary and the Children's Hospital. The gathering, presided over by Lord Provost William Meff,[6] took place in April and led to the creation of a Joint Hospitals committee to examine the feasibility of the project. By 1922 a decision had been reached to build the new Infirmary and other components of the scheme at Foresterhill. The 112 acres (45.3 hectares) would be purchased from the Town Council for an overall £35,000 (approximately £875,000 at 1991 prices).

The years of drift

The years 1922 to 1927 were described in the local newspaper as those of drift,[7] though Logie in more forthright terms called them those of 'threat, strife and frustration'. The main reason was the organization of the hospital service in the country as a whole. The increasing range of the Public Health Acts in the 1920s allowed local authorities through their public health services (whose original role

Plate 14 Ashley Mackintosh.

is sketched in Chapter 6), to take on the task of provision of hospital and laboratory services. The very success of the service in Aberdeen as a consequence of the work of Matthew Hay was to threaten the future of the scheme through the convictions of his assistant and successor J. Parlane Kinloch.[8] The latter proposed to take into his care in the fever hospitals many conditions such as pneumonia, tuberculosis, poliomyelitis and the venereal diseases which at that time were commonly treated by general physicians and surgeons in the voluntary hospitals. Such action would segregate a large proportion of the hospital medical practice of the day and, just as importantly, remove the patients from the teaching environment. From the time of his appointment in 1923, Kinloch made clear his hostility to the voluntary hospital system and also, perhaps to reinforce his views, raised questions about the financial involvement of the Town Council in the Joint Hospital scheme. In 1926 at his instigation, the council took over Woodend Hospital from the parish council and proposed to develop there 200 beds for medical and surgical patients, so posing a serious threat to the voluntary system in that the new hospital would be entirely financed by the ratepayers and staffed by doctors employed by the local authority. Newspaper reports of the time speak of 'the first municipal general hospital in Scotland'.[9] The board of directors of the Royal Infirmary and their permanent officials who had been working enthusiastically on the details of the joint scheme suddenly found that it was endangered because of what appeared on the surface to be an unseemly wrangle between doctors as to who should treat which diseases and where this should be done, but was in fact an ideological clash over the delivery of health care. University staff were also alarmed at the potential loss of patients for teaching.

It should be emphasized that these difficulties were not unique to Aberdeen. Parlane Kinloch's entrenched position behind the Public Health Acts was shared by medical officers of health in many large cities including London, and led to the development of hospitals which were initially, and in some instances for years after the start of the National Health Service in isolation from the network of voluntary acute hospitals.[10] Their architectural legacy – often gloomy and outdated – is still there for all to see. In Aberdeen the effect was to induce hesitancy in the Town Council because of Kinloch's influence with a resultant deadlock which lasted until 1928 and cast grave doubts on the possibility of ever building a new Infirmary. Already siren voices were beginning to call for wider intervention in the provision of hospital services by the state rather than the local authorities, though it would take World War II and the social upheaval that followed to bring this about. In that the financial support of the voluntary hospitals such as the Royal Infirmary was at this time entirely by contributions from the general public in the form of personal donations, collections in church and workplace and legacies, it is easy to imagine how the possible introduction of a service based on government was a disincentive to such contributions and hence a challenge to the continued existence of the voluntary system.

The deadlock was finally broken, as is often the case, by a powerful personality. Andrew Lewis[11] (Plate 15) had been elected Lord Provost of the city in 1925. He was an enthusiast for the joint scheme and within two years had raised £410,000[12] for the Infirmary by his personal efforts and his contact with monied people in the North-East. Towards the end of 1926 the directors of the Infirmary asked him to convene a meeting of all the interested parties on the same lines as that of his predecessor William Meff. The result was a consultative committee set up in 1927 to consider the whole question of hospital services in Aberdeen. Through its activities a compromise was ultimately reached. Lewis had seen clearly that the joint scheme could prosper only with the co-operation and under the aegis of the Town Council, which had up to this point been ambivalent. He had identified the real problem which was to demonstrate that money could be raised for the building of the new Infirmary. In March 1927 he was able to announce that in a few days of campaigning in the community he had received definite promises of £130,000 with more to follow – an astonishing *coup de theatre*.

Another catalyst to the development and one which somewhat antedated Lewis's decisive action was the purchase in 1925 by the directors of the Children's Hospital of 17 acres at Foresterhill. Their old hospital in Castle Terrace was a grim edifice which had attracted unfavourable comment from Queen Mary during a visit in 1912. An appeal in 1919 raised £70,000 for a new hospital but, with the directors embracing the Joint Hospital scheme, they saw their plans unnecessarily and repeatedly postponed. By 1925 a further appeal had increased these resources to £140,000 and they went on to buy the site and build their new pavilion-style

Plate 15 Andrew Lewis, Lord Provost of Aberdeen 1925–9.

hospital which was opened in January 1929. Such action bought valuable time for the ARI: the town council reserved the rest of the Foresterhill site for five years to enable the necessary funds for the Royal Infirmary to be raised. Lewis used the presence of the Children's Hospital as an argument in his public appeal in 1927 for money to build the new Infirmary speaking of the 'new . . . hospital arising on the sunny slope overlooking the Westburn and Victoria Park open to the healing winds from the south and west'.[13]

By 1927 all seemed to be decided and the matter of a formal start to the development now became important. Since the days when Queen Victoria had made Balmoral her highland home,[14] frequent formal and informal visits by the royal family to Aberdeen had strengthened the affection in which they were held by its citizens. So it was seen as fitting that a date was set aside in August 1928 on which the foundation stone of the new Royal Infirmary could be laid by the Prince of Wales who would be in residence at Balmoral. The local daily paper stated in somewhat fulsome terms[15] that: 'there is no more popular and romantic royal personage in this or any other country than our bachelor Prince. His readiness to associate himself with any movement for the welfare of the country has endeared him to all classes, while his sunny smile and unassuming demeanour have made him a national idol'.

At the time the Prince promised to return to open the hospital but this commitment was to remain unfulfilled (see below). The first turf was cut in July 1930 and the construction of the medical block of the Infirmary began a year later. It was not a propitious time to begin work on a new and costly project. All the monies had to come from public subscription when worldwide trade was in depression and large-scale unemployment rampant, with political upheaval between 1929 and 1932 accompanied by collapse of the banking economy in the United States. It needed vision and stout hearts to proceed with the building of a hospital which was finally to cost £535,000 (about £13 million today) amidst the prevailing climate of unemployment, poverty, poor housing conditions, hunger and such dispensations of charity as soup kitchens.

The building programme

Though we have run ahead of events in our account, it was 1929 when the directors were in a position to invite the honorary medical staff to state their requirements for beds and accommodation. The planning committee considered that the 580 beds requested could not be funded and settled for 500. As had applied in the past and was to be repeated in the future, methods of hospital construction were studied in a variety of settings ranging from Inverness to Woolwich and by the scrutiny of plans available from the United States and South Africa.[16] It was finally agreed that four storey blocks would be most appropriate in that these would conform with the site and would be less costly both to erect and to administer. The initial brief was to produce a series of buildings to include: an administrative block;[17] out-patient departments for all specialities along with two minor operating rooms and a casualty department; an electrical department;[18] an out-patient unit for venereal diseases (see Chapter 9); standard ward blocks for medicine and surgery with, in the latter, attached operating theatres; a laundry, mortuary and chapel; and a five storey home to accommodate 276 nurses.

It soon became clear that the ideal scheme could not be achieved with the funds available. Out-patients would perforce have to remain at Woolmanhill though this was not looked upon with favour by the medical staff and would lead in future years to a great deal of difficulty and wasted effort (see, for example, p.131). Initially the nurses' home was also dropped in favour of accommodation in the old Infirmary at Woolmanhill. In order to save money the possibility of using the large pool of unemployed labour for the work of excavating the site and laying roads, footpaths and drains was also explored as this would have attracted a government grant. A calculation by the city engineers rejected this idea in favour of using private contractors with fixed estimates and guaranteed time scales.

Plate 16 Building Foresterhill. Aerial view of the greenfield site, 1934. The nurse's home is on the left.

The fiercest debate centred, however, on a proposal by the consulting architects to build in the most economic method – steel and brick. This departure from the long architectural tradition of using local granite led a number of individuals and organizations to threaten withdrawal of financial support; the silver city by the sea was also the granite city and this building material was famous the world over. After consultation with the local stone merchants, a compromise was reached so that granite was incorporated alongside concrete dressings and as can be seen today, the North-East's material is dominant in the buildings of the day though surrounded now by concrete and glass (Plate 16).

Anxious but undaunted the directors pressed ahead with their now continuously revised building programme. Fortunately some organizational help was at hand in 1931 from the Aberdeen branch of the British Medical Association which felt that it should be possible to merge some of the voluntary and municipal services. A regional consultative committee was set up[19] and a hospital plan was produced which proposed that Woolmanhill should contain all out-patient services irrespective of whether they were being provided from the voluntary sector, the local authority or central government. Casualty, all out-patient departments and the management of venereal disease (predominantly on out-patient basis) would remain down town and the funds so released would ensure the building of the nurses' home at Foresterhill.

Many small difficulties remained to be overcome but by 1933 building was proceeding apace.[20] During the next two years, though the ward blocks were completed without much alteration, the nurses' home had to be reduced in size

Plate 17 Peter Scatterty Memorial. The largest bequest from a single benefactor to the 1936 Foresterhill project is commemorated and is in the reception area on the first floor of the special block (Otolaryngology wards 1 and 2).

to 258 beds. Increased costs were also incurred in the boiler house which was to supply the Children's Hospital as well and provide steam for the joint hospital laundry.[21] Further changes were made to re-design the special block so as to accommodate advances in therapy, to provide a lodge for the 'gate porters' and to include a mortuary and post-mortem theatre in the new university building being erected concurrently (see Chapter 19). These variations were the main cause of setbacks and delays as was the stringency of funds from year to year. There was only one strike in a period of six years of building when plasterers withdrew their labour for four months.

The last hundred thousand

By 1935 the deficit on the building scheme amounted to £70,000 and a further £30,000 had still to be found for furnishing and equipment. Another fund-raising exercise was needed and the directors put their faith in Lord Provost Edward Watt[22] who justified this by producing the money within 12 months[23] (Plate 17).

Plate 18 The opening ceremony, Foresterhill, 23 September 1936. The Duke of York holds the gold key which has been presented to him by the architect, J.B. Nichol, just visible next to the pillar. Lord Provost Watt is to the right of the Duchess. The head porter is Alexander Petrie.

The opening

All the vicissitudes of construction and finance notwithstanding, it was foreseen that the new Infirmary would be ready for occupation in the autumn of 1936. By custom the royal family – headed by the one time Prince of Wales, now King Edward VIII – would be resident at Balmoral at that time and the return of the king to fulfill his promise was widely anticipated. In the event it was his brother – the Duke of York (subsequently King George VI) accompanied by his Duchess (now Queen Elizabeth the Queen Mother) who performed the ceremony in the natural amphitheatre in front of the main entrance (Plate 18). Several thousand people gathered to hear his speech in which he paid tribute to Matthew Hay (who had died in 1932), Andrew Lewis and Edward Watt and went on to read a message from his brother, the King: 'The opening of the new Aberdeen Royal Infirmary. . .is a landmark in the progress of a far reaching scheme, which, by concentration of many hospital services in one area will. . .prove of the greatest benefit to all the people of Aberdeenshire. I recall with pleasure that I laid the foundation stone. . .in 1928 and I shall look forward to visiting the Infirmary later. . .'

Meanwhile the promulgator if not the direct author of these words had unexpectedly arrived at Aberdeen joint (railway) station[24] to meet his future wife Mrs Wallis Simpson who, when Edward VIII abdicated later in the year, was to become the Duchess of Windsor. In the event he never returned, but 30 years later the Queen Mother opened Phase I (see p.72) and remarked that she well remembered the day.

Some of the objectives of the joint scheme were not destined to be achieved but the overall concept remains in Norman Logie's words 'a monument to the vigour, tenacity, independence, longsightedness and generosity of the people of Aberdeen and the North-East'.

Though times have changed through social evolution and the developing needs of medical practice, the vision of those who set up the original concept will forever remain part of Aberdeen's history.

5

Post-war Planning and Development

Neither the whole of truth nor the whole of good is revealed to any single observer although each gains a partial superiority of insight from the peculiar position in which he stands.

William James[1]

Contemporary history is the most difficult to write. The fact that many though not all of those who participated in the growth of the Aberdeen Royal Infirmary on the Foresterhill site after World War II are still alive is both a help and a complication. What follows is an attempt to blend different perspectives into a coherent, if not quite homogeneous, account.

The end of the war saw Britain gripped by new social ideas such as the National Health Service but exhausted both in terms of the will to carry them out and the economic resources needed. Many will now have forgotten the fact that food rationing ended only in 1952–3, conscription (National Service) in 1960 and that severe shortages of both basic materials (such as bricks, cement and building machinery) and of consumer goods (furniture and other household items) persisted well into the late 1950s. Against such a background, to the historian at least, it is scarcely surprising that our hospital 'stock', already severely affected by six years of semi-neglect during the war (and some would say also before it), should continue to decline.

The National Health Service, the child of the Beveridge Report published during the dark days of 1942–3, inherited this inadequate physical base on the appointed day (5 July 1948 in Scotland) but was unable to do much about it for some years. Not that in Aberdeen the buildings were crumbling; the foresight of those in the inter-war years had, as we have seen, secured both the Foresterhill site and the main buildings which stand to this day. With the exception of Woolmanhill which was to languish untouched except for internal tinkering (see p.131) until it was abandoned in 1976 for all but scheduled out-patients, the need in Aberdeen was for expansion. This was vigorously pursued.

The East Wing

By 1952 the supply problem had eased somewhat and regional boards were given a hint that small sums of capital might be available for limited building projects.

Advances in medical knowledge and techniques, coupled with pressures from medical, nursing and other staff back from the war, persuaded the Board to apply for resources to build a small extension at the east end of the Infirmary adjacent to the existing special block (see p.52).

Pressure for space from the medical staff was intense but in the long run four claims emerged as having top priority. The first was a central records and registration department to change what was a largely chaotic state of affairs with records held on individual wards. The second was a laboratory for blood transfusion, the development of which is outlined on p.196. Third was pharmacy whose history is traced on p.197 *et seq.* Finally there was nurse training, whose advocate was Miss Florence Kaye, Matron of the Royal Infirmary from 1935 to 1958,[2] who with foresight sensed the need for nurses to have periods of intensive study off the wards and in a place of their own.

It was possible also to cater for two other urgent needs: an ambulance bay and porter's lodge so that movements of patients and visitors could be controlled; and a night casualty department to meet a need that is discussed on p.129.

The architect chosen by the board was Mr Geoffrey Fairweather[3] of Messrs Pite, Son and Fairweather. After his death in 1955, Bruce George (see also p.64) of the same firm took over (in 1959 the firm's name was changed to George, Trew and Dunn).

As planning proceeded, what emerged was a four storey building with a link at ground floor level to the extreme east end of the main infirmary corridor and further links at first, second and third floor levels to the three wards of the existing special block. Records, the ambulance bay and the porter's lodge were found on the ground floor; blood transfusion and pharmacy on the second floor; and the nurse education department on the third floor (Plate 19).

The architectural treatment was designed to match the existing pre-war buildings (Plate 20) and the contract went to the local builder Alexander Hall, who subsequently continued their involvement in Foresterhill with Phase I. In those more informal times, J.C. Duffus the then chairman of the board of management for the ARI[4] laid a wager with the chairman of Alexander Hall that the building would not be completed on time. Mr Duffus lost his £20 because all went according to plan and the building was occupied in 1956. We shall encounter the east wing again when the link building is described on p.78.

Though the ARI was fortunate to get the east wing extension this was only a beginning. By the mid 1950s, it was accepted that a major development of the Royal Infirmary was essential if this, the chief hospital in the region, was to accommodate the ever-increasing demands of the population of the North-East and of the Islands. Provision was required for the many advances in medicine

Plate 19 Building the East Block, 1955. The style is still traditional.

Plate 20 Overall view from the north-east after the completion of the East Block. This is the end of granite. The Porter's lodge and entrance shown in Plate 22 was attached to the very left hand corner of this view. Drawing by Graham Barrie Clilverd.

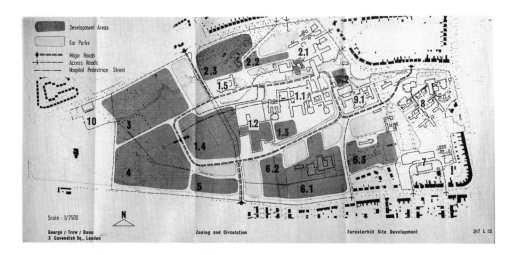

Plate 21 Development plan late 1950s (see text).

Zone 1: Royal Infirmary: 1.1, existing ARI; 1.2, extension phases 1, 2 and 3; 1.3, future OPD*; 1.4, future hospital*; 1.5, administration.
Zone 2: University Medical School: 2.1, existing medical school and extension, medical physics, animal house, Foresterhill refectory, and future medical centre; 2.2, future biological sciences block and new medical school*; 2.3, university residential area*.
Zone 3: University development*.
Zone: Hospital development.
Zone 5: Industrial area B: boiler house B; frozen food factory or store.
Zone 6: Hospital teaching and housing: 6.1, Foresterhill College and hospital educational buildings; 6.2, teaching health centre; 6.3, hospital residential area.
Zone 7: Industrial area A: 7.1, boiler house A; 7.2, CSSD and laundry; 7.3, future transport area.
Zone 8: Royal Aberdeen Hospital for Sick Children.
Zone 9: Maternity Hospital: 9.1, existing building; 9.2, future developments.
Zone 10: Hydro board and ambulance station.

* Denotes planning development only.

and patient care and also to permit a rationalization and redeployment of adult beds in the Aberdeen area. Furthermore, there was a need to allow for the progressive upgrading of the original hospital which, while still comparatively modern, would need to be re-organized and refurbished in the next 20 to 30 years as part of an overall policy of improvement and of concentrating the specialist services on the Foresterhill site. The overall objectives and a draft site plan were agreed in the late 1950s though there were subsequent modifications (Plate 21).

Expansion to the west

The place most obviously available for large-scale development at Foresterhill was located to the west of the existing buildings of the Royal Infirmary on land having, as does virtually the whole of the site, a south-facing slope. In preparing the development plan, advantage was taken of the gradient of the site to link the new with the old buildings by designing the lower ground floor level to correspond with the main ground floor level of the existing Royal Infirmary. The service departments such as the operating theatre suite, X-ray department, staff dining and changing rooms were obviously best located at this level and connected to the main hospital corridor of the existing buildings. Provision was also made for future connections at both the ground and lower ground floor levels to Phases II and III and to other future developments.

Phasing the development

Financial constraints, both capital and revenue, combined with the need to find trained nursing staff matched to the foreseen total additional requirement of some 500 beds and supporting services, determined that the expansion would require to be phased. Phase I would comprise wards for general surgery, thoracic surgery, cardiovascular investigation and some private patients – a total complement of 129 beds; an operating theatre block with four theatres and central sterile supply department; an X-ray department with six main rooms and an X-ray theatre; a central concourse for visitors which would include a shop, a cafeteria and a bank; a patient reception suite and a central records department to serve the whole of the Royal Infirmary. Provision was to be made to allow extension of the operating theatre block and the X-ray department in Phase II.

Phase II, as had always been envisaged, would be a larger project than Phase I – to provide some 400 beds; further theatres and X-ray provision; in-built accommodation for the university departments of medicine, therapeutics and gynaecology; various special departments and support services and an accident and emergency department (the latter originally known as Phase III).

The content of Phase I

There seems little doubt that what went into Phase I was in great part the outcome of informal discussion between Dr A.M. (Sandy) Michie, OBE – who had become medical superintendent of the ARI shortly after the war and whose knowledge of and sensitivity for the issues was based on his strong roots in the North-East – and two senior medical officers to the regional hospital board, Dr Knox[5] and Dr Beddard.[6]

Dr Michie[7] recalls that the main 'pressure points' which dictated the discussion about what should be included were clinical, organizational and social. On the clinical front there were too few beds available to deal with orthopaedic emergencies, for example, the eight or so fractures of the femoral neck following a frosty winter's day in Aberdeen. There was also severe pressure on thoracic surgery; tuberculosis was on the decline but surgery was still the mainstay of the management of cancer and a backlog was building up. In addition the thoracic unit was ill-housed at Woodend and a fair amount of pleading on its behalf was taking place. There was a looming problem of dialysis for renal failure which was being pioneered in the professorial medical and surgical units[8] but was going to need a more permanent base.

The facilities for X-ray – then the only form of imaging – were grossly inadequate so that patients (Sandy Michie among them) were denied reasonable facilities when they had to undergo complicated investigations (see p.178). It was further realized that extra theatre capacity was bound to be required not only to deal with thoracic surgery but also to take into consideration the increasing length and complexity of modern general surgery.

As to organization, it was clear that the space for records in the east wing (p.56) was inadequate and that a new telephone exchange had to be created – in 1957 that for the ARI was housed in a room no larger than six feet by four feet; it is worthy of note that the planning eventually achieved, ahead of most hospital complexes in Britain, a massive and efficient PABX (private automatic branch exchange) which encompassed the whole hospital group and medical school. The regional hospital board needed more space in its offices at Albyn Place; next door lay the (then) Watson Fraser Nursing Home, so transferring these beds to the Foresterhill site would make this accommodation available.

Last, though not least, was the social aspect. The distance of Foresterhill from the centre of Aberdeen, though admirable for long-term planning and development, meant that both patients and relatives needed what might be called domestic or social facilities. One has only to look at a contemporary photograph (Plate 22) to realize that, with the then somewhat draconian rules about visiting hours, relatives were queueing in the cold and wet with nowhere to have a cup of tea, or to buy flowers and minor gifts, let alone the necessities that are so often forgotten in the hurry and stress of a hospital admission.

Though it was not yet common, it was also appreciated that banking facilities on site would be needed both by patients, their relatives and the staff. As a man in touch with his community, Dr Michie remembers that 'I was the one who was getting the complaints' – though this of course also made him uniquely capable of responding to them and impressing the regional hospital board with his views.

It was from this *melange* of pressures that the early concept for Phase I developed. It could have been thought that, given the need for orthopaedic and traumatic services, it would have been better to re-house this department primarily but, though short of facilities, they were well placed on the ground floor of the existing surgical block with an adjacent orthopaedic out-patients' department. It was judged preferable to move the professorial surgical unit which was at that time on the first floor, so as to free more accommodation for the orthopaedic department.

That there were also long waiting lists for surgical admissions in 1958 is undoubted but these did not seem to loom large in the decisions about planning. To a certain extent this may have been because other techniques of management, mainly the development of 'day surgery' in which Aberdeen was a pioneer had

Plate 22 The congestion just before visiting hours referred to on p.60.

already begun to mitigate this.[9] However, the initiative to provide adequate beds and operating facilities has probably made it possible for Aberdeen to be, as we write, one of the few places in the United Kingdom where waiting for an elective surgical bed is minimal.

These outline concepts were taken up by Dr Denys Beddard with the Scottish Office in 1958, and at the end of 1959 formal approval was given to start planning for a ward block of 129 beds (on three floors) with certain central services, and the first part of a treatment block containing operating theatres and very extensive X-ray facilities.

The transfer of the beds of the Watson Fraser nursing home to the uppermost of the three ward floors enabled the cost of these to be largely met from the (then) board of management's endowment funds.

So the Royal Infirmary became, in company with six other projects in Scotland,[10] and as a result of the efforts of a few far-sighted people, part of a general effort throughout Britain to upgrade and extend hospital accommodation. In retrospect this programme can be seen to have been too little and too late: future historians will pronounce on whether this was due to a lack of funds or a continued lack of political will. For those in Aberdeen at the time, however, here was an opportunity to do something new and exciting. It was grasped with enthusiasm.

Planning

A professional planning committee (PPC), chaired by the board's senior administrative medical officer and comprising representatives of the senior medical staff, senior nursing staff, the professional and administrative staff, was charged with the preparation of the functional brief for the Phase I development, and this was completed in the spring of 1960.[11] At a later stage, another – equipment – committee, chaired by the group medical superintendent, undertook the choice and provision of equipment, lighting and of electrical outlets plus the detailed layout of individual rooms. Room data sheets were prepared in plan, ceiling and wall elevations. It met at the unsocial hour of 7.30 a.m.

The approach to planning which placed the primary onus on a PPC was the brainchild of Dr Denys Beddard, though it seems likely that Sir George Godber, who was later to become his chief at the Department of Health and Social Security in London, influenced his thinking. The committee considered all aspects of the brief and when necessary other specialists were co-opted for advice – a concept that emerged from Dr Beddard's view that if every specialist (including consultants from the mechanical and electrical engineering services) was represented on the committee it would be impossible to reconcile their views. This approach also meant that the members had to work hard and acquire at least a nodding acquaintance with areas that were not necessarily familiar to them in their everyday work.

At all stages of planning it was made clear that the PPC dealt only with function. The outcome of their deliberations would be a functional brief for the architect. It was then his task to turn such proposals into three-dimensional spatial relationships and to rationalize a functional proposal with the practicalities of such matters as plumbing, ventilation, the supply of electricity and the distribution of food and equipment. The ultimate user should see a sketch plan to try to ensure that there was nothing glaringly wrong with it in terms of how space would be used. But planners should not be draughtsmen. To achieve this symbiosis between function and design it is essential that the architect should be present when function is debated. Furthermore he should be a sympathetic listener, which is not commonly the case as some planners have learned to their cost. The consultant architect was in consequence invited to attend all the meetings of the committee. These took place weekly. In those days the only aircraft that plied the Aberdeen–London route was a somewhat lethargic DC3 and, in addition, the journey from Heathrow to central London could be relied on to take two hours at least. The overnight train was then (even if not now) a more reliable form of transport. At the height of the planning exercise this meant that Bruce George, based in London, had to spend two nights on the London–Aberdeen train sleeper every week, which for Phase I involved a total of more than one hundred thousand miles and such adventures as arresting an intruder into his sleeping compartment at 3 a.m.

For other members of the PPC, planning on such a scale was a new experience and few if any realized at the outset the extent of the commitment which would be called for, nor the additional workload which each would require to carry on top of his or her normal everyday tasks. Late afternoon and evening meetings became routine.

Homework for individual committee members in the preparation of specialized detail became an accepted way of life. One member recalls[12] that Monday, the day of the PPC meeting at 5.30 p.m., was a 'receiving day' for his surgical team and from the end of the PPC meeting he had to make tracks for the wards both to see what emergencies had come in and to teach on what was at that time a well-attended evening round for students.

Another[13] was once required by his professor (seeking no doubt some recompense for the frequent absence of a lecturer on planning business) to calculate the hours spent on the PPC; it amounted to more than 400. However, as all recall, no one thought too much about this frenetic activity; planning became part of the tapestry of living in and developing the National Health Service for the future.

Denys Beddard chaired the committee with great effect. The PPC approach as seen by its secretary is recalled by Buff Hardie:[14] '. . . I cannot get away from the thought that my own career as an administrator in the health service was very much bound up with the Aberdeen Royal Infirmary development. . . Late in the 1950s I had joined the administrative ranks of the then North Eastern Regional Hospital Board. . .I had my head well below the rampart and it was my intention to keep it there as long as I could. That ambition was thwarted at a fairly early stage when I was given, as my first substantive task, the job of secretary to the professional planning committee for Phase I of the Royal Infirmary development. The role of the secretary to the committee was to ensure that its members had the date, time, venue and papers for the next meeting (thus early did I learn what administration is all about) and following the meeting to write a minute detailing all the decisions taken. That was then passed to Dr Beddard who used it as an aide-memoire in the preparation of the functional brief for Phase I. It was he who shaped the layout and the presentation of the information in the brief but it was a rewarding experience for a tyro administrator to see, as the document took shape, verbatim extracts from the committee's minutes being included. All this was at a time before anyone had heard of job satisfaction but I guess that is what I had.

'The concept of the functional brief was new and not one which I have ever read of in any health service journals. Its objective was to describe in specific detail what was to happen in the new building – what was to be done and by whom, how, where and with what they were to do it. At meetings of the committee no preconceived notions of what rooms should be provided were admitted; no one was allowed to draw squares on paper; the expression 'etc' was sternly eschewed, where there was a temptation to use it, every item which would have been covered by it had to be specified. This discipline was rigidly enforced by the convener and the other members of the committee responded by playing the game according to these rules throughout the two years of their regular weekly sessions, which went on until the chairman made what became a ritual declaration of "Well I think we have reached saturation point. Does anyone

fancy a snifter?" Once the functional brief was completed and enshrined in a
bluebook. . .it received the board's approval and was then passed to the architect
for him to express the spatial requirements of the activities it described in the
form of outline sketch plans. These were discussed with the PPC and subjected
to a series of amendments and adjustments before they were finalized to the
satisfaction of both the functional planners and the architect.

The architect for the project was Mr W.N.B. (Bruce) George, senior partner of
the London firm of George, Trew and Dunn. He was and is an urbane, civilized
man with whom the members of the committee established a very happy and
productive rapport. As well as his technical and artistic skills he had a great gift
of advocacy in the pursuance or defence of a point.'

He recalls further that at one stage a meeting had to take place with civil
servants from the Scottish Office where the board invited a clinical member of
the PPC to attend who did not take kindly to the mandarins and their somewhat
patronizing attitudes, and goes on to say that 'the meeting had the outcome
which the Board was seeking. It represented another triumph for the negotiating
skills of Lady (May) Baird[15] then well into a 20 year period as chairman of the
board, a veritable giant in the history of health care in the North-East of
Scotland, not least in the development of the Royal Infirmary. It has often
occurred to me during the Thatcher era that May Baird undoubtedly was prime
minister material: she had all the Thatcher qualities, including toughness,
leavened with charm, compassion and a sense of humour. .. . .But in terms of the
acceptability of women at the top level of politics she was in her prime a
generation too soon.

'The meetings of the PPC at which all such momentous, and a myriad of far less
important decisions, were hammered out could be quite lively. In this context
'lively' is a euphemism and that was a figure of speech seldom encountered at
meetings of the committee where exchanges were frank and direct.

'I recall one distinguished member who had said, rather sanctimoniously, to
reinforce a point, "Nothing is too good for the patient", being told that this was
an "extremely immature view" and that in a Health Service with finite financial
resources some things were too good for the patient if they were not essential
and resulted in some other patient being deprived of something which was
essential.

Such philosophical exchanges were not for minuting but they contributed
greatly to the health service education of the committee's perspiring secretary.
After one particularly tousy[16] session when the fourth, fifth or sixth version of a
sketch plan was being discussed with Bruce George, Denys Beddard felt
constrained to apologize to him for the abrasive and contentious performance of
some of the committee members. The impeccably mannered architect replied that
the meeting had been relatively tame compared with his experiences 'in another
project in which senior men of distinction had conflicting views. . .'

In the light of the very considerable knowledge now available on hospital
planning – though few would wish to claim that even now it is easy to get things
right – it is possible to forget that in 1959 professional people in the hospital
service were very ignorant. It is not so much that the information was absent;

rather it was difficult to find. In both North America and Scandinavia great strides had been made but nevertheless much that had been done in these two geographical areas was not always suited to the United Kingdom scene. Though parallel developments were taking place throughout Britain there was no easy mechanism for the exchange of information and there was a certain amount of proprietorial jealousy from which those on the planning committee were not exempt. Thus, everything was worked out from scratch and Dr Michie reflects, for example, that, as a trivial example, 'no one knew where we should put the clocks in the operating theatres and a long debate ensued before the matter was resolved. There was animated discussion whether mini-hand basins should be provided in the toilets in the X-ray department or merely, as is more usually the case, a single one to serve a bank of water closets. The more expensive former solution was chosen though not without something of a tug-of-war between those who wanted the aesthetic and those who were going for economy.'

The planning structure which has been described by Buff Hardie, and which used the PPC in conjunction with an architect who had 'partner responsibility', was a pivot around which ideas developed. It was in many respects ideal. It gave flexibility combined with the power to make fairly quick and clear-cut decisions. There was a commendable lack of bureaucracy about its meetings and the deadhand of central planning had yet to manifest itself.[17] Aberdeen was fortunate for Phase I at Foresterhill to be at a time when post-war planning was still relatively simple. It could be argued with much truth that the ultimate success of the project and the award it received (see p.72 below) were the outcome of this freedom.

All this is not to say that the pursuit of professional planning objectives took place without difficulties. The design of the ward unit (considered in more detail below) was revolutionary with its emphasis on the control of cross-infection by isolation and positive pressure ventilation. It was initially greeted both locally by colleagues not on the committee and at St Andrew's House in Edinburgh with a considerable measure of incredulity and something of patronization. However, as Gordon Smylie recalls,[18] it was finally the expert advisers at government level who, in consort with Dr Blowers and Professor R.E.O. Williams 'refused to put a limit on the degree of bed isolation needed and so the Aberdeen plan was eventually licensed as an experiment in the control of infection'.

Another feature of infection control that greatly influenced design was the introduction, in an ever-increasing stream, of 'disposables'. Disposable syringes, forceps and containers saw the end of local 'boiling up' and sterilization of re-usable syringes, stainless steel bowls, jugs and surgical dressing instruments at ward level (the task of persuading senior nursing staff to part with local ward boilers in each ward of the original hospital was, it is recalled, an exercise strained by emotion). Disposable bedpans replaced metal bedpans – no longer would the nursing staff require to undertake the special weekly cleaning with lysol.

In similar vein, improved bed design, cotton blankets and mattress coverings saw an end to hard 'draw sheets' and rubber mackintosh sheeting. The foundation of this revolution was the sterile pack and tray system which came into operation – at first on a restricted scale – but eventually as the standard method of providing the 'ingredients' for all ward, departmental and theatre procedures for all hospitals in the region.

The other matter that added to the enjoyment of the planning process was an atmosphere, for the most part, of mutual respect and lack of suspicion amongst the group.[19] There were differences of course and all were learning during a time of rapid change about the 'idea of the hospital'. The younger members especially tended to be too dogmatic in the pursuit of what they saw as their concepts of perfection. Looking back it was certain that in the professional advice given to the architect, there was over-confidence in understanding of problems such as those of cross-infection, intensive care and closed-circuit television, all of which will be considered in more detail as the tale unfolds. There was an enthusiasm however to grapple with the problems posed by this first big post-war development in Aberdeen.

The final recommendations of the PPC for Phase I, the bluebook already referred to, were ratified by the hospital board in June 1960 and formally submitted to the Scottish Home and Health Department for approval. During the preparation of the brief, sketch plans had been produced and provisionally agreed, concurrently by the committee and the Scottish Home and Health Department which had been kept fully informed throughout. The word 'informed' is used advisedly for at this time central control of the planning process was minimal and the brief was developed almost entirely by the PPC.[20]

Because of the easy flow of information to the Scottish Home and Health Department, approval to proceed to the contract stage for Phase I followed rapidly after the formal submission. Planning for Phase II followed essentially similar lines as Phase I. In late 1963, as the Phase I development was under construction, a professional planning committee, composed again of doctors, nurses, administrators and others representing the Regional Hospital Board and the University of Aberdeen, put forward recommendations to their respective bodies for the second phase of the expansion of the Royal Infirmary.

The Phase II PPC first met in the house of Dr Denys Beddard, the senior administrative medical officer, in Rubislaw Den South in the spring of 1963. However, there were delays caused by differences with the Scottish Home and Health Department and with the necessary financial provisions. Serious planning did not commence until early in 1964 and in fact a great deal of the work was carried out during the sunny months of May and June when a typhoid outbreak gripped Aberdeen and much elective medical work temporarily ceased.

We defer consideration of the further development of Phase II until later (p.73).

Ward plans for Phase I and Phase II

At the time that the Phase I brief was being prepared there were in vogue two ward designs: the Nuffield Trust concept which provided a ratio of three single rooms to every 16 beds; and a multi-bed open ward with beds organized within bays or sub-divided by semi-partitions.

Two considerations dominated the Phase I PPC's thoughts. First, several of its members who had worked in the United States, where single rooms were uniformly provided, felt dissatisfied with an open plan in terms of privacy and amenity; they admitted that economies were possible both in capital expenditure and running costs by the use of open plans but nevertheless they wanted to break the view that Florence Nightingale was still, after a hundred years, the sole arbiter of how patients should be housed and nursed. They were not necessarily entirely right in these views and, not having been patients themselves, may have underestimated the positive social features of an open ward where a degree of self help and support between patients is more easily possible. However, they were adamant that the concept of privacy should receive more consideration.

Second and more importantly was the looming spectre of cross-infection. At this time the potential for one patient to infect another and the possibility of such infection becoming endemic in a building, had been well recognized by the pioneering work of Colebrook on burns, first in Glasgow and later at the Birmingham Accident Hospital. It was now very clear that the same was true for surgical wounds. Experience from Guy's and St Bartholomew's, which arose particularly as a result of the painstaking work of Dr R.E.O. Williams (later to be professor of microbiology at St Mary's Hospital Medical School) and his colleagues chiefly implicated *Staphylococcus aureus* and focused attention particularly on airborne carriage either from patient to patient or from staff to patients.[21] It seemed especially to be the case that a single, uncontrolled focus in an individual could spread organisms widely and bring the activities of a ward to a halt. Further, quite devastating attacks of enteric infection – acute diarrhoeas resembling the condition we would now call pseudo-membranous enterocolitis – could result from the use of broad spectrum antibiotics and invasion of the gut by resistant staphylococci. It seemed appropriate at the time to take careful bacteriological advice on whether or not ward design could contribute to the limitation of cross-infection.

In consequence the bacteriology department of Aberdeen University was asked for its views on the respective merits of the two basic designs for surgical wards. The onus for marshalling the evidence and giving this advice fell largely on Dr H.G. Smylie whom Buff Hardie has described as 'a combative member of the PPC'. Gordon Smylie had been accosted in the corridor by Hugh Dudley who waved an outline ward plan at him and said 'What do you think of this?' Gordon's reaction was to tear it up forthwith which he threatened to do.[22] This was, however, the start of a fruitful participation on the PPC which led to the following recommendations:

1. Bays or semi-partitions in an open ward plan offered little or no control of cross-infection.
2. The nature of both staphylococcal cross-infection and the hospital antibiotic environment pointed to a possible solution by a high degree of compartmentation within ward areas.

3. The success of this 'architecturally cellular' interior would be dependent not only on the isolation of patients which it provided, but almost as much upon efficiently controlled ventilation.
4. Controlled ventilation to acceptable hospital standards is virtually impossible in an open multi-bed ward. When the same large interior is broken down into smaller compartments of air, i.e. single rooms, controlled ventilation becomes technically feasible.
5. As a consequence of the bacteriological principles mentioned above, the higher the percentage of single adequately ventilated rooms in any hospital building, the greater would be the opportunity to minimize hospital cross-infection.

This advice was accepted as a basis for the development of a new concept of ward design and it was agreed within the PPC that 40 per cent of all the beds should be provided in single rooms.

In addition, and independent from the problem of cross-infection, the following features emerged.

1. The nurses' station should be located at the hub of the ward and related more closely to the single rooms than to the multi-bedrooms. It should have facilities for the handling of drugs.
2. The clean (supply) and dirty (disposal) utility rooms should be directly related to the nursing station.
3. The clean utility room should be stocked from the corridor via pass-through hatches.
4. A separate disposal lift and storage bay should be planned adjacent to the dirty utility room for the removal of soiled material and waste.
5. A room should be provided for the reception of newly admitted patients where preliminary examination and any urgent treatment could be administered thereby avoiding disturbance to other patients. This room should be adjacent to the dirty utility room and to a bathroom with a W.C.
6. An administrative centre should be provided to concentrate the accommodation for both clinical and non-clinical staff such as house officers, ward sisters and clerk-receptionists and should include a tutorial room, a side-room laboratory, an investigation room and an interview/sisters' retiring room.
7. The single rooms should be planned so that 60 per cent were provided with individual lavatories and the remainder designed for what was at that time regarded as an intensive care unit, with a proportion of the beds having a high degree of observation.
8. That a system of efficiently controlled ventilation should be incorporated to assist with the control of airborne cross-infection.

Beds were allocated as follows: (1) 12 to a cardiovascular investigation unit; (2) 30 to a thoracic surgery unit; (3) 58 in two ward units for general surgery; and (4) 29 beds to replace accommodation for private patients situated in the Watson Fraser nursing home. All three floor plans were to incorporate the principles outlined in the brief but the evolution of the plan for the 58 general surgical beds did in fact determine, to some extent, the layout of the other two floors.

The intensive care beds were to be directly available to each of the two ward units on the floor they served and were therefore arranged as a cross-link between two parallel ward units. In retrospect this concept was to prove wrong, largely because of the rapid advance of the speciality of critical care and its need for expensive high technology equipment. The remaining single beds were planned to be contiguous with the intensive care beds in order to provide the maximum flexibility for general purpose isolation. Patients using these rooms would be those at risk from, and those who were known to increase the risk of, hospital cross-infection. This degree of compartmentation also provided flexibility in the use of the wards by the sexes (again we have to realize that the PPC was designing a ward in a particular cultural time; now segregation is no longer an issue and when HAFD retired from clinical practice in 1988, his ward unit had complete mixing of the sexes brought about through both liberation of attitudes and the imperatives of economics). The administrative accommodation was to be common to both ward units and so it was planned as a second cross-link at the end opposite to the intensive care unit.

This arrangement resulted in a 'racetrack' layout with the bedrooms and administrative accommodation on the perimeter surrounding a central core of service rooms, ducts and vertical circulation which, being in intermittent use could, without detriment, be lit artificially and ventilated mechanically. Positive pressure ventilation began the process of control of airborne infection in the patients' bedrooms. Consequently the system delivered filtered air through high level diffusers to the periphery of the racetrack.

Extraction took place through or under the doors to extraction grilles in the core of the building. Originally about 75 per cent of the air was to be re-circulated after filtration and 25 per cent was fresh but this was ultimately abandoned. A maximum of six air changes per hour was possible. This quality of circulation and filtration was relatively new at the time and Gordon Smylie and HAFD made a trip to the Caterpillar factory on Tannochside to look into their 'clean air' provisions. The journey was notable for the fact that it was made during a snowstorm and that the car went off the road at least once. In spite of this attention to detail the ventilation did prove troublesome both in relation to filtration and humidity (see p.81). In the private beds on the top floor ventilation was more basic.

The Phase II ward plans were similar with a slightly modified racetrack. The continued use of the racetrack design, with the necessity for artificial ventilation and lighting, did not go unchallenged. Some of the committee felt that the Foresterhill site was well provided with light and ventilation and that full use should be made of these natural advantages. There were lengthy discussions about having a long narrow building, with all rooms having an outside window, and about the mechanical considerations and costs of a square or rectangular building with comparable floor area. The advocates of the racetrack design won but in practice, years later, the artificial ventilation can still cause difficulties.

The treatment services block

Here were to be found the operating theatre suite, X-ray department and certain central hospital services. The X-ray department and the theatre suite (initially four operating theatres), were planned so that in each case future extensions could take place without being inhibited by, or interfering with, the use of the first phase.

The operating theatre suite

The operating theatre suite was of particular interest. Previous suites had been designed to allow as much flexibility of use as possible and had, therefore, consisted usually of a number of open communicating spaces in which staff, materials and patients could circulate freely. This, however, offended against many principles of ventilation, control of infection and economy of effort and, in planning the operating suites at Foresterhill, account was taken of Blowers' findings on downward displacement ventilation[23] and of the experience already gained of package systems in operating theatres and also of the advantage of restricted circulation with interchange barriers. The theatre suites were therefore designed around a system of management the aims of which were briefly:

1. to provide restricted access to the theatre with both patients and staff having to make a complete change before reaching the central corridor of the suite.
2. to provide isolation of each operating theatre from its neighbour so that contamination of one would not cause contamination of the others.
3. to evacuate dirty materials to the exterior rather than back into the suite. This was accomplished by discharging dirty material through an underpass to the disposal bay situated outside the clean inner core of the suite. Dirty disposal from the theatres would be dealt with by a disposal team entirely separated from staff inside the suite. This also maintained the efficiency of the ventilation system in the theatres and reduced dirt in the suite as a whole.
4. to exploit a package system from a central sterile supply department (CSSD) to the full in the interests of economy of labour and high bacteriological standards especially in relation to sterilizing rooms. This was only achieved after the CSSD opened.
5. to have a sensible flow of patients through the suite from the induction of anaesthesia to the end of a recovery period and in consequence to speed up turnover. These results were achieved with no increase in the number of sterilizing rooms over the Nuffield design and by the use of a single disposal area for the four operating rooms.

A theatre design of this kind implied a certain rigidity of organization which had not previously been attempted. The objection to this had usually been a lack of flexibility for changes in function but the committee considered that, if planned from first principles, there was no reason why this design should not prove to be a considerable advance on current concepts of management.

It was fairly universally agreed that the thespian aspects of operating exemplified in both the description of operating rooms as 'theatres' and the provision of galleries for viewing were no longer relevant. Though the surgical members of the PPC thought that there would be still some need to demonstrate procedures and the 'pathology of the living' it was agreed that closed-circuit television (CCTV) would be best for this purpose. Therefore galleries were not included and, because there was little agreement on the choice of television equipment or on how it should be financed, the suites were wired for this purpose but nothing else was done. A rudimentary CCTV communication to the X-ray department eventually developed but fell down on technical grounds because at the time digital image transmission with its high quality had yet to be developed. But as Professor Lewis Gillanders has remarked:[24] 'The CCTV concept could be regarded as ahead of its time. In 1991 the use of high resolution television and a network of monitors seems likely to become the preferred method of displaying images in various parts of the hospital complex.'

A further feature which it was intended to deploy was physiological monitoring using centralized equipment for both the operating theatres and the recovery area. However, though physical provision was made it was overtaken by events after the suite was opened (see p.80).

The recovery room within the suite was supplemented by holding facilities in the theatre exit room and was to be provided with cubicles for grossly infected patients and for the dying. The anaesthetizing areas were designed so that the anaesthetic room proper and the exit room could be thrown into one to make a large space available when necessary.

The ventilation system in the theatres was plenum: that is positive pressure ventilation by downward displacement of air using Blowers' system, which at that time represented the most adequately proven technique.[23]

The X-ray department

This consisted in the first phase of six main rooms with an X-ray theatre. Films were to be mechanically transported and automatically processed. In the X-ray theatre, the procedures contemplated were cardiac catheterization angiocardiography, aortography and peripheral arteriography. The theatre was to be fully equipped with apparatus for pressure recording and ECG monitoring. This ideal remained unachieved though it is now regarded as routine.

A fuller description of the emergence of imaging in Aberdeen will be found in Chapter 12.

Teaching and research

Provision was made in a number of ways for teaching and research: bedside teaching could take place in the two specially designed tutorial rooms on the wards into which a bed may be wheeled (a traditional Scottish technique that may have been instituted by James Syme of Edinburgh in the 1830s or 1840s). One of the tutorial rooms was designed for 20 students and was wired for CCTV from the operating suite (see above). The tutorial rooms were regarded as multi-purpose and available for clinical tuition to student nurses and others. Several rooms were provided in the general surgical wards for clinical staff taking part in clinical research and a room was made available for clinical investigations adjacent to a research laboratory. On the thoracic ward a small clinical investigation room was provided into which a patient could be taken for special procedures.

The cardiovascular investigation unit was designed to have four laboratories for clinical research including space which could provide a base for research students.

Building Phase I

The construction of Phase I began in 1963. A considerable amount of excavation was involved and the sloping site with the possibility of underground streams led to informal prophecies of difficulties from the builders. However, they and the architect were both familiar with the site and were favoured by dry weather so few actual difficulties were encountered.

Phase I was occupied in September 1966 and formally opened by Her Majesty Queen Elizabeth the Queen Mother on the 18 October 1966 (Plate 23). In 1969 a Civic Trust Award was received and the citation stated: 'This is an extremely competently designed building. Its simple lines and crisp detailing are outstanding. Good materials have been sensibly used. Despite the fact that the hospital is to be built in several phases, the first stage is admirable in its clarity. It will undoubtedly set a standard for future building for some time to come. Skilful use has been made of the falling site to allow for a low level connection to other buildings in the development. The handling of public spaces and circulation problems is quite brilliant. The building creates an atmosphere of quiet efficiency, without the impersonal quality of much of the large hospital work today.' (A plaque to record this award is sited under the name of the firm of architects at the west entrance to Phase I.)

To assess the validity of the new design in controlling cross-infection in surgical wards a study of the incidence of wound infection in the old and new buildings was carried out over a period of four years from September 1964 to September 1966 in the old buildings and from September 1966 to September 1968 in the new. The results were published in 1971.[25] A substantial reduction of both postoperative wound infection and cross-infection of about 10 per cent appeared to have been achieved in the new design. However, the study could not assess other factors which, in retrospect, may have played a part in the general decline particularly in staphylococcal wound infection in the hospital, and indeed in the country, as a whole.

Norman Matheson, whose interest in and contributions to the control of surgical infection has earned him and the Royal Infirmary an international

Plate 23 Her Majesty the Queen Mother opening Phase I in 1966.

reputation, has evidence to suggest that wound infection rates in the 'old' surgical wards in which he cared for patients were no different from those in the new. This does not of course detract from the virtues of the design which is permissive to dealing with any new infectious challenge. At the time of writing it seems that this might be necessary because of the endemicity of multiple antibiotic-resistant staphylococci which are extremely difficult to eradicate from more conventional designs. Furthermore, the planning of the wards interlocked other desiderata with the objective of infection control to produce an overall result which has largely stood the test of time.

Phases II and III

Though in the bureaucracy-free days of the mid-1960s Phase I proceeded apace, the same was not to be so true for Phases II and III. The PPC's brief was completed in October 1964. The outcome in terms of bricks and mortar was to be a block of nine floors linked to the Phase I block with the bed areas and 'embedded' university departments (or parts thereof) accommodated on the top five floors.

The medical wards of the second phase, it was planned, would be 'sandwiched' between surgical wards to bring surgical and medical disciplines into closer working alliance. A further four operating rooms and ancillary accommodation, as an extension of the Phase I provisions, would complete the eight room theatre suite.

In the four Phase I operating theatres the floor area was only 360 square feet. Strenuous efforts were made to have the size of the Phase II theatres increased to 420 square feet; in the end a compromise figure of 400 square feet had to be accepted. Practical experience has shown that the plea for more space was fully justified; with modern technical and support equipment and staff, small operating theatres become very congested.

Similarly the Phase I X-ray suite (now to include other forms of imaging) would be extended and completed. The accident and emergency centre, connected to Phase II at basement level (because of the fall of the site), was to be a relatively independent building with its own entrances off a new main hospital roadway. It would have its own two theatre suite, X-ray department, fracture clinic and short-stay beds together with the casualty area with examination and treatment rooms.

Special provisions in the Phase II development were to include an expanded pharmacy department (to incorporate a sterile fluids production unit previously housed at Mile End with the laundry and CSSD); maintenance workshops; staff changing areas; a staff dining room of 200 places and a main hospital kitchen.

'Embedded' clinical academic departments were in the late 1960s regarded by most as ideal as they could keep clinical scientists in close contact with patients. This was to be a corner stone of the next development and was carried through to completion and use. These units, however, did not survive in the long term, the university departments being finally withdrawn to the medical school.

Overall the second part of the expansion of the Royal Infirmary constituted a formidable planning exercise and the preparation of the functional brief, and the detailed planning which followed acceptance of the planning committee's recommendations to its parent bodies and the Scottish Home and Health Department, once again called for very considerable commitment by those involved and, again, many additional hours of work.

Having in mind the size of the Phase II project and the complex nature of the further development, a multi-disciplinary team of officers was formed – the project team with: responsibility for support to the planning committees; preparation of specialist detailed planning; the equipment requirements; staff recruitment and training; and the commissioning.

The detailed planning requirement of the second phase ranged widely. For example, the theatre table system and related services for the operating theatres; the complex requirements of the radiographic rooms; the patient floor patterns in the accident department; signposting; working conditions in the maintenance workshops; and the very particular needs of the new pharmacy with its sterile work areas, stills and bottling plant (rumour had it, with regard to the last two items, that, in addition to sterile fluids, a malt whisky called 'Foresterhill' or possibly 'Glenburn' was to be produced).

The equipment requirements of the Phase II development were many and varied and constituted a formidable task for the equipment section of the project team. In all, some 3,000 different, individual items of equipment were defined for purchase. If this figure seems excessive, it is of note that, at the time, a requirement for a single anaesthetic machine and associated equipment comprised 71 different items, including the 38 items forming the machine itself. This in turn necessitated 71 separate decisions.

Although the major portion of planning Phase II had been completed during 1964, the committee continued to meet at intervals during the next six years. A variety of problems caused delays and had to be dealt with. For example, changes in the fire regulations meant both that new baffles had to be inserted into the small ventilating ducts and that additional fire escapes had to be provided in the diagonally opposite corners of the buildings. The latter alteration resulted in the loss of two or three beds from each floor of the tall north-south block (Plate 24). Work on the site commenced in the spring of 1971 and the first areas of Phase II were made available for use in early 1976. As regards the actual bringing into use of the ward floors, changes in the Health Board's priorities over the intervening years, the availability of trained nursing staff, and financial considerations, led to: (1) alterations in the use of some of the Phase II ward accommodation as originally planned[26] and also in the related bed redeployment exercise; and (2) a phased programme of occupancy of the ward areas.

Notwithstanding the additional problems thus occasioned, the first areas of the ward floors were brought into use in 1979 and the final stages of occupation achieved in 1984.

Commissioning was not without its difficulties. Buff Hardie writes: 'In 1976 I was appointed secretary of the Grampian Health Board. When I arrived it was to find that the major exercise confronting the board was the bringing into use of the Phase II block which was then in the last stages of completion. It was an exercise fraught with difficulties.

'In the good old days of Phase I any such capital development attracted automatically, as a new additional revenue allocation to the hospital board concerned, all the running costs appropriate to such a building. It was on the basis of this doctrine known as RCCS (revenue consequences of capital schemes) that Phases I and II had been planned, and Phase I had been brought into use. However, by the time Phase II had reached that stage the rules had been changed, RCCS had been abolished and the health boards had to find the running costs for new capital schemes from within their existing revenue allocation. This moving of the goal posts would have been a serious blow whatever the nature of the Phase II development but it had been deliberately planned in a way which made it particularly expensive to run.

'In addition, at that time, in the mid- and late 1970s the North Sea oil boom was a major contributing factor to a severe shortage of trained nursing staff in

Plate 24 Phase II in 1982. Phase I is behind. Foresterhill Health Centre is in the right
 foreground. The sloping nature of the site is apparent in this view from the
 south-west. Drawing by Albany Wiseman.

Aberdeen which had a considerable effect on the Phase II building which
required high levels of nursing staff. The net result of all this was that in the late
1970s the board found themselves the custodians of the most expensive hospital
block in the Kingdom but without the money to run it and if they had had the
money they could not have found the nurses to staff it.

'This crippling shortage of resources, both financial and manpower, was compounded by the fact that, since the original planning stage, the board's priorities had changed and there was a clamant need for the Phase II building to be put to a use that would meet the new pressing requirments of the 1980s. Given that because of the financial and manpower constraints, the building could only be brought into use gradually one floor at a time, there was more opportunity for continuing debate as to what the board's most urgent priorities actually were and how the new building could best be used.

'Phase II eventually was fully occupied but, because of the factors outlined above, its occupation was inevitably a slow and protracted process, not being helped by the fact that the years of decision making . . . were the heyday of the massive consultative machinery with which health boards were blessed following the 1974 health service re-organization.

'Every move or proposed move or, it sometimes seemed, proposal to suggest a proposed move, had to be debated by an inordinate number of advisory committees and other bodies each of which solemnly approved minutes and submitted comments from its own standpoint with the effect that the volume of advice which the board received was often totally intractable.

'The administrative effort expended in deciding on and implementing the occupation of the various floors of Phase II was enormous; as we reached the end of the road, I reflected on the halcyon days of the Phase I planning and allowed myself to wonder if the whole apparently interminable process of occupying Phase II might not have been better accomplished by one judiciously selective cocktail party and no committee meetings. Not that a career in the Health Service bred in me a dislike of committees *per se*. It is easy to mock committees, and certainly the ill-conceived and badly run committee is a recipe for disaster, but in a multi-disciplinary organization like the Health Service they are inescapable and I always felt that the Professional Planning Committee for Phase I demonstrated that the right committee with a carefully chosen membership and a clearly understood objective can achieve much'.

Other developments at Foresterhill 1960–1990

Though the foregoing account has concentrated on the mainstream of the development of the new ward facilities and services for patients, the full use of these would not have been possible without concurrent growth in other areas.

CSSD and laundry

At the time of planning of Phase I much interest was being expressed in the semi-industrial centralized provision of sterile goods and in Edinburgh, Bowie was experimenting with total pre-packaging of theatre instruments.

The ARI committed itself down the road of central sterile supply and at the time of the Phase I planning exercise a new building was being developed in the south east corner of the Foresterhill site which would contain a new laundry and a central sterile supply department (CSSD). The laundry was planned with a very much increased capacity over the original one and incorporated a higher degree of automation particularly in the handling of soiled and foul linen. Clean linen from the new unit was to be despatched to the wards, etc in large paper sacks not baskets; the sacks being returned with used linen to the laundry for processing and disposal of the sacks. At hospital level as part of the 'paper bag scheme', eventually introduced into all the acute hospitals, colour-coded small paper bags were designated for the general disposal and incineration of waste. Arrangements made with the local authority for it to deal with hospital waste saw the end of the hospital's own incinerator.

The CSSD was designed to provide all ward and theatre packs, theatre clothing packs, and instrument trays. At first it supplied the Phase I development, then the original Infirmary and other hospital units on the site and, eventually all hospitals in the region. At the outset of the planning of this production unit, all the 'ingredients' required for every single ward, departmental and theatre procedure in the major Aberdeen hospitals were listed down to the last cottonwool ball and from this detail was determined the contents of the basic packs, supplementary packs, clothing packs and, in like vein, theatre instrument trays.

In later years, this exercise would have been easily and very quickly coped with by a computer. At the time it was very much a pen and paper marathon for a particular administrator and for decision taking by another hard working committee. The CSSD building was commissioned in 1966.

Cardiology

On p.143 *et seq.* will be found the sequence of events that resulted in the eventual concentration of cardiological services on the Foresterhill site in a series of purpose designed buildings centred on ward 3 on the ground floor of the medical block.

Laboratory services – the link building

Before the advent of the NHS, hospital laboratories were often set up in almost any vacant shed or basement store and few pathologists, bacteriologists or clinical biochemists enjoyed the luxury of purpose-built accommodation.

With growing demand for prompt laboratory help, however, it became clear that clinical laboratories should be easily accessible and as near to the patient as possible, sometimes actually within the patient-care area. How then did it come about that in 1969 a new laboratory building was opened at Foresterhill, primarily to meet the needs of patients, yet almost as far from the main medical and surgical wards as it could be and, in the words of one of its users 'awkwardly joined to the Infirmary and apparently doing its best to obstruct traffic flow around the site?'

The answer lies in the history of laboratory services for the Royal Infirmary and in the sources of building funds at that time. At Foresterhill, laboratory services for patient care and for clinical research had developed in the university departments of pathology, bacteriology and clinical chemistry – later re-named chemical pathology and now titled clinical biochemistry – and by the late 1950s it was clear that the accommodation for these departments within the medical school building was hopelessly inadequate for a service load many times greater than had been envisaged when the building was designed in the middle 1930s. The solution was simple: build new laboratories.

The problem was where was the money to come from? The Scottish Home and Health Department was unlikely to fund a new university building and the University Grants Committee (UGC) was equally unlikely to build new laboratories for the hospital. The NE Regional Hospital Board had no wish to change the well-established arrangements for university staff in these paraclinical departments – to divide their time between teaching, research and provision of services for patient care, nor was there any strong wish for change within the faculty of medicine. The UGC would indeed have been prepared to consider a case for new teaching accommodation at Foresterhill but other departments in the university with urgent space problems of their own would have been most reluctant to allow this project to jump the queue of the university's already extensive building programme. However, a glimmer of hope existed in the form of the so-called 'medical sub-head', a special packet of money set aside centrally for new academic buildings to be incorporated in a teaching hospital building scheme. The rules would have to be bent considerably but a hint was received from the UGC that, if the hospital side was prepared to put up a substantial proportion of the money required, something might be done.

Immediately this possibility became known, almost all the university departments at Foresterhill leapt on the bandwagon. Lists of 'minimum' space requirements proliferated and soon there came a sharp warning from the UGC that 'the tail must not wag the dog'. After heated debate a more modest scheme evolved comprising new departmental accommodation and laboratories for pathology, haematology, chemical pathology, medical illustration and forensic medicine. Also office space for the dean and executive dean, new tutorial rooms and a modest provision of research accommodation for clinical specialities.

Bacteriology would expand into laboratories to be vacated by chemical pathology and the former pathology accommodation would be divided amongst other departments. The Scottish Home and Health Department signified its willingness to pay a fair share of the cost and the new scheme just managed to slip through the UGC net for acceptance as a medical sub-head project.

Recourse to medical sub-head money, however, had its problems. To qualify, new academic accommodation must be an integral part of new hospital buildings – physically part of the hospital, not merely a new academic building which happened to be on a hospital site.

There were of course good arguments for extending the existing medical school building rather than creating a second one and so the idea of a link building emerged. To add to the architects' difficulties, the Infirmary and the university building were on opposite sides of the main roadway through the Foresterhill site, the floor levels and even the ceiling heights were different and while the hospital's communications were based on a single long corridor at groundfloor level, the medical school had corridors at each floor level. The compromise arrived at, not without misgivings, was a bridge building having the same floor levels as the medical school, with a lift and staircase tower leading down to the Infirmary corridor. To allow fire appliances and other large vehicles to pass through the site, the road had to be lowered to form a single lane underpass.

The building work had of course to be done without interrupting either hospital or medical school activities. On completion the laboratory departments had to be transferred to their new abodes without any break in the services for patients. Somehow all this was achieved and the link building came into use in 1969.

And so we have a building whose primary purpose was to provide better patient care services, purpose built but in quite the wrong place, with a continuing burden of thousands of man-hours wasted in specimen transport, limited liaison between ward and laboratory and slower processing of urgent samples, all because of the restrictive terms of the agreement on shared funding. But it was that or nothing and in fairness to everyone concerned it must be said that the possibility of mechanical specimen transport systems was thoroughly gone into but given up as impracticable for the time being.

Every cloud though has a silver lining of some kind; one surgeon (long since deceased) had a good word for the new building: 'At least I can get to the library on a wet day without needing an umbrella'.

What was learnt about post-war planning

The 'retrospectoscope' is one of the most powerful but also one of the most abused tools of history. Looking back on planning for the post World War II development at Foresterhill there were some lessons which emerged.

First, there is a tendency to overdesign on the basis of a brief which specifies a particular use and which does not allow for change, especially when there is rapid technological innovation. The intensive care beds in Phase I; the concept of a central monitoring room in the theatres; and the embedded academic departments in Phase II are all examples.

Second, birds of passage should not have their pet ideas too readily accepted; central monitoring was again a case in point for, as Buff Hardie recalls, 'the theatre suite in Phase I was built on this basis but by the time the theatres were in use Hugh Dudley had moved; the notion of the remotely located recording equipment did not commend itself to his successors and, not surprisingly, the operating rooms seemed too small. It was a situation endemic in the health service where fashions change, preferences differ, people move and they who plan and they who use are seldom the same people.'

Third, the PPC approach was sound though ultimately it proved unsuited to the heavyweight bureaucracy that built up in the Department of Health and Social Security and Scottish Home and Health Department and which by the 1980s had reached Byzantine complexity. Also though a powerful tool, it did inevitably lead to identifiable tensions and recriminations when either professionals overruled architects or the reverse.

Perhaps too little attention was given by both sides to the fine detail of function though it should be re-emphasized, as has already been pointed out (p.64), the Phase I planners were working in an experiential vacuum.

Douglas Needham comments perhaps a mite bitterly: 'The clinicians were overruled or not consulted quite consistently. I could go on and on about the nonsense of the internal fittings: baths so placed that attendants could not support ill patients; lights in rooms encased in shades like black coal scuttles and placed vertically over beds (rather than one each side) so that (a) patients had to be looking directly into the light and (b) there was no illumination laterally for patient examination; door handles that stuck out dangerously; towel rails set so close to the wall that a towel could not be threaded behind it, etc'.

These matters are perhaps as much a difference of attitude and knowledge rather than of what ultimately turned out to be correct function. Bruce George rightly points out that the equipment sub-committee looked at all these matters and thought that the drum shades which were an approved hospital standard fitting at the time were appropriate; that reading lights were provided on the mobile bedside lockers and that the door handles were thought to be the best for arm operation when a nurse's hands were engaged in carrying trays or equipment. The last were in common use in Scandinavia and the USA.

Ventilation proved at the time to be controversial. The British have a love–hate relationship with fresh air, enjoying a 'fug' but wishing always to retain the freedom to throw open windows to permit contact with uncharitable meteorological conditions such as Aberdeen frequently provides in winter (not to mention at other times). Controlled ventilation was not to everyone's taste and 'balancing' the ventilation to provide equable conditions often led to complaints. There can be hardly anyone in Aberdeen professional circles who is not familiar with the story of Sandy Michie taking a group of distinguished visitors around the wards. Entering a single room on the top floor, they were confronted by a lady, well known as something of a character in Aberdeen society, sitting bolt upright in bed under the protection of a large black umbrella which shielded her from the down rush of air emerging from a ceiling louvre immediately above her head. Her mute but pointed protest did not go unheeded. Conviction can also triumph over economics and a member of the PPC for Phase I noted on a visit to Aberdeen in 1990 that '. . . the windows in Phase I now are openable not only on the top floor but on those below also – so the Aberdonian love of God's good wind has gained a small victory. . .'

The same member (CDN) notes also that the ventilation system was designed to operate at low relative humidity which while suitable for most surgical patients was not right for those with chronic respiratory disease – again a lack of flexibiliy in forward thinking.

Perhaps one of the editors of this section on post-war planning may be

Plate 25 Aerial view of the site, 1973. Matthew Hay's vision has achieved reality
though there are further developments to come.

permitted the final word. After leaving Foresterhill and the ARI he went to help
found a new university in the antipodes. The motto of this institution attributed
to Leonardo da Vinci was *ancora imparo* a free translation of which is 'I am
always learning'. Such was the course of post-war hospital development in
Aberdeen; a continuous and profitable learning process for all involved, the
outcome of which has been a hospital complex with many virtues and few
defects (Plate 25).

6

Medicine

To the lay person 'medicine' has the general meaning of care for the sick. To the professional it implies a particular discipline which endeavours to alleviate or cure without recourse to gross intervention such as manipulations or invasion of the body which characterizes surgery. At the time the Infirmary was founded it was the mainstay of management though once antisepsis and anaesthesia had been introduced (see Chapters 7 and 11) surgery became increasingly important in the affairs of the institution.

As our account of the early days of the Infirmary describes (Chapter 2), the first physician (James Gordon[1]) was appointed in 1742. The clinical resources available to him were minimal. The cause of even the commonest diseases was unknown; methods of physical examination and the scientific techniques used to make a diagnosis were still far in the future. So it was that the Infirmary was predominantly a temporary refuge for a few patients chosen mainly but not entirely from the poor of Aberdeen; most were returned to an independent if not useful life.

Disease from the environment

In 1742 Scotland was a rural society; Aberdeen had fewer than 16,000 souls within its burgh. Though formal statistics date only from the founding of the registrar-general's office in Scotland in 1855, earlier more limited sources show that urban death rates in the poorer areas were high so that one of every five children born did not see the end of the first year, and life expectancy at birth was but 43 years for a female and 41 for a male.[2] The greatest prevalence of disease and the highest mortality rates were in the overcrowded areas which in Aberdeen were around the mouth of the Dee, the harbour area and to the north along the shore line. The size of the city grew over the ensuing 150 years with the urban migration which accompanied the industrial revolution.

Accounts of life in Scottish towns attest to the insanitary conditions which prevailed[3] and are a striking commentary on the collapse of the ancient standards for personal hygiene and pure food, which had been established in Graeco-Roman times and which were accompanied by impressive arrangements for

Plate 26 Alexander Kilgour, physician. This memorial medallion is in the entrance hall of the 1936 building at Foresterhill.

urban sanitation and good water. As alarming epidemics of infectious disease swept through Europe, codes of personal and public hygiene were being established anew and in the early 19th century were accompanied by a growing reform movement as political power began to shift to the middle classes of the expanding towns. The concern of enlightened local authorities was provoked both by the intuitive link between poverty, poor housing and disease and the feeling that the provision of improved public hygiene was a duty.[4]

It is not surprising, therefore, to find that in 1840 'a committee of the town council with the medical gentlemen attached to the Infirmary and the dispensaries' undertook an inquiry into the sanitary conditions of the poor of Aberdeen. The report[5] was submitted by Alexander Kilgour (Plate 26) as secretary to the committee.[6] Recent epidemics in the city were reviewed: deficiencies in sanitation and other causes believed by the committee members to influence the propagation of 'fever' were considered and much improved drainage, sewerage, domestic and personal hygiene with the provision of better water supplies were recommended. The need for more hospital accommodation, separation of the sick from the healthy and measures to prevent 'contagion' were also emphasized.

Political and civic measures were to be of great significance in the gradual reduction of the impact of acute epidemic disease on the medical practice of the Infirmary. The third Public Health Act of 1875[7] empowered local authorities to appoint medical officers of health, to undertake major projects in sanitary engineering, to provide a supply of pure water and to undertake the building of hospitals and sanatoria.

Plate 27 David Finlay, Regius professor of medicine 1891–1912.

One of the first medical effects of this was the opening of the City Hospital in 1877 so that patients with infectious disease were no longer admitted to the Infirmary. Medical officers of health took over from the superintendent of police the duties of the sanitary department. In Aberdeen, prominent for his work and to be encountered in many parts of this history, was Matthew Hay who held the post of medical officer of health from 1888 to 1923.[8]

Yet well into the first decade of the 20th century, the role of medicine was still as a collective science to draw on what are fundamental disciplines to establish the foundations of knowledge that would enable doctors to acquire their most important skill – achieving a diagnosis based on history and clinical findings, and increasingly confirmable by special investigations. Apart from prevention which resided mainly in the public health measures that have been described above, advances in therapy were still to come. Gradually this non-interventionist attitude was to change and specialities within medicine were to grow. They altered the face of medical practice in Aberdeen as elsewhere.

In the years up to the end of the World War I in 1918, medical practice was still dominated by generalists such as David Finlay[9] (Plate 27) who was Regius professor of medicine from 1891 to 1912 and his successor Ashley Mackintosh[10] still remembered as the 'master clinician'. Specialization was already underway with the introduction of electrocardiography (see p.143) which led to the birth of cardiology and it received a considerable boost in the field of metabolic medicine with the discovery of insulin in 1926. The effect of this on the management of diabetes and particularly in Aberdeen through the work of Alexander Lyall[11] (Plate 28) is discussed on p.151. These two fields apart, clinical medicine remained largely a general pursuit until well after World War II.

Exceptions were in the fields of cardiology, dermatology and venereal disease, haematology and rheumatology. When Ashley Mackintosh, who, like all his

Plate 28 Alexander (Sandy) Lyall, physician and clinical chemist.

Plate 29 Stanley Davidson, the first full-time Regius professor of medicine 1930–8.

colleagues was in part-time practice with attendance at consulting rooms and nursing homes, retired in 1930, there was a view that greater effort should be put into the university department of medicine so as to promote research. The first whole-time chair in the United Kingdom was created with Stanley Davidson (Plate 29) as its occupant.[12] He believed that in addition to other areas of investigation it was a duty of a department of medicine to be prepared to take part in the investigation and treatment of any disease which was a major cause of invalidism in the region served by the University.[13]

Chronic rheumatic disease was one such problem and it was his view that a special unit should be established exclusively for these disorders. Various reasons, including the outbreak of war, delayed the project but it was fostered by his successors until in time a hospital service in rheumatology was established (p.166). He was in fact more influential in research in his own field of haematology and the development of this, which began under his guidance, is discussed on p.154. Both he and his successors encouraged the development of specialities, first as an interest of general physicians and later as a full-time practice for those who had acquired special skills.

General medicine persists at Foresterhill with wards devoted to it in 1991. Many[14] though not all[15] of those who, through long service to the ARI, had helped convert it from a contemplative art into an increasingly active and interventionist therapeutic discipline are still alive. However, there is now an intricate patchwork of specialist care so that patients can have access to the skills of those in cardiology, dermatology, endocrinology, gastroenterology,[16] haematology, nephrology, neurology, oncology, rheumatology and thoracic medicine all of which, however, remain linked with the mainstream of that collective discipline which is Medicine. They are also associated with simultaneous developments in surgery and other methods of treatment. So the accounts of specialities takes into consideration all the disciplines involved though perhaps it gives primacy to the carriers of the gold-headed cane – the practitioners of Medicine.

7

Surgery

The history of surgery in the Royal Infirmary of Aberdeen divides into two periods, both equal in length but completely different in character and the year which marks this division is 1867, when Joseph Lister published his first paper on the treatment of patients using antiseptic principles.[1] During the first 125 years, surgery in Britain was practised by some remarkable individuals such as Cheselden, Hunter, Astley Cooper, Syme and Liston but an operation was always a treatment of last resort, holding terrible forebodings for patient and surgeon alike. After ether and chloroform were introduced in the 1840s, the threat of infection remained as an apparently insuperable bar to any broadening of the scope of surgery.

Little is known about the surgery practised in Aberdeen in the 18th century though for 100 years it was unusual for more than two operations to be performed in a week so the surgeons worked for their living as general practitioners and training was obtained by being apprenticed to a practising surgeon (see also p.30). After a period of dispensing medicines and carrying the surgeon's bag on his rounds, simple tasks such as incision of abscesses would come the trainee's way and experience would gradually widen. In Edinburgh and London, apprentices could attend a school of anatomy but in Aberdeen there was little formal teaching until Dr Andrew Moir opened an anatomy school in the 1830s.[2] The surgeon of those days was dependent on detailed anatomical knowledge to enable him to operate swiftly and safely on the conscious patient in a dimly lit theatre. By the 1870s the student curriculum was in fact unduly biased toward anatomy and in 1877 Alexander Ogston[3], then surgeon to the Infirmary protested about the years spent studying chemistry, botany and anatomy 'while the most valuable part of the curriculum – the study of medicine – is compressed with few exceptions into one year'.[4]

Many admissions were for injuries sustained in the crowded streets and dangerous factories of the industrial revolution. Fractures were often compound and so great was the threat of infection that it was considered safer to amputate forthwith above the fracture. This was one of the principal operations of the pre-Listerian era; surgeons of the calibre of Syme and Liston could perform an amputation through the thigh in less than one minute. Even so, mortality from infection could be as high as 50 per cent.[5] Abscesses, boils and carbuncles were common and would mostly be treated in the home. Hernias were only operated on when strangulated. Aneurysms of the major arteries were fairly common and enterprising surgeons practised ligation. The only truly internal operation performed was lithotomy for bladder stones.

It is hardly surprising that all those who were able to do so would avoid hospital admission. Ogston, writing of his student days in the Simpson pavilion of the 1860s, recalls 'how the wards, even the very corridors, stank with the mawkish manna-like odour of suppuration. Each stuffy ward was presided over by an old woman whose only qualification was her ability to make a poultice'. Ogston's impression was that 'not a single wound healed without festering, and small wonder'.[6] Nurses did not generally wash patients, and new patients used the same sheets as the last occupant. In the typhus epidemic of 1863–4, the managers of the Infirmary protested that typhus patients had been nursed in the surgical wards and the matron had died of the disease.[7]

During 1843, with the new Simpson pavilion and operating theatre open, 74 operations were performed, all without benefit of anaesthesia, including seven major amputations, nine lithotomies and two mastectomies. Three cataracts were treated, probably by couching, and one hare-lip was repaired.[8]

In his memoirs Ogston recalled the theatre he attended as a student. 'There was no appliance for washing the hands, nor was there any in the robing room opposite. There hung a row of old frock coats, covered with the dirt of years and encrusted with blood stains; these were donned by the surgeons before going into the wards or operating room. At the foot of the stained coarse old operating table lay a wooden tray of sand, smelling of cats. On a shelf around lay the instruments, open for anyone to handle. Suture needles were stuck in a jampot of rancid lard, which never seemed to be changed'. The theatre which Ogston describes was below the rotunda of the Simpson pavilion. It was opened in 1840 and illuminated by gaslight. As the time for an operation approached, the students filled the semicircular tiers of benches demanding that those at the front should remove their hats. Distinguished visitors sat at the front of this amphitheatre and would comment on the progress of the operation. Nowadays the occupied part of the Simpson building is neat, clean and quiet; it is difficult to imagine the smells and noise and clatter which would have assailed the terrified patient as he or she was carried through the narrow door at the top of the main staircase into the crowded room and bound to the stained wooden table.[9]

By 1848 chloroform was administered to some patients, with variable results. The surgeon William Keith[10] (Plate 30) describes in 1849 the case of John Smith, farmer of Glenbucket,[11] who was sounded for stone. 'Chloroform was administered freely. After a struggle, requiring his limbs to be steadied by four assistants, and then a good-humoured indulgence in a display of celtic eloquence which lasted for five minutes, he went into a state of complete anaesthesia'. However, Keith commented that, in two cases of lithotomy, violent convulsive struggling came on during induction after the patients were secured to the table, 'which deterred the writer himself from using chloroform in like cases'.[12] Ogston records that 20 years later Keith still adhered to this decision, so everything

Plate 30 William Keith (1803–71), noted lithotomist.

depended on the dexterity and anatomical knowledge of the operator. Working in the perineum, by daylight only, with no time for retraction or swabbing, the operation must have been conducted mainly through the sense of touch. Children were cut for stone and the awful distress of the patients must have laid an immense strain on the surgeon and his assistants. Abernethy's assistant tells that 'he had seen him after a big operation with tears in his eyes, lamenting the possible failure of what he had just been compelled to do by dire necessity and surgical rule'.[13]

Keith was appointed surgeon to the Infirmary in 1838 and in 1843 he reported every patient with a stone in the bladder who had been treated over five years (remarking on how easy it is to show good results if only selected cases are reported)[14] and the next year published a remarkable account of his lateral approach for lithotomy, based on an experience in 42 patients.[15] Keith then had charge of 56 beds as did his only colleague William Laing but the annual total of operations was but 70–90.

Keith had never performed the operation before his appointment to the staff but he remarks that 'I have borrowed ideas from every quarter, adopting what my judgement taught me was right'. He made dissections on the cadaver and had specially modified instruments made. He was ahead of his contemporaries in stressing the importance of the preparation of the patient especially in the elderly. Bed rest, a good diet and ample quantities of thin gruel and tea were ordered along with leeches applied to the suprapubic area. However, plethoric 50-year-olds needed 'a process of fining down', with two to three weeks of a thin diet. Without anaesthesia, three assistants were needed to restrain the patient: two held the legs and one pressed upon the shoulders so that the perineum always overhung the end of the table. A fourth assistant had the crucial responsibility of holding the urethral staff firmly in place. Keith described the vital importance of the correct siting of the incision, and remarks that the account given by Sir Charles Bell is 'calculated fearfully to mislead the young and inexperienced surgeon'. He gave a vivid description of how he reaches the bladder without injury to the rectum or to major arteries, based on his post-mortem studies and reported that he had removed stones up to three inches in diameter.

Post-operative vigilance was vital, when the patient's 'safety and progress rest, under God, on the surgeon's skill and care. For six hours after the operation he should never be above an hour absent from the bedside. Then the surgeon must visit every four hours for 36 hours and then every six hours for a week.' This 'enables the surgeon to keep everything right, which is easier and safer than having to set them right. While he rests on the blessing of God for success, let him watch and strive as if the cure depended on his unaided efforts'.

Keith was able to report only one death among 18 consecutive patients between 53 and 79 years of age at a time when many clinics had a mortality of 20–30 per cent.

Ogston remarks that in 1861 when he became a clinical student that although chloroform was available, 'usually it was not used'. In that year 108 operations were performed, including 14 major amputations, 10 lithotomies and five litholapaxies. One arterial aneurysm was treated by proximal ligation and a vesico-vaginal urinary fistula was repaired.[16] The American gynaecologist James Marion Sims of New York – the pioneer of the repair of vesico-vaginal fistula – visited Aberdeen in that year and commented on the skills of Keith.[17] It is not impossible that he played a part in the repair of this fistula.

One of the problems of pre-Listerian surgery was the arrest of haemorrhage. Main vessels were tied off with silk thread, the end left long and the thread withdrawn after some days – a course which was liable to precipitate secondary haemorrhage associated with sepsis developing along the tract of the thread. The alternative method of acupressure, using pins or wires to compress the vessels, was introduced by J.Y. Simpson and enthusiastically promoted by William Pirrie, the first professor of surgery at Marischal College.[18] However, in 1869, a year before he joined the staff, Ogston demonstrated that ligation with silk was more reliable.[19] After much experiment, beginning in 1875, Lister showed that the need to leave the ligature long was overcome by using absorbable catgut though these conclusions were much contested.[20] After visiting Lister, J.C.O. Will who was a member of the ARI staff made many experiments with chromic acid as a treatment to delay the absorption of catgut.[21]

Plate 31 Alexander Ogston in his home at 252 Union Street, 1896.

The experience of Ogston (Plate 31) links in a remarkable way the pre-Listerian era with the second period of 125 years after 1867. As a student he saw all the problems of surgery practised without anaesthesia or any understanding of the cause of infection. In 1869 he decided to investigate Lister's work on antisepsis in Glasgow by paying him a visit. By then, however, Lister had moved to the chair of clinical surgery in Edinburgh but did not have charge of beds, so he advised Ogston to visit the wards of his successor in Glasgow, Hector Cameron, where he would see Listerian techniques in operation. Cameron took Ogston to his ward and 'five minutes later found me convinced of the truth of the marvellous discovery. I was shown a knee joint which had been opened . . . the limb was perfectly well and the wound clean and healing. I saw that a miraculous change had come over our science . . . .I felt inclined to sit down and think out what the great revelation implied in the future'.[6] However, when he returned to Aberdeen, Ogston was faced with the incredulity of his surgical colleagues who had 'all been brought up to believe that suppuration was one of the necessary and inevitable stages of the healing of a wound'. Moreover, the managers of the Infirmary objected to the extra expense of the clean dressings and lotions which he required. Nevertheless, as Ogston followed antiseptic principles he found that these allowed him to operate safely on bones and joints and enabled him to describe in 1877 the operation for genu valgum which became internationally known as Ogston's procedure.

He did not, however, obtain such wide recognition for a much more important piece of investigation. The work of Pasteur and Lister had produced a growing belief during the 1870s that there was a connection between germs and sepsis but few recognized that specific germs caused specific diseases. Ogston suspected there was truth in this theory and between 1877 and 1880 he carried out a series of crucial experiments. These are described in detail in Porter's account[3] and were a considerable tribute to both the science of bacteriology and Ogston's intellect. Working with pus from 70 abscesses he identified the staphylococcus and fulfilled Koch's famous postulates which relate disease and organisms several years before the latter were published. When Professor Bulloch wrote Ogston's obituary in 1929 he reviewed the interaction between Koch and Ogston and concluded that it was Ogston who 'correctly interpreted the exact aetiology of acute suppurative processes in man'.[22] However, when Ogston presented his findings to his colleagues he was disbelieved and it was only when he addressed the congress of the German Chirurgical Society in Berlin in April 1880 (he spoke good German) that his work was immediately recognized as valid and he was elected to its membership.[23]

Lister's work caused a fundamental re-orientation in surgical practice but it is curious nowadays to consider how greatly he relied on antisepsis to achieve his results. We are told that he lectured to the Edinburgh students in the surgical amphitheatre wearing a stained frock coat and seated on an old chair.[24] Then four students would carry in the patient, who was laid on an aged kitchen table. No one scrubbed up. The carbolic spray – 'the unconscious caretaker' as Lister called it – was started up, the anaesthetic was induced and Lister began to operate, explaining each step. In Aberdeen Ogston seems to have followed these rituals closely and, in the famous photograph of him at work, everyone wears ordinary clothes with sleeves rolled up to the elbow.[25] It seems strange that such a thoughtful surgeon did not appreciate the greater safety which would come from following the example of the great ovariotomists – Wells, Keith, Tait, Sims – who laid strong emphasis on the cleanliness of hands and of instruments; for example visitors to Spencer Wells' theatre had to swear that they had not attended a post-mortem room for at least seven days.

A photograph taken in 1890 in the operating theatre under the dome of the Simpson building shows that the surgeon and his assistant had progressed to wearing freshly-laundered overalls (Plate 32). In that year Lister abandoned the use of the spray and in Germany between 1890 and 1900 Neuber and von Bergmann in Berlin introduced steam sterilization of all linen and dressings and the boiling of instruments. Gradually antiseptic techniques based on Lister's chemical methods gave way to asepsis and the exclusion of micro-organisms from surgical wounds.

At this time new buildings were going up at Woolmanhill (see p.40) and, when they opened in 1892, there were three male and three female wards on three floors, connected by a lift to two theatres in the basement – one able to

---

Plate 32 Operation in 1890 under the dome in the Simpson building in front of a gallery of medical students (dressers). The surgeon Alexander MacGregor, at that time medical electrician to the Infirmary, and his house surgeon are wearing white coats – washed but not sterilized. The steam sterilizer was a thing of the future. A Lister carbolic spray can be seen (lower right).

Plate 33 The basement operating theatre at Woolmanhill, circa 1910.

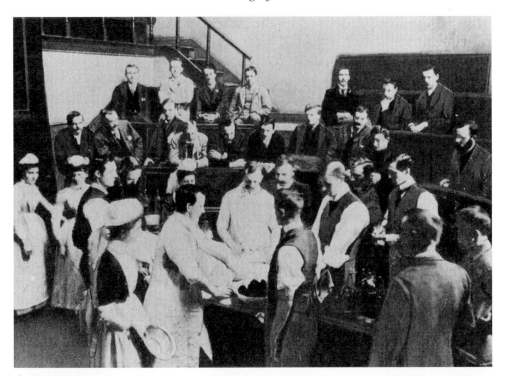

accommodate 200 spectators and the other 60 (Plate 33).[26] These looked remarkably similar to the old amphitheatre under the dome but scrub-up sinks and an autoclave had been installed, and though the operating table was still of wood, metal trolleys were in use. The new block was lit by electricity yet the lighting over the operating table was restricted to three naked bulbs.

With the opening of the twin theatres, the number and range of operations increased and the report of 1893 contains for the first time a section on 'operations on the digestive organs'.[27] However among the 12 laparotomies there were six deaths. By 1900, 906 operations were performed; 42 carcinomas were excised (22 in the breast, nine on the jaws, six on the lips and five on the tongue) with only two recorded deaths.[28] Tuberculous neck glands were removed from 49 patients and 15 had varicose veins ligated; 12 appendicectomies were performed and eight appendix abscesses drained. For the first time a kidney was removed and a cholecystostomy performed. There were 11 ovarian cystectomies, and all the patients recovered. Ovariotomy was by this time a standard operation.[29]

Although Fitz of Boston had in 1886 established acute appendicitis as a pathological entity which required urgent treatment[30] and McBurney had published his famous paper in 1889,[31] it took another 10 years for British surgeons to accept the need to operate on appendicitis as an emergency. The first mention of acute appendicitis in the proceedings of the Aberdeen Medico-Chirurgical Society was in January 1900, when Scott Riddell read a paper.[32] He remarked that the point of maximum tenderness is not always at McBurney's point, and that 'it is never safe to diagnose appendicitis in a young female without a rectal examination'. He stated that 'no case of acute perforative appendicitis if left to nature recovers. With operation the patient has a chance'. However, at a time when intravenous fluids were hardly used and patients were often referred late, Riddell had a mortality of 20 per cent and this was the general experience.

In other reports to the Medico-Chirurgical Society, Riddell expressed concern about the delay he experienced in seeing patients with intestinal obstruction who were still being admitted under the physicians. In 1907 he reported on a Maydl's operation performed on a six-year old girl with an ectopic bladder: the trigone was separated and implanted into the sigmoid colon, after which she could retain urine in the rectum for about four hours before voiding. In 1908 successful primary colonic anastomoses were described after resections for irreducible intussusception and for carcinoma.

John Marnoch[33] published 60 cases of gastric ulceration on which he had operated.[34] In 42 elective operations the favoured procedure was gastro-jejunostomy which had been widely used since the start of the century. In 18 patients he had closed an acutely perforated ulcer by suture; mostly in young women (duodenal ulcers were still unusual). Although nine of these 18 patients died, there were only two deaths in the last nine patients treated and Marnoch attributed this to patients being seen sooner and the post-operative use of Fowler's position and infusion of water per rectum.

Improving standards of nursing also made an important contribution to the outcome of surgery. Back in 1844 the surgeons had complained that there was only one ignorant and overworked nurse to care for two wards. Come the 1880s, trained nurses were creating new standards of care throughout the country and by 1904 Woolmanhill wards were staffed by nine sisters and 63 nurses and students.[35]

By 1908 the increasing range of surgery especially within the abdomen led the three senior surgeons, Riddell, Marnoch and Gray,[36] to inform the Hospital Board that there was acute need for new theatres.[37] The annual numbers of operations performed had risen from 403 in 1893 to 1,972 in 1907, achieved only by working unduly lengthy lists. Theatre ventilation was quite inadequate and facilities for washing, sterilization and storage were out-of-date. The amphitheatres were also used for student lectures and lists could only commence after teaching had finished – 'a most undesirable state of affairs'. By 1908 some 600 abdominal operations were being done in a year, including 220 appendicectomies, 150 hernia repairs and 44 gastric operations. In 50 patients with intestinal obstruction there were only seven deaths – a low figure for that time. Six ectopic gestations had been successfully treated. The Board recognized that the volume of surgical work could only increase and decided to erect a vertical stack of three theatres backing on to Spa Street and communicating directly with the three surgical floors. These, provided by Lord Mount Stephen,[38] opened in 1912.

During World War I, the surgical staff had to cope with the additional work generated in the military hospitals which were established in the Central School, the Girls' High School and Woodend Hospital. F.K. Smith,[39] an assistant surgeon, perhaps as a consequence of overwork, developed a duodenal ulcer, which was treated by a posterior gastro-jejunostomy performed by Professor Marnoch. About half the patients who had this operation, which remained popular throughout the 1920s and 1930s, secured an excellent result and F.K. (as he was known) was fortunate to be one of them.

Henry Gray was absent throughout the war and went to Canada in 1923. He was the first surgeon in Aberdeen to insist on all operating room staff wearing a sterile cap, mask and gown (Plate 34). He performed the first Caesarean section in Aberdeen and one of his lists could include the plating of a fracture, a cerebral decompression and a resection of the bladder. On the western front he was largely responsible, with Robert Jones of Liverpool, for the introduction of the universal application of the Thomas splint for transportation of lower limb wounds; coupled with wide excision this reform resulted in the mortality of compound femoral fractures falling from 80 per cent to around 20 per cent. He was succeeded by Mr G.H. Colt[40] who had been Professor Marnoch's assistant since 1910 and became widely known for his ingenious method of wiring aortic aneurysms (devised while still a medical student). In 1937 he reviewed over 20 years' experience.[41] Among many publications he made a detailed review of 239 admissions for tuberculous mesenteric adenitis and was the first surgeon to report torsion of the hydatid of Morgagni.

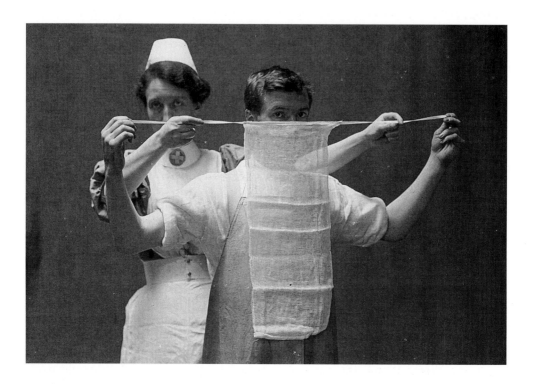

Plate 34 Henry Gray preparing to operate, circa 1900. (From the George Washington
  Wilson collection.)

As the 1920s opened, the volume of work rose steadily, reaching over 3,000 in-
patient operations in 1925 and over 4,000 in 1931. These figures were achieved by
a relatively small staff – three senior and three junior honorary consultants, one
resident surgical officer and three house surgeons. In the treatment of peptic
ulcer, 43 elective gastro-jejunostomies were performed in 1934 but only seven
partial gastrectomies. Among 76 perforated peptic ulcers the low mortality rate of
five per cent was achieved.[42]

When it is remembered that the population served by the Royal Infirmary has
increased only by some thousands over that of the 1930s these numbers seem
small. In 1934 for instance, 18 colorectal carcinomas were resected but by the
1960s over 150 colorectal cancers were being removed in Aberdeen each year
with over 100 patients having a radical resection with a view to cure.[43] It seems
reasonable to believe that although the same number of large bowel neoplasms
occurred in the 1930s, relatively few were being selected for treatment. Many
were never referred by their family doctors who knew of the risks of major
surgery at that time especially among the elderly.

By 1934 the new Royal Infirmary was being built at Foresterhill – 'the
promised land on which all eyes are set' as Scott Riddell described the plans in
1927.[44] When the new Infirmary opened in 1936 F.K. Smith, then senior surgeon,

performed the first operation. His assistant was James Learmonth[45] who had followed Sir John Marnoch in the Regius chair in 1932.

For the first time a separate urological unit could be conceived and was put under the charge of F.K. Smith. This was a time when ward sisters played a particularly important part in the running of a surgical unit and they were well exemplified by Miss Hay, who was the sister on F.K.'s unit. She ran the ward with a remarkable combination of complete efficiency and wise compassion. Rarely off duty, with a phenomenal memory for former patients, mentor to many hesitant house surgeons, she (and many like her) appear to have derived the greatest satisfaction from what seems now to have been a life of almost unrelieved hard work and responsibility.[39]

During World War II, William Anderson[46] dominated the surgical side of the Infirmary. His pioneer work in neurological and thoracic surgery in Aberdeen continued after 1945 until specialist units were formed. W.C. Wilson[47] who had succeeded Learmonth, was in the Middle East during 1942–3 where his extensive experience of the care of burns was employed as the officer-in-charge No.1 Medical Research Unit, RAMC. The few remaining staff were extremely hard-pressed to cover the work in the Infirmary and Woodend Hospital. As the staff re-assembled after 1945 the strength of the surgical units was enhanced as younger surgeons were demobilized and joined the units as assistants. It was, however, not only an increase in their staffing which was bringing change to the character of surgical units but the rise of new technology and of teams, the latter fostered by the war and leading to the growth of specialities.

The operation books show that in 1946 over 7,000 operations were performed. Tuberculosis was still a common affliction. One or two thyroidectomies were being done each week and most peptic ulcers were treated by partial gastrectomy. Seventy perforated peptic ulcers were closed, with over 90 per cent being duodenal ulcers in men. Suprapubic cystostomy was still a more common operation than prostatectomy and colonic resections were generally carried out by the Paul-Mickulicz procedure.

As July 1948 and the advent of the National Health Service drew near, few could foresee how these practices would in turn become a part of history. Over 200 years ago, Percival Pott gave good advice:

> Many and great are the improvements which the chirurgical art have received over the last 50 years, and many thanks are due to those who contributed to them; but when we reflect how much still remains to be done it should rather excite our industry than inflame our vanity.[48]

General surgery at the ARI after the NHS

For the 15 or so years after the start of the Health Service, general surgery continued to be dominated by those who 'from the war returning' became distinguished practitioners of its craft and science; they gradually replaced seniors who had kept the service going against all odds during the difficult years of the war.[49] William Anderson died in harness in 1949 and George Gordon Bruce[50] retired in 1957. William Wilson, in post as professor of surgery from 1939 to 1962 fostered a number of younger men in his department including such senior lecturers as Michael Woodruff, who was to become professor of surgical science at Edinburgh, Brian Brooke, who went to a readership at Birmingham and from there to the chair at St George's Hospital London, and Andrew Wilkinson, who became professor of paediatric surgery at Great Ormond Street. Greig Murray[51] was appointed professor of surgery at King's College Hospital – the first to hold the chair there since Lord Lister. William Burnett[52] went from a lecturership in the department to a senior lecturership with Charles Illingworth in Glasgow and thence to the chair of surgery in the University of Queensland. Charles Clark,[53] first lecturer and then senior lecturer in Aberdeen with Wilson and later Professor George Smith, went on to Leeds under Professor John Goligher as a reader and thereafter to University College Hospital, London as professor.

Wilson will best be remembered for his sponsorship of others but he had a profound but quiet influence on the development of surgery in Aberdeen as a whole and at the Royal Infirmary. He was particularly responsible for the post-war development of the specialities such as neurosurgery (see p.154), though some of these, such as plastic surgery (see p.157) and urology, were slow to start. In particular, though F.K. Smith had professed urology before World War II and had designated beds in ward 6 at the west end of the Foresterhill surgical block, the idea of an independent unit lapsed in the 1940s. Norman Logie[54] kept a special interest in the field but it was only after Phase I opened that planning made possible a urological department in 1967. Technical advances in the field have increased its work so that there are now three consultants and a service for the management of urolithiasis, though Aberdeen has yet to acquire a lithotripter.

Wilson was succeeded by George Smith, who held the chair for two decades from 1962–82 during which many developments and changes took place. The number of beds allocated to surgery increased, a further general acute unit was opened at the ARI and, as planned, cardiothoracic surgery moved into the Foresterhill buildings in 1966 (see p.146). The continued development of renal medicine and renal replacement therapy allowed renal transplantation to begin in 1975 undertaken by Jetmund Engeset. The 1960s were also notable for the transfer of surgeons who had received much of their higher surgical training in the professorial unit to consultant posts in the NHS so to produce a fertile intermingling of the academic and the practical – a 'collegiality' that would stand Aberdeen in good stead in the ensuing years.[55] A network of interchanges, principally with North America, was established and many opportunities also arose to provide research experience at Foresterhill for surgeons from Jordan, Kuwait, the Gulf States, Thailand, Pakistan, Afghanistan, Kenya, Nigeria and Zaire. Surgeons from the RAMC and the RN were also attached. Most important, however, was the creation of a comprehensive research and training programme within the Aberdeen teaching hospitals and centred on the Royal Infirmary. The research component of the training varied over the years but five broad areas could be identified:

1. Infection related to surgery.
2. Micro-circulation and platelet pathophysiology.
3. Hyperbaric studies with special reference to diving (see p.103).
4. Environmental studies particularly of cold.
5. Body metabolism in relation to sepsis, operations and stress.

In summing up 20 years of great activity on what he refers to as 'the Hill', George Smith comments:[56] 'By 1979, after the Aberdeen surgical training programme had been going for 16 years, a survey showed that 155 had joined it for part or the whole of their course, 113 registrars had entered the latter cadre. While 18 were still in post, of the remaining 95, 83 had become senior registrars and then consultants in general surgery. Of the remaining 12, nine had transferred to other branches of surgery and one each had gone to radiology, pathology and family practice. By this time also, seven full professors, eight readers or associate professors and 27 senior lecturers or assistant professors had become established from the group with a world-wide distribution.

'Over 500 papers, communications and chapters in books had been contributed by surgeons and trainees at Foresterhill. In addition, nine textbooks were published, while of the 272 higher degrees awarded in the medical faculty over a 20 year period, 63 originated from the surgical division.

'Perhaps the most important thing of all was that the university and hospital staff had become more of a single entity. In 1961–2 the university calendar showed, under the entry Surgery, one professor, two senior lecturers, one lecturer, five part-time lecturers and 12 part-time assistants. By 1981–2 the figures were one professor (two clinical professors had recently retired and one moved out of surgery), two readers, 38 senior lecturers, 16 lecturers, 18 clinical tutors and two research fellows'.

Foresterhill at this time provided not only a centre of clinical excellence in surgery and basic surgical research but also a base for studies in what might be called 'surgical natural history'. Prominent among these were: the continued assessment of the surgical treatment of colon cancer by Peter Jones;[43] the assessment and surgical management of thyroid disease begun by William Michie,[57] who in turn had built on the experience of Gordon Bruce, and which was to be continued by Norman Matheson; the development of vascular surgery by George Mavor[58] further established by Engeset; and the prevention and management of surgical sepsis again by Matheson[59,60] who also pioneered the introduction of better techniques of intestinal anastomosis. It is fair to say in this context that the unique position of Foresterhill and the ARI as the focal point of all major surgery in the North-East of Scotland ensured a steady and channelled flow of experience which was exploited in the best possible way.

Changes were to follow after 1982. The physical structure and organization of general surgery underwent gradual metamorphosis from the opening of Phase I in 1966 and the move of the Academic Unit. The disintegration of the traditional compact self-contained unit based on a Nightingale ward and an attached operating theatre accelerated with the transfer of the two general surgical units to Phase 2 in 1980 and was completed with the relocation of Ward 7 from Woodend into the ARI.

Zygmunt Krukowski writing as a contemporary general surgeon at the ARI in 1991 comments on these changes which were part of the view that large operating theatre suites should be more efficient and, from an anaesthetic perspective, safer: 'It is a curious observation on the diversity of the medical profession that anaesthetists draw strength and support from a large grouping both on a clinical and administrative level; that well-organized guild – anaesthesia – aspiring to an image of a beehive throbbing with co-ordinated activity (albeit it with the odd drone), contrasts vividly with the traditionally individual approach of the surgeon ploughing on alone which the less than charitable liken to an elephant blundering through a thicket. There is little doubt that a large theatre suite is administratively more attractive with the greater flexibility which stems from a large pool of staff and the resources that can be provided, but the de-personalization which seems to be the inevitable consequence impinges on job satisfaction and the morale of those who work there'.[61]

Other major organizational changes were a consequence of continued progressive sub-specialization – an inevitable force in a sizeable teaching centre such as the ARI. The requirement to develop vascular surgery as a separate discipline was achieved with the relocation from Woodend. The four general surgical units were reduced to three with the predictable consequence that they had to undertake the remaining general surgical workload and sustain an increased frequency of emergency 'receiving' with smaller staff numbers.

Krukowski remarks: 'Simple arithmetic shows that a reduction in junior staff by a quarter, an increased frequency of emergency receiving from one in four to one in three and the diminishing extra hours recommended for junior staff are all incompatible with traditional work patterns and training. There is a dawning realization that radical re-organization of surgery, including the introduction of a shift system for junior staff, is necessary. The resident house officer could become a faded memory when he or she clocks in and out with the other staff. The gains to juniors from a shorter working week will have implications for their ultimate career post'.

Paediatric surgery was also moving towards a speciality separate from general surgery with the establishment in 1988 of an exclusively surgical paediatric consultant post, thus breaking a longstanding link between general surgery at the ARI and the activities of the Children's Hospital.

All these changes leave the impression, strong in some quarters, that general surgery is, at the ARI as elsewhere in the country, a crumbling edifice through loss of traditional spheres of activity to sub-specialities and other disciplines. The current general surgeon will be replaced by one of different style, without the versatility of his or her predecessors which have illuminated some of the pages of this history but possessed of a more refined repertoire. The first indications of this are in the impact of laparoscopic techniques on abdominal surgery since the late 1980s.

Committees flourished during the 1980s. The Surgeons' Committee, predominantly a general surgical enclave, mutated into a Division of Surgery which encompassed all specialities. Conceived with the idea of unifying and strengthening the advice available from all, its title as one individual has commented 'lends weight to the concept of a collective noun as a description of the group'. *Ad hoc* groups, sub-committees and specialist sub-groups proliferated although the business of decision-making and of formulating policy continued to remain – at least to some – as obscure as before and now buried beneath an ever larger volume of word-processed and photocopied output.

In contrast to the infrequency of surgical operations in the early years of the hospital the annual number of operations in 1990 exceeded 32,000 and about 8,000 of these were done as day case procedures. The duration of hospital stay has steadily and dramatically reduced – in no small measure due to advances in anaesthesia. For example, after inguinal hernia repair or operations for varicose veins it is usual for patients to go home the next day and after cholecystectomy they are commonly discharged four and sometimes even three days later; after laparoscopic cholecystectomy, discharge one or two days later is routine.

Serious wound infection, which dominated the outcome of surgery in the past and was still a problem of considerable size 20 to 30 years ago, has almost vanished and after abdominal surgery it has in some units become almost a rarity. This remarkable change may be partly attributable to the natural history of the pathogenic potential of bacteria but is probably mainly dependent on the appropriate use of antibiotics as well as on refined and defined surgical technique.

Hyperbaric medicine in Aberdeen

In the late 1950s the therapeutic possibilities of oxygen at high pressure were promising and, when George Smith came to Aberdeen and was followed by Nelson Norman, a pressure chamber was soon established behind the Medical School[62] with funds provided by the Medical Research Council. Apart from research its most impressive clinical use was in the treatment of poisoning by domestic (town) gas, the chief component of which was carbon monoxide. For this purpose, portable 'monoplace' chambers were produced one of which was installed in the casualty department at Woolmanhill and another was commissioned by Ernest Ridley for use in radiotherapy. However, leaky gas appliances were less common in Aberdeen than elsewhere and the discovery of natural gas (methane) in the Southern North Sea soon led to the conversion of the gas grid in the United Kingdom to this product so that carbon monoxide poisoning from this source largely disappeared.

Though the therapeutic aspects of the work which was based on the Royal Infirmary declined in the 1960s for these reasons, the discovery of oil in the Northern North Sea at ocean depths not tackled in the past led to saturation diving being introduced with the possibility of serious decompression illness should unscheduled decompression take place. Gradually through the enthusiasm of those in Aberdeen there was a move towards a national hyperbaric centre and this was eventually set up on the Foresterhill site with the Grampian Health Board Hyperbaric Medicine Unit (1982) as part of it but heavily dependent on the Royal Infirmary for its support and staffing.[63] However, the focus of initial treatment has moved to the oil rigs themselves and at the time of writing re-organization and staff change is taking place and will be the subject of record for future historians.

8

Nursing

The general involvement of those who were the predecessors of today's nurses when the Royal Infirmary opened its doors has been recounted in Chapter 3. Mrs Strachan's duties were predominantly house keeping but she was able to hire those who could tend to the seriously ill and first did so in May 1744.[1] This practice continued throughout the 18th century and included such tasks as 'watching', 'waulking' or 'waking', the last of which indicated that there were staff available at night. Margaret Grubb in 1744 was the first nurse to specialize; she looked after patients under salivations of mercury[2] at a salary of one shilling and sixpence (7.5p) a week. A midwife[3] was employed following the opening of the lying-in ward until its closure in 1766.

As to patients with mental illness, they were consigned in Bedlam to the care of the town sergeant[4] until in 1768 this duty was transferred to James McEdward who had been hired as a strong young gardener.[5] Such patients could have 'servants' to meet their needs sometimes employed by their relatives and sometimes by the hospital. In the early records of payment there is often no distinction between these and the nurses, though an exception occurs in 1765 when it is recorded that there were three nurses and five servants on the books. What training these nurses may have had is unknown though by this time midwives were being encouraged to attend for instruction.[6]

With the grant of the first royal charter (see p.24), the conduct of affairs became more formalized and the rules to govern the behaviour of housekeeper, nurses and servants are considered in detail on p.26. The housekeeper's role remained chiefly managerial but it is clear that she was responsible for the nurses. These duties were re-confirmed in 1801.[7] Recorded misbehaviour amongst the nurses was rare but in that year a certain Ann Joss refused to attend to hear about her duties and was dismissed.[8]

During the first half of the 19th century and in common with the rest of the country, the image conveyed to us of the hospital nurse in the Aberdeen Royal Infirmary is not flattering. Ogston wrote[9] perhaps partly with hindsight and in caricature but surely with more than a grain of truth that: 'In the old Aberdeen Royal Infirmary[10] each stuffy ward was presided over by an old woman whose only qualification was her ability to make a poultice; whose dress was a mutch [11] on her head, a printed calico dress round her capacious figure and a big apron;

who kept a tom cat called after the physician she served, such as Alexander Kilgour or Benjamin Wilson. Dr Kilgour[12] himself coming out of the admission room downstairs. . . would be greeted by the deaf old crone'.

Standards had clearly deteriorated since the 18th century with its emphasis on cleanliness and the 'goodness of air' reinforced by the discipline of twice daily housekeeper's rounds and unannounced inspection by the managers. Laxity in observance of the rules is also recorded in the dismissal in 1827 of matron (now the accepted title) Janet Gordon who had been appointed as 'matron or housekeeper' in 1818. She was charged on counts of allowing her son board and lodging, not visiting the wards, not giving proper attention to the physician's instructions and of sending hospital provisions to her sister. All but the last were found proven.[13]

Money – or the lack of it – may well have been a root cause of this abysmal behaviour and also of poor recruitment.[14] In 1816 pay for nurses and servants (which must be assumed to include free board and lodging which was to continue well into the 20th century) went up from £5 per annum to £5.50; a further increase to £8 took place in 1837 with an extra £1 (danger money) for fever nurses.[15] The matron at this time received £35 a year. Pay for nurses did improve by £2 a year in 1870 after the managers had obtained scales from Edinburgh, Glasgow and Dundee which showed that by comparison with the first two cities Aberdeen's nurses were at a disadvantage.[16]

Two other matters were however combining to generate change in nursing. First and more important was the experience of Florence Nightingale in the Crimean war of the 1850s and her subsequent persistent and determined advocacy of nursing as a dignified and dedicated profession.[17] Second, and as the century wore to a close, the increasing need for expert care with the widening of the scope of medicine and surgery. In 1873 at least the first of these may have influenced the managers to set up a committee to 'enquire into the whole subject connected with the nursing department'.[18] The event marked a real turning point and evidence was obtained from the matron, the medical superintendent and the medical staff.

The committee's report gives us an exact account of the working hours experienced. The day nurses rose at 6 a.m. and began work shortly thereafter continuing until 10 p.m. when they were relieved by the night staff. The latter were responsible for the patients until 6 the following morning but then helped the day nurses to sweep, scrub and make beds and on two days a week they helped with the laundry which took until mid-day. Thereafter they could go to bed at 3 p.m. having dined with the day staff under the eye of the oldest nurse. There was no sitting room and little privacy as three to four women shared one bedroom. Off duty was not stated except for attending church, though there were arrangements for an afternoon or evening off when they wished.

As to the majority opinion of the medical staff this can be summarized from a statement by Alexander Ogston:[19] '1. The nurses are underpaid. 2. The diet is inferior in quality. 3. Nursing accommodation is insufficient. 4. Nurses are recruited from an inferior class. 5. They are expected to do work other than nursing. 6. They have too much to do.'

He recommended that trained nurses should be employed – in particular protestant deaconesses from their Institution and Training Hospital in London.[20] Unfortunately for Aberdeen they were not available to teaching hospitals though six had been employed at Perth Infirmary where their services were held in the highest regard.[21]

Apart from generating a groundswell of opinion, no firm recommendations seem to have resulted but in 1874 the nursing committee reported that, though there was a staff of 21 nurses, three more were required for infectious disease (typhus and scarlet fever). An appointment of a head nurse was recommended and also of two women to act as scrubbers – presumably to relieve nurses of this duty – at a cost of £62 per annum. Marion Dobbie,[22] who had trained in Liverpool under Miss Mary Merryweather – an original Nightingale – became the first head nurse later in the year with duties which included recruitment, oversight of nursing care and training. For reasons which are not known, but can be imagined given the conditions of the day, she remained for only a year and was succeeded in November 1878 by Margaret Bothwell.[23] This lady was a direct product of the Nightingale school at St Thomas' and had then spent time at the Royal Infirmary of Edinburgh. She appears at least initially to have been made of sterner stuff than her predecessor in that she managed to have her nurses relieved from scrubbing floors and carrying coals. The period of training was extended to 12 months but her request for a uniform was turned down.[24] Her final achievement may have been a year later when she secured textbooks for the nurses and so began their library.

Miss Dobbie's and the first year of Miss Bothwell's appointments straddled what was in theory an improvement in the selection and training of nurses. The trustees of the estate of Robert Donaldson[25] provided money to support three or four months attendance at the Infirmary by women who would be then qualified as it was put 'to carry out intelligently the orders of a medical man'.[26] This scheme ran for at least 10 years but inevitiably those selected and supported tended to go elsewhere to institutions where they could command higher wages. Even those that remained were, according to the medical superintendent, not well enough trained and were required to do menial work. By 1884, at which time there were 27 nurses employed in the Infirmary, the nursing committee was asked to consider methods of attracting a higher standard of personnel. Salaries were again found to be inadequate compared to those in other Scottish cities and were raised though discrepancies remained at the top end of the scale.[27] Uniforms were provided and a systematic course of instruction for probationers[28] over two years, given by the head nurse and the medical staff, was instituted. An examination followed with the award of a certificate for those successful.

The influence of Miss Bothwell seems to have waned because criticism of nursing performance was not stilled by these radical improvements and culminated in a letter from Dr Angus Fraser which, *inter alia*, referred to a patient of R.J. Garden[29] who had exsanguinated from a secondary haemorrhage after an amputation. When Garden arrived neither the house surgeon nor a nurse could be found and the patient was *in extremis*. Wrath seems to have been more concentrated on the nursing than on the medical staff and the board acted with

(a)   (b)

Plate 35 Two formidable ladies. (a) Rachel Lumsden; (b) Elizabeth Edmondson.

dispatch. Both the housekeeper and Miss Bothwell were given three months notice and Miss Rachel Lumsden (Plate 35a),[30] at that time matron of the Children's Hospital, was persuaded after an unofficial approach to accept the post of lady superintendent. It was next decided that the medical superintendent would have to go[31] and Miss Lumsden took over in absolute charge in the combined post of superintendent, head nurse and housekeeper/matron.

The tenure of this patrician and philanthropic lady was eminently successful. She instituted a three year training scheme for her nurses, the first such in Scotland. Four trained nurses were brought from London to become ward sisters. She advised the board on the planning and staffing of the Jubilee extension scheme and in 1892 was instrumental in establishing a superannuation fund.[32] She was followed, albeit briefly, by one of her assistants Miss Tatham[33] and then in 1898 by Miss McNaughton[34] who was referred to as matron, the post of medical superintendent having been restored.

For the future of nursing in Aberdeen the next incumbent of the post, from 1912 proved to be a crucial figure. Miss Elizabeth Edmondson[35] (Plate 35b) immediately established her authority. Shortly after her appointment she informed the managers that she could not continue her duties unless she had entire control of laundry, kitchen, nurses' home, cleanliness and care of wards and superintendence of the work of nurses and maids; demands which were immediately approved.[36] Her dominance of the Aberdeen nursing scene from then on is attested by the fact that Scott Riddell[37] who was appointed non-resident medical superintendent at the outbreak of war, demitted office a year later saying that his post was a sinecure and unnecessary because of the efficiency of the matron.[38] She then became hospital superintendent and matron, a post which she held until 1935.

Her firm hand on the nursing and other affairs of the Infirmary is apparent and many changes followed from her suggestions. A home for nurses outwith the hospital had been first proposed in 1913[39] but was deferred because of the war. However, in 1919 the board purchased 15–16 Albyn Terrace and it was opened the following year with a matron in charge. Again at her insistence, a building[40] was provided in 1927 to house the preliminary training school (PTS). She was also responsible for shortening the hours that nurses worked and for the engagement of more cleaners to relieve nurses of menial duties.[41] What she could not do was to raise the level of pay for nurses in training. Through the 1920s they received 13 shillings and 6 pence (67.5p) per month.[42] A sister was paid £70–75 a year. The matron's salary was a princely £300.

This remarkable woman is remembered as a tall, imposing figure who did her rounds with a flowing head shawl and sometimes wore a mink cape. She was a strict disciplinarian but also compassionate. 'I could pretend', she said, 'to close my eyes'. One of her aphorisms to nurses on duty was to exhort them to treat patients as '. . . . guests'. She encouraged leisure activities for nurses and led the carol singing on Christmas morning. Her influence continued to be felt among the nursing profession in the Infirmary long after she retired but, although often invited, she never returned.

The second period of what might be called the 'reign of matron-superintendent' then came to an end. J. Crawford Knox[43] became medical superintendent and Florence Kaye[44] matron, both of whom were in post in time for the move to Foresterhill. From here we can best consider the subsequent development of nursing at ARI under the headings of buildings, recruitment and training, pay and conditions and finally the organization of the nursing task.

Buildings

The Albyn Terrace nurses' home became redundant with the opening of the Foresterhill home and was sold (including its tennis courts) to become a boarding house for Robert Gordon's College (Sillerton House). The Foresterhill home on five stories contained 285 bedrooms, with sitting rooms, lecture rooms, study and demonstration rooms and a large recreational hall – a gift of the Crombie-Ross trustees.[45]

In spite of its size it was soon to prove too small and in 1947 buildings in Queen's Gate and Great Western Road were acquired. The occupancy of all these would change with social patterns. The strict discipline in force up to the mid-1940s gradually relaxed so that in 1948 sisters were given keys to the home when out late. By 1954, nurses in their third year of training were allowed to live out and in 1969 those with homes in Aberdeen were encouraged to live there. Finally in 1970 all nursing staff in residence were allotted keys, so bringing to an end the tradition of 'lights out' and late passes.

Recruitment and training

At the time of the move to Foresterhill, when Miss Kaye was appointed, the annual intake of student nurses was around 36 a year giving a total of about 100 in training. Because of the greatly increased size of the new hospital, twice this number was required. In the mid- to late 1930s the north-east of Scotland was an excellent recruiting area and the standard of applicants was high.[46] This happy state of affairs did not persist for, with the outbreak of war in 1939, there were difficulties in staffing the Infirmary with trained nurses. Many left to join the armed forces, mostly to the Queen Alexandra's Imperial Medical Nursing Service (QAIMNS) and some would lose their lives.[47] Throughout the war fully half the trained staff entered the services and could not be adequately replaced.

Nursing standards were maintained through hard work and dedication.[48] By 1942 shortage of student nurses was beginning to cause concern as young women turned to better paid employment. Direction into the profession was resisted but once a nurse was trained she could only be employed after approval from the Ministry of Labour and National Service.

Recruitment after the war remained satisfactory – though influenced by pay and conditions of service – but in the 1970s the problems experienced during the latter years of the war recurred upon the discovery of North Sea oil. The shortage had a severe effect on the provision of clinical services with closure of wards and delay in the opening of Phase II (see p.75). Strenuous efforts were made to attract staff: married nurses were encouraged to return to the profession and nurse 'banks' were established to provide emergency cover. Gradually the shortage was overcome and new developments such as the opening of Phase II, Accident and Emergency at Foresterhill, the Coronary Care Unit and Intensive Care were able to proceed. Meanwhile the inevitable demand for more nurses which was the consequence of increasing technology and shorter working hours (see below) led the NE Regional Hospital Board to set up a study into nursing requirements in order to ascertain the staff necessary for day duty in each ward and department. The outcome was a series of reports which became known as the 'Aberdeen formula' and in 1976 were recommended for use throughout Scotland by the Home and Health Department.[49]

Training

Recruitment and training are almost inevitably linked. We have seen how Rachel Lumsden and Elizabeth Edmondson formalized local arrangements for education and certification. In 1919 the Nurse Registration Act[50] removed the need for local certification and by 1925 the Infirmary examination and certificate had been discontinued in favour of those for State Registration (SRN) .

Such had been Elizabeth Edmondson's contribution that, in this year, all the nurses from Aberdeen passed. Up to and largely through World War II their training continued to be, after a short introduction in the preliminary training school (PTS), an apprenticeship in the wards where, under the supervision of a sister or staff nurse, they carried out all the nursing duties required.

The first mention of tutoring was in October 1921 when it is recorded that the 'home sister'[51] should give instruction assisted by the ward sisters. Catherine Muirhead became sister tutor with charge of the nurses' home in 1927[52] – the same year as the opening of the PTS. The first full-time tutor was Sister Stephen previously of ward 6 (medical).[53] The formal appointment of a sister to the school of nursing continued (ultimately as principal nurse teacher) until Foresterhill College – the first one of its kind in Britain – opened in 1967. By 1943 a new grade of 'assistant nurse' had been authorized under the Nurses Act (Scotland)[54] but the managers – perhaps a trifle disdainfully – noted that this did not apply to the Infirmary.[55] Block training was introduced by Miss Kaye in 1948 to allow nurses to have systematic teaching and to sit examinations while free from clinical duties.

Two years later the Aberdeen Pre-nursing College was inaugurated with 100 pupils.[56] It allowed school leavers the opportunity to take subjects such as anatomy, physiology, hygiene and dietetics before starting practical nursing. In its first three years, 82 students presented for the preliminary state examination and 78 were successful. This was followed by a group training scheme in 1954 – after the union of the schools at ARI and Woodend – so as to include all nurses under the board of management of the Aberdeen General Hospitals. Experiment was later conducted in single patient assignment, but though this was considered a success it was never carried through because of shortage of trained nurses.

Successive changes in requirements introduced by the General Nursing Council throughout the decades 1950–70 caused further problems – particularly the need to second pupils to other hospitals for training in specialities such as paediatrics. In-service training for staff nurses was begun in 1959 and in 1967 a full-time sister for in-service training was appointed. Three week courses for nurses who wished to return to the profession were organized and study days for sisters and nursing auxiliaries began. In the 1970s a national system of assessment was gradually introduced so that reports were written on all the activities of an individual. All nurses were not only assessed but also counselled as to their progress, achievement and future goals. Gradually there developed a change in the training of nurses away from the apprenticeship system in the wards towards education based in a college. The first indication of this change had been Miss Kaye's block system already mentioned. Eventually the 'Aberdeen Formula' suggested that only 60 per cent of trainee nurses' time should be given to service and, with the advent of Project 2000,[57] the student nurse will be supernumerary to service for the great majority of her (or his) training, working out of the College of Nursing on the Foresterhill campus.

Pay and conditions of service

The stringent conditions of pay and terms of service which had their origins in the 18th century were to continue in Aberdeen and elsewhere and, as we have seen, were to affect recruitment. By 1931 the hours of work had nominally come down to 56 per week. National salaries were reviewed in 1943 and a rise of approximately a quarter (remarkable in wartime) followed, with four weeks holiday and superannuation.[58] Uniforms were to be provided free.

Also at this time Aberdeen University was about to introduce a comprehensive full-time student health service – the first of its kind in Britain. Dr Alex Macklin[59] was appointed to the post which included medical charge of the nurses' health service and carried an honorary appointment as assistant physician at ARI. Beds were allocated for the purpose on the top floor of the medical block, ward 5, an arrangement persisting since the opening of Foresterhill and which hitherto had been a responsibility of the medical registrar overseen by the senior physician and surgeon as appropriate.[60] The beds were transferred to the third floor of Phase I when it opened in 1967.[61]

In 1947 further reductions in hours to 48 were advocated but in Aberdeen lack of staff made 52 the practicable figure. For the first time, assistant nurses, ward orderlies and part-time nurses were allowed into Foresterhill.[62] Yet a further reduction was recommended by the Whitley Council[63] in 1964, this time to 42 hours. That was achieved the following year and the unattractive practice of 'split shifts' was gradually eliminated. Further reductions were still to come – down to 40 in 1970 and 37.5 in 1979.

But shorter hours were not enough because pay still remained comparatively low. In 1969, dissatisfaction over this came to a head with the national 'Raise the Roof' campaign which was supported by the Infirmary staff. The result was an increase of 20–30 per cent for trained nurses which at last allowed them to buy a small house or flat. 'Pay as you eat' was also introduced and this saw the end of the tradition of Christmas and New Year staff dinners and gradually the disappearance of the Christmas day gathering on the wards, a loss which many older doctors and nurses much regretted. Finally in parallel with all these changes – which were mostly for the better – went others. Nurses gradually became both more free and more specialized. The day of the long serving unmarried sister was over. More married during or after training to give, on average, two years of service before leaving to start their families. When they returned it was with a wish to work part-time.

Shorter hours also liberated their lives. Specialization grew with the development of medical techniques; the need for skilled nursing staff also determined how patients could be best looked after (see, for example, ITU, p.173). These changes also invoked organizational ones prominent amongst which was the Salmon report of 1968.[64] Titles changed – 'matron' and to a large extent 'sister' disappeared to be replaced by 'officer' – responsibilities altered and new tiers of staff were first created and then abolished. The process continues to this time but may be viewed by future historians as no more cataclysmic and perhaps of less importance than the work of Rachel Lumsden and of Elizabeth Edmondson 60 to 100 years ago.

The Aberdeen Nurses League

Not least amongst the activities of Florence Kaye was to found in 1937 the Nurses' League which has since had an annual meeting and runs a journal of high quality. In spite of the recommendations of the managers in 1876,[24] nurses trained at Aberdeen Royal Infirmary had no tangible recognition in terms of a badge and this was remedied by the League with a distinctive design which underwent changes over the years as training schools amalgamated and titles of health boards changed.[65] The current version bears the legend – Grampian Foresterhill College.

9

The Early Specialities

Introduction

The emergence of speciality at the Aberdeen Royal Infirmary must be seen in both national and international contexts. With few exceptions, of which ophthalmology and ENT are examples, the concept of the generalist had a firmly entrenched position in the UK for the first half of the 20th century even though it was grudgingly recognized that centres which concentrated their interests on restricted fields could produce excellent results. Orthopaedic surgery which had had its pioneers as early as the late 19th century was the first to appear after ophthalmology and ENT, though even it had a mixed parentage (the first Scottish professor had been successively a general surgeon, a thoracic surgeon specializing in tuberculosis and then the first in Scotland to ligate a patent ductus arteriosus) and in Aberdeen as we shall see was only given full rein in 1953 (p.143). Cardiology advanced on the back of a technological revolution and venereology on changing social patterns. Neurosurgery, though given a remarkable boost by the early efforts of Macewan in Glasgow in the first decade of the 20th century, was ultimately driven by the American pioneers such as Harvey Cushing and his numerous British acolytes. Plastic surgery, which was the outcome of the mutilations of two World Wars, and cardiothoracic surgery followed. All were of course also dependent upon technical developments such as the diathermy for haemostasis (neurosurgery), skin transfers (plastic surgery) and the endotracheal tube which permitted positive pressure ventilation of the lungs during anaesthesia (thoracic surgery). The history of these specialities as a whole cannot be gone into in detail here and the reader is referred to specialist works on the subject. What we shall try to do is outline their development in Aberdeen and particularly how this affected the ARI.

The story of the development of the specialities is intimately bound up with the evolution of craft postgraduate training which is outlined in Chapter 19.

OTOLARYNGOLOGY (ENT)

Although a department for diseases of ear, nose and throat was first mooted in 1904 and instituted in 1909, we learn from the biography of Sir Alexander

Ogston[1], that, finding too little to do after being appointed junior surgeon in 1870 and having given up ophthalmology, he applied for and was appointed to, the additional post of aurist. He had previously met Czermack, inventor of the laryngoscope, during a tour of continental teaching centres and had studied under his successor Turck in Vienna. Ogston operated on the frontal sinus in 1884 and later published a paper on lesions of the labyrinth.[1]

Henry Peterkin[2] applied to the board of management in 1907 to use the surgical admission room for lectures to the medical students but J. MacKenzie Booth,[3] who was later to retire early through ill health, had previously asked for use of the surgical theatre in 1904 to give lectures on the ear and larynx. MacKenzie Booth treated 608 ENT conditions in the dispensary in Castle Street in 1894 and in 1907 he anticipated the use of a photocopier as a teaching aid by devising a system of phographing lecture notes and diagrams for students. Both he and Peterkin were founder members of the Scottish Otolaryngological Society.

Peterkin, then assistant surgeon, was appointed surgeon in charge of the newly instituted ENT Department in 1909. In 1912 he was given beds in the new casualty and out-patient block. However, his appointment as the first university lecturer in diseases of ear, nose and throat was not until 1927. He retired in 1935 and was succeeded by H. Ross Souper[4] who died the following year and the latter was replaced in turn by Jack Otty[5]. He and John Gerrie[6] had come to the department as assistants and were together throughout the war years. E. Godfrey ('Wilkie') Collins[7] moved east from Inverness to fill the assistant vacancy after Souper's death and not long after in 1939 joined the 15th (Scottish) General Hospital ; he was taken prisoner at Tobruk and consequently did not return until the war was over. (Charles Weir,[8] a member of the same unit and a mere three miles away at the time considered himself fortunate to have eluded capture.)

Until the move to Foresterhill, in 1936, the ENT wards at Woolmanhill were on the first floor with a small room upstairs for 'special' cases, possibly malignant. The custom in these days was for the sister to live 'on the flat'. Miss Pickford,[9] who was theatre sister in the Peterkin era, recalls having to prepare her theatre for a clean surgical afternoon list following out-patient tonsil cases in the morning. The guillotine removal of tonsils was, in practised hands, an eminently successful operation but involved meticulous timing by both surgeon and anaesthetist. In Peterkin's day even adult tonsils were guillotined as out-patients and the story is told of an unfortunate man collecting a rather shocked lady patient and being advised by the sister to ensure her warmth by getting into bed with her (it was presumed he was the husband but was in fact a taxi driver). Guillotining was ultimately replaced by dissection in Aberdeen but, in some of the peripheral hospitals, guillotine sessions were to continue until 1967.

Dr W.G. Todd as the resident to Jack Otty in 1943 recalls being instructed to treat the first patient in Aberdeen to receive penicillin (Plate 36).[10] Professor Cruickshank had obtained some penicillin mould from which his laboratory prepared a brownish fluid containing a few units per millilitre. Nevertheless, this injected four times a day into a large carbuncle of the upper lip was associated with resolution of the lesion and aborted the danger of intracranial spread.

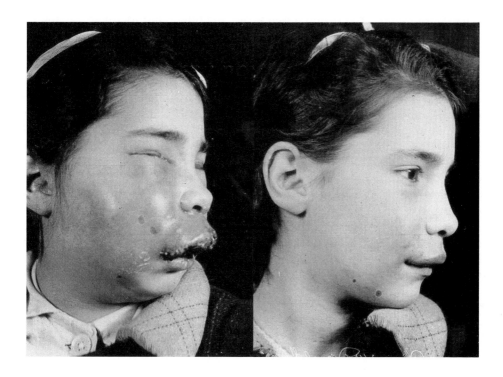

Plate 36 Patient treated by penicillin. The dramatic early effects of antibiotic treatment. Before and after photographs of the patient referred to on p.116 who had a severe staphylococal infection of the upper lip – a condition which, at that time (1943), nearly always led to death from cavernous sinus thrombosis. Reproduced by kind permission of Mrs Joan Burns (née McDonald) of Glenrothes who – 12 years old at the time – still remembers doctors gazing at her and shaking their head, muttering that there was of course no hope of cure.

After the war, staff changes were occasioned by the departure in 1946 of Jack Otty to Bradford and by the sudden death of John Gerrie at the BMA Conference in Harrogate in 1949. Meantime Ian MacNaughtan came from Edinburgh in 1947, followed in 1949 by Ivan Thomson and by Charles Weir a year later. These three with 'Wilkie' Collins, all from Edinburgh originally and following their war service, formed a stable tearn until Collins' retirement in 1967. The ensuing vacancy was filled by W.J. Newlands also from Edinburgh.

In the 1950s surgeons from the department, usually with an anaesthetist in company, travelled to eight peripheral hospitals for operating lists. There were also clinics held at Stracathro as well as children's tonsillectomy lists but these were abolished progressively on the grounds of safety.

Along with advances in the surgery of deafness, technical developments in the field of audiology were significant and a comprehensive regional service of hearing assessment in children was set up by Ivan Thomson. Another departmental development of note was the establishment of a weekly joint clinic with the oncology department in 1956 (see p.164). All cases of malignancy were discussed and monitored through diagnosis, treatment and follow up by the four consultants along with Mr James Philip and Dr Ernest Ridley.[11] This service has been continued. Advances in anaesthesia and antibiotics significantly widened the scope of operations in malignant diseases of the ear, nose and throat.

No account of the department's activities during the war years and for long after would be complete without mentioning Sister Jamieson, known far and wide as 'Jimmy'. She ran the wards – and originally the theatre as well – until persuaded reluctantly after the Salmon Report re-organization,[12] to join the administrative staff, which promotion she had steadfastly refused on several previous occasions. Her comprehensive knowledge and experience were a considerable support to junior staff and indeed often to her consultants.

The decade 1967–77 saw the replacement of the four consultants who had been together for 17 years by Messrs Newlands, L.C. Wills (an Aberdeen graduate), K.A. McLay from Glasgow and H.A. Young from Newcastle. A fifth consultant, F.A. Stafford, also from Newcastle, was appointed in 1988 on the retirement of Dr Nina Gillan, who as a clinical assistant had operated on countless tonsils and adenoids in the Children's Hospital for many years. Stafford resigned in 1991.

Finally it should be noted that though this is now the department of otolaryngology as in other centres, the familiar acronym ENT has not been overtaken by ORL – yet.

OPHTHALMOLOGY

The early history of the Infirmary includes sporadic references to diseases of the eye which were undoubtedly a considerable source of morbidity in the 18th and 19th centuries. As we have already seen (p.30), cataract was being treated in the 18th century. The formal establishment of the discipline is somewhat complicated by the fact that there were two institutions caring for those in need: the Eye Institution which was founded in 1829 and the Eye Department of the Infirmary which begins to be mentioned some nine years later. The record[13] shows the first eye operation was done at the Institution by John Cadenhead (Plate 37).[14]

The Institution catered for out-patients only and because of this, Cadenhead petitioned the managers of the Infirmary to grant him a ward in the new hospital for 'the reception of patients labouring under severe cases of eye disease'.[15] As might be expected from other encounters – some of which are described in this history – there was opposition from the general surgeons and physicians but, in May 1838 at a general meeting of the managers, it was resolved that two wards should be set aside for ophthalmic patients under his charge.[16] Thus it is to Dr Cadenhead that we owe the foundation of the eye department and in this endeavour he received the active support of James McGrigor.[17] However Cadenhead's position was not officially recognized in monetary terms until 1847 when he was voted an annual salary of 10 guineas. He continued in post until his

Plate 37 John Cadenhead, pioneer ophthalmologist.

death in 1862. In characteristic flowery terms reserved for the departed, the managers then recorded 'their feelings of regret at the death of Dr Cadenhead who lately filled the important position of ophthalmic surgeon for upwards of a quarter of a century. Dr Cadenhead had zealously served the Hospital, giving, it might be said, in many instances sight to the blind by his care and skill'.[18]

James Reissberg Wolfe[19] was the next appointee but, in keeping with his nomadic career, left for Glasgow and founded the Ophthalmic Institute there after only five years. He was succeeded for a brief period by Alexander Ogston after the latter's appointment as a junior surgeon in 1870. Though not having much to do initially and able to take on the post of aurist as well, Ogston rapidly changed to a distinguished career in general surgery and was followed as ophthalmologist by Dr A. Dyce Davidson who was to be struck down at the early age of 44 by a cerebral haemorrhage while in the middle of a lecture to students.[20]

The next ophthalmic surgeon was also a Davidson – J. McKenzie[21] – and during his time the new surgical block at Woolmanhill was built (see p.40) and there the eye department was given what at the time seemed adequate space. McKenzie Davidson is especially remembered as one who started a new method for X-ray localization of foreign bodies in the eye and so attained world-wide recognition (Plate 38). He resigned in 1895 but continued as surgeon at the Eye Institution, a post which he held until 1897 when he went to London. His impact on radiology is discussed on p.175.

Davidson was succeeded in turn by C.H. Usher[22] who was to remain in charge until his retirement in 1926. He is commemorated by a medallion plaque in the main entrance of the original Infirmary buildings at Foresterhill. Dr Usher's published works were numerous. On his retiral in 1926 he was succeeded by W. Clark Souter[23] who had been his assistant for many years.

Dr Souter was a first-class surgeon and the best of teachers – always explaining that one should be a doctor first and an ophthalmologist second.

Plate 38 Device developed by McKenzie Davidson for the localization of intra-ocular foreign bodies. Using a principle similar to what was later to become known as tomography, this apparatus was used to re-create from skiagrams (X-ray films), placed on the mirror, the path of the X-ray beams which had produced the image. The stereoscopic position of a foreign body in relation to the anatomy could then be calculated. See *British Medical Journal* 1898; **1**:10–3. The apparatus is now in the Marischal Museum.

However, like many a chief at that time, he tended to keep his most interesting cases to himself and likewise with surgical procedures. This led to complaints from the assistant staff, so in 1937 H. Edgar Smith,[24] an assistant for many years resigned and Beatrix B. Law,[25] a junior assistant, was appointed full surgeon with one third of the department's beds and two out-patient clinics per week. J.R. Mutch[26] and C. Cockburn were appointed assistant surgeons. It was an unsatisfactory arrangement but persisted until 1946 when Souter resigned and Law became sole chief.

In 1936, as part of the general exodus of the Infirmary from Woolmanhill to Foresterhill, the eye department was housed in ward 13 of the special block – a very satisfactory arrangement – and out-patients continued to be seen at Woolmanhill. However, it was found necessary to move the unit to another ward in the main surgical block. After some years the department was on the move again and this time to Woodend where it was housed in wards 9 and 10, and part of 11. On 14 October 1989, ophthalmology returned to the original Foresterhill surgical block and now occupies wards 17 and 18 with a total of 41 beds. There are two operating theatres and currently 14 surgical sessions per week. Seven consultants, including the professor, are attached to the wards.

For out-patients, it may be stated that Aberdeen has now one of the best facilities in the UK. A fine building was erected at Foresterhill for that purpose: it contains five orthoptic service clinics, a refraction clinic, and an accident and emergency service. Some idea of the work done is evident from the fact that in 1989 no less than 45,000 patients were seen.

The Eye Institution in King Street closed in 1958. It had dealt with out-patients and emergencies, and its closure greatly increased the workload for the eye department at the Infirmary.

Dr Law retired in 1961 having been in charge for some 15 years. Charles Cockburn succeeded her as consultant in charge and he continued until 1974, when there was a change in arrangements, and the senior surgeon at the time became acting chief. W.S. Milne was appointed. He retired in 1977 and the post was held by Fiona M. Bennett until 1983, when P.K. Ray took over until his retiral in 1986.

In 1984 the University of Aberdeen established a chair in ophthalmology[27] and with the appointment of J.V. Forrester to the post a new chapter in ophthalmology in Aberdeen began. This department was one of the few in the university during the 1980s created entirely from private funds and it has since grown rapidly and established areas of clinical and basic science research. The clinical department in Aberdeen Royal Infirmary has improved its standing with increased numbers and quality of staff and has developed special expertise with resultant change of status to a centre of referral from other parts of the country.

DERMATOLOGY AND VENEREOLOGY

As with diseases in the eye, skin disorders must have been very common in 18th and 19th century Britain, yet dermatology as a speciality was largely a development in Europe and America and in many instances continued to be practised by general physicians and, interestingly enough, by surgeons.

In Aberdeen Robert Garden,[28] who graduated in 1872, studied for two years thereafter in Berlin, Wurzburg and Vienna before he returned to his native city to take up practice as a surgeon. In spite of this direction in his career, he published a textbook *Skin Diseases* in 1889.[29] His aim was to provide a text for the student attending his classes – to present in a 'convenient form the essentials of a subject as regards classification, definition, diagnosis and treatment'. This book was based on the classificatory scheme of Hebra whom Alexander Ogston described as 'a jolly little ball of a man, as German as he could look'. Though Ogston went on (p.93) to make the classical contribution on the infective nature of *Staphylococcus aureus*,[30,31] – an organism which is commonly found on the skin – he too did not practise dermatology, turning his attentions to surgery. Garden did not mention Ogston's work, published eight years before the textbook, but perhaps we can account for this in that the interchange between surgery and dermatology was not likely to have been great.

John F. Christie[32] a graduate of 1895, also travelled to Germany for postgraduate study in surgery and dermatology. After his return to Aberdeen he was appointed lecturer in skin diseases in 1901 and in consequence a separate department in this speciality came into being. Such an organization had been formally recognized in 1901 when at a meeting of the Infirmary board of directors[33] it was noted 'The lecturer on skin diseases shall have charge of this department and be styled assistant physician in charge of the department for diseases of the skin. He shall attend at the Infirmary on Mondays and Fridays . . . to give advice and treatment to patients suffering from diseases of the skin. He shall have power to select from among such cases, for admission to the wards in rotation, those which he considers suitable for indoor treatment either in the medical or surgical wards of the Infirmary, as he may decide. Such cases shall be under the care of the physician or surgeon in charge of the ward to which they are admitted'. It is clear, as has been repeated on numerous occasions during the development of the specialities, that although Christie was able to admit he was not allowed to have full control. During 1902 more than 1000 out-patients attended and 31 in-patients with skin disease were discharged. Amongst the conditions treated were eczema, psoriasis and 'ulcers' but there were also those with tubercular disease of the skin for which at the time treatment was by excision. By 1903 Christie had been placed in charge of all cases of erysipelas. In 1910 he was appointed a full physician and he continued as the specialist in skin diseases until his death in 1931. During the 1914–18 War he was honorary consultant dermatologist to the military hospitals in the Aberdeen area. On his death in 1931, he was succeeded by Dr Thomas Anderson[34] who had graduated in 1926. Anderson had been able to study in Paris at the Pasteur Institute and also at the St Louis Hospital and was to dominate the department from then until his retirement in 1968. The introduction of the National Health Service in 1948 was followed by a time of expansion and clinics were organized in the Orkney and Shetland Islands, various peripheral hospitals and, for some years, in Inverness. Anderson was President of the British Association of Dermatology in 1967/68. His relatively conservative attitude – not unique to him in the Aberdeen scene – may not have led him wholly to welcome the advent of the NHS but in his speciality the health service brought in new blood, increased the potential of the department and widened its horizon. Alan Lyell, who described toxic epidermal necrolysis (now known eponymously as 'Lyell's disease') during his appointment in Aberdeen[35] was the second consultant dermatologist. In 1962 he moved to become head of the Skin Department at Glasgow Royal Infirmary and to pursue a distinguished career in dermatology and the history of medicine.

The department of dermatology has moved both physically and intellectually with the times. In 1936 it shared in the migration to Foresterhill where it occupied a ward in conjunction with oncology and dentistry – strange bedfellows – until nearly 30 years later when an independent ward (ward 5, now renumbered 29, on the top floor of the medical block) became available. In 1988 R.A. Main who had been a consultant dermatologist from 1962 retired after steering the department towards a more scientific approach based on the new science of the skin. He also revolutionized teaching of his subject. There are now three consultants[36] and the department has an active programme of research in clinical care, particularly in the fields of industrial medicine and immunology.

Throughout Europe venereology was allied to dermatology in the latter years of the 19th century. It began to emerge as a separate speciality during World War I when in 1916 the venereal diseases regulations were introduced. These required local health authorities to provide suitable clinics to manage the diseases by co-operation with local hospitals. In the clinics, diagnosis and treatment were both confidential and free. The regulations were reinforced by the Veneral Diseases Act of 1917 introduced specifically to protect the public from treatment by unqualified practitioners who promoted 'quack' remedies for the prescribed diseases – syphilis, gonorrhoea and chancroid.

As a consequence of the regulations, the Aberdeen Venereal Disease Clinic opened in 1917 within the out-patient department at Woolmanhill with an additional service based on the City Hospital. Christie was appointed as temporary chief in charge in 1917 and G.M. (Daddy) Duncan[37] the pathologist at the Royal Infirmary undertook the laboratory work and monitoring of the treatment regimens.

Christie was confirmed as chief officer, Aberdeen venereal centre in 1920 and was also recognized as a lecturer in venereal disease by the university. The annual report of the medical officer of health for 1920–21 showed that there was indeed a need for the centre in that 475 patients with syphilis and 277 with gonorrhoea had been treated at Woolmanhill. With the increase after World War I in maritime trade in and out of Aberdeen, control of the international spread of infection also became important as a substantial number of patients attending the Aberdeen clinic were merchant seamen.

These arrangements persisted until 1931 and Christie's death. Thereafter F.J.T. Bowie[38] who was at the time head of the Municipal Hospitals' Venereal Disease Department became Chief Medical Officer to the Venereal Disease Department at the ARI though the part-time association with the dermatologists continued with Thomas Anderson as a part-time assistant medical officer. This era of dermato-venereology persisted in Aberdeen – as in many other places in the country – until 1962 though since the end of World War II it had been recognized that it was a less than satisfactory method of providing a specialized service and that career venereologists were essential to plan and implement preventive, diagnostic and therapeutic regimens for an ever-increasing range of sexually transmitted infections.

Bowie brought the Venereal Disease Department to a high level of efficiency with his meticulous records and his ability to carry out, often over many years, the complex and difficult pre-antibiotic treatments with toxic drugs. When he retired in 1957 he left a department dealing with 750–1,000 new patients a year of whom about a quarter were non-venereal.

For a brief period, Thomas Anderson assumed the responsibility of the clinic until the appointment of Hugh W. Rutherford[39] a chest physician, first on a part-time basis but ultimately full-time until 1980. During these years there was a dramatic and progressive increase in the clinical work load; a combination of the 'permissive society' and an almost total abandonment of barrier methods of contraception in favour of oral contraceptives led to a considerable increase in all forms of sexually transmitted infection apart from syphilis. The control of gonorrhoea and non-specific genital infection became more difficult because of antibiotic resistance, though at the same time the diseases were easy to cure by short courses of an increasing assortment of these agents.

Rutherford was succeeded by Aileen Downie, a previous assistant in the clinic and James Finnie continued as an associate specialist until his retirement in 1989. The workload continued to increase with the addition of viral infections – first genital herpes and warts and later HIV infection. By the mid-1980s, 3,500 patients a year were being seen. The 'open all hours' policy had been abandoned in 1978 in favour of an appointments system. The clinic, essentially unchanged since its foundation was extensively re-furbished and re-equipped throughout the decade to provide what is now an appropriately re-named Department of Genito-urinary Medicine (venereal disease) on the top floor of the Woolmanhill out-patient department.

OBSTETRICS AND GYNAECOLOGY

Gynaecology is usually associated with the practice of obstetrics. As a description of a speciality the word first appears in 1847[40] but, in Aberdeen as we have seen (p.22) the care of the pregnant woman began at the Infirmary in 1762. Thereafter it seems that there was only intermittent interest at the Infirmary in women and their conditions, including pregnancy. The Maternity Hospital was founded in 1893 by renting a house in Barnett's Close adjacent to the Dispensary[41] and it was there that a succession of distinguished practitioners had their main business. Yet, as recounted in more detail in Chapter 7, it is clear that a number of surgeons were performing gynaecological procedures at the ARI – especially ovariotomy – in the second half of the 19th century.

The creation of a chair of midwifery at the time of the fusion of the two universities recognized the importance of midwifery for teaching. Its first occupant was Robert Dyce (Plate 39)[42] who was succeeded in 1869 by Andrew Inglis.[43] However, it is to the third occupant of the chair from 1875, William Stephenson,[44] that we can trace the development of proper consideration for diseases of women. Though primarily a paediatrician and obstetric physician, he pleaded in his inaugural address for three things: a Children's Hospital; maternity beds; and beds for diseases of women.[45] He got the money for the first within a year – a tribute to the universal drawing power of children and their illnesses. The second materialized after his continued pleading[46] in 18 years. The third was ultimately achieved in 1895 – 20 years from his appointment and as a result of his continuing advocacy. Even then it was merely the designation of beds because it was not until the 7 December 1897 that the minute book of the Infirmary records that the managers 'remitted to the medical reference committee to arrange as to the lock[47] wards and the proposed gynaecological department in the Infirmary and to report'.[48] With a celerity that disgraces our current practices, the committee did so on 16 December and were strongly of the opinion that such a department should be organized under the charge of a physician – 'the

Plate 39 Robert Dyce, foundation Regius professor of midwifery 1860–9.

professor of midwifery at the university being suggested as is customary in other hospitals'.

Before this formal organization of a department of gynaecology, we learn that in 1891 Dr MacKenzie Booth[49] had been appointed third surgeon in 1891 to look after six beds at the north end of the male surgical ward on the first and second floors of the new, that is the Jubilee, building.[50] In addition he was to have charge of the six beds of the female lock ward and six beds in the ward for disease of women. His main career was however to be in ear, nose and throat surgery. He was succeeded by Robert McKerron (see below) but in addition William Stephenson's name appears by 1898 as a gynaecologist and it is to be presumed that he was now in charge of a department.

Table I Disorders of the female generative system treated in the Royal Infirmary

Year	1890	1891	1892	1893	1894	1895	1897	1898
No. treated	54	61	65	68	59	51	74	90

There are unfortunately only sporadic records of the gynaecological patients treated during the early years of the department; Table I gives a summary of the diseases of the generative system treated in the last decade of the 19th century which spans the founding of the department. Included within them are three colporrhapy operations in 1893, six mastectomies in the same year and 16 in the next, and in 1898, an ectopic gestation of five months' duration.

Little is known of the fortunes of the department for the first decade of the 20th century but Stephenson retired in 1912 though he remained a consultant on the staff of the Infirmary until his death in 1919 at the age of 81. He was succeeded in 1912 by his student Robert Gordon McKerron also, by training, a paediatrician.[51] As is not uncommon in the split organization of medical schools and hospitals in Britain, it was not until the following year that he is recorded as having been appointed as a gynaecologist on the staff of the Infirmary.

The next important development to affect gynaecology occurred in 1922. In the years since World War I irradiation had become established in the treatment of cancer of both the uterine cervix and of its body. The loan of a quantity of radium from the Medical Research Council which is described on p.160 was followed by the first record of its use for this purpose in 1923 when two patients with cervical malignancy and one with cancer of the body of the uterus were treated. Hysterectomy was also being used for both diseases – twice in that year for the cervix and three times for the body. There were a total of 19 patients with malignant disease and this is the first time that a detailed classification of the gynaecological disorders managed is available.

Table II Workload of gynaecological department

Year	1913	1914	1935	1936	1937	1939	1947
No. of out-patients	122	211	548	678	770	905	1221

Over the first half of the century and before the inception of the NHS there was a steady growth in the work of the department (Table II). In February 1931, G.S. ('Jeff') Davidson,[52] who was the first north-eastern obstetrician to be formally trained in gynaecological surgery, was appointed temporary assistant gynaecologist to act as a substitute for Professor McKerron who was ill with severe rheumatoid arthritis at the time. G.P Milne recalls[53] that had it not been for this disease, McKerron would not 'have dreamt of letting anybody else in if he could have helped it' particularly as Davidson had been tutor in surgery in the Royal Infirmary for the past seven years, was obviously an experienced operator and 'completely overshadowed' McKerron. Six months later, and we can presume as a result of the pressures of work and his own illness, McKerron petitioned the Board of the Hospital for the appointment of an assistant and within the next 10 days the post was advertised. By November, the local candidate, Davidson, had been appointed in competition against John Chassar Moir a native of Angus but an Edinburgh graduate, who was to go on to be in competition with Dugald Baird for the chair of obstetrics in Aberdeen, to discover ergometrine, become first a reader in his subject in London, and then to be Nuffield professor of obstetrics and gynaecology in Oxford.

Davidson's problems were not completely at an end because the general surgeons continued to carry out a great deal of gynaecology. The result of this was that he had difficulty in generating a referral pattern because of professional loyalties.[53] The growth of the speciality and the medical and social conditions of the 1930s continued to impose pressure on gynaecological beds and services throughout the decade. By 1934 the waiting list for in-patient treatment had, within the year, gone up from six to 145 in spite of attempts before and during that period to deal with the problem by allocating surgical, ENT and dermatology beds to gynaecology. The City Medical Officer of Health (Dr H. Rae) was approached and from this sprang an association between gynaecology and Woodend Hospital (42 beds) which was to endure for 55 years until all gynaecological services returned to Foresterhill in 1989.

McKerron formally retired in 1936 but was temporarily re-appointed until Dugald Baird[54] took over the Regius chair of obstetrics in 1937 and was appointed a staff gynaecologist at the ARI in the same year. By this time the department had in 1936 shared in the general migration to Foresterhill where it occupied ward 6 on the left-hand side of the main corridor. Later, after the ophthalmology department was shifted to Woodend, the department of gynaecology moved to ward 13 (renumbered ward 6) on the second floor of the special block and there it remained until its transfer to wards 42–43 Phase II in 1981. It has markedly increased in size and the number of patients treated has continued to grow (Table III). Senior staff numbers have risen from four in 1947[55] to eight in 1967,[56] during which time Dugald Baird, in post as professor of midwifery from 1937–64, fostered a number of these younger men in his department, an elite group within the speciality known as 'Baird's boys', who went on to hold professorial chairs in other universities.[57] In 1990 the department, now with 13 consultants, continues to have a number of major research interests one of which is the investigation and treatment of infertility whose foundations in Aberdeen were laid in the 1960s by John Wyper.[58]

Table III Gynaecological workload since the introduction of the National Health Service

Year	1951	1960	1970	1980	1990
New patients	2211	2350	4052	5256	11396
Return patients	3137	2785	2704	2576	7226*

* 2093 were return patients to the colposcopy clinic.

Dr J. Elizabeth Macgregor[59] established screening for cervical cancer in Aberdeen in 1960 by invitation of Dugald Baird, who with his senior lecturer, Dr James Lawson, had for a number of years been interested in its epidemiology. So began a cytopathology service, the success of which would depend on the co-operation of general practitioners within the region for the acquisition of smears from women between the ages of 25 and 65 years. Testimony to the success of the project is that 30 years later the unit has been awarded a Harris Birthright[60] grant in open competition with other centres in the UK.

There are now 102 in-patient beds in ARI though at the time of writing this is set to fall to 86 by the end of the current decade partly because of the opening of a new unit in Elgin. The department's ambit extends to include peripheral clinics throughout the North-East and the Islands and specialized clinics for colposcopy, malignant disease, cystometry and infertility.

It is a fitting postscript to record the continued generosity of the Aberdeen public who through the local Evening Express Laser Line appeal in 1981 donated £350,000 for a gynaecological laser. This equipment acquired, the residue of the funds were put towards a whole body X-ray scanner (see Chapter 12).

ACCIDENT AND EMERGENCY

In Chapters 1–3 we have read how in 1739 it was agreed that an Infirmary should be built. Amongst the reasons given was that medical assistance was needed for individuals '. . .that met with misfortunes of dislocations or broken bones. . .' Here was the start of provision for the treatment of injury.

We have little information about the arrangements for injury in the first phase of re-development at Woolmanhill in 1840 (see Chapter 3) but presumably, when the surgical and medical blocks were erected in the 1890s, some in-patient provision for injuries became available. However, this cannot have been to the extent of providing what was considered necessary at the time. The minute of the medical committee of the 26 December 1900 states 'in the opinion of the Medical Committee the present accommodation in the out-patient department in the Royal Infirmary is insufficient. There is no possibility of altering the present accommodation to make it suitable'. In fact there were two huge and intimately related problems: where was the required accommodation to be found and who was going to pay for it?

In 1908 a committee appointed to report on additional accommodation suggested that new premises be provided on the other side of the road, that is on the east side of Woolmanhill opposite the existing buildings. Evidence that things had come to a pretty pass is provided by a comment of the medical committee which referred to the first floor of the main block then occupied by nursing staff: 'one of the rooms on this floor is used for the observation ward for drunk people but this could be provided on the other side of the road'. Fortunately this unsatisfactory situation was not to persist for much longer. Lord Mount-Stephen,[61] who had been treated at the Royal Infirmary, gave a generous donation for improvements and this allowed the annual report for 1908 to state that it was proposed to erect a building which would contain rooms for treating and dressing casualties and surgical patients, surgical and medical admission rooms as well as having admission rooms and wards for ear, nose and throat patients. The building was to stand on a piece of ground known as Sim's Square opposite Woolmanhill and which had been given by the trustees of Mr Thomas Primrose.[62] The casualty and out-patient department was opened on the 25 November 1912 and remained largely unchanged until 1958. A handsome brass tablet, in grateful recognition of the generosity of the two major donors was placed on the wall of the waiting hall. It was removed after the 'appointed day' for the introduction of the NHS (5 July 1948), never replaced and its whereabouts are no longer known. David Proctor, the creator of the modern department, comments somewhat ruefully: 'philanthropy was no longer acknowledged or considered necessary'.

Accommodation

There was a large tiled room with two small wooden-walled cubicles opening off it. The chief entry was from the main hall where benches were provided for those waiting. Another door gave direct access from the outside of the building for patients brought by ambulance and led directly into a small extension of the main area which was known as the 'police room'. Internal modifications took place over time. One of the cubicles became the place where general anaesthesia was given by the houseman who had to possess an alert eye for and response to cyanosis in that it was described by a visiting lady member of the board as like the 'lowest deck of a troop ship on the China station' (while no one would quarrel with the comparison, the lady's ability to make it gave rise to varied and sometimes ribald conjecture). A massive wooden dresser dominated the centre of the main area. On it were taps and small sinks, dressing, bandages, jars of swabs – it was a dispensary for most of what was required for treatment. In time a huge sterilizer stood against one wall. Its height was such that no nurse under six feet tall could hope to avoid scalding her forearms on its rim while desperately fishing in the depths with Cheatle forceps for an elusive piece of surgical hardware. The resulting scars provided speedy and specific identification of her place of work.

Staff and arrangements for patients before 1952

The casualty department, or casualty 'ward' as it was confusingly called for many years, had no medical staff of its own. Cover at all levels was provided by staff seconded from major units. With in-patient facilities on the same site this arrangement was satisfactory and doctors were available round the clock. By 1936 there were both full-time and a part-time junior casualty officers, the latter having main duties in the skin and VD departments. In 1937 a senior casualty officer was appointed at a salary of £200 per annum with a lunch and tea allowance of £78 in lieu of quarters.

As Chapter 4 relates, and in pursuance of the grand plan for the development of the Foresterhill site, in-patients moved there in 1937. Casualty was left behind and so began the isolation of the department from the main body of the Infirmary which was to last for 22 years. Casualties were received at Woolmanhill from 8 a.m. to 7 p.m. daily and were seen at other times at Foresterhill in a casualty room near the eastern end of the building by members of the wards 'receiving' at the time. Medical cover then became a particular problem but this cumbersome arrangement worked amazingly well for many years.

During World War II medical staffing was difficult to maintain. The board minutes note in 1942 that it was not possible to get a qualified junior casualty officer and a fifth year student was temporarily appointed. After the war the senior casualty officer post was included in the surgical registrar training programme for doctors returning from the forces. The prospect of even a brief six months was too much for those single-mindedly bent on getting their surgical qualifications and many forms of escape and evasion from what was regarded as the professional equivalent of Devil's Island were employed – even to the extent in one instance of submission to surgical intervention for the sort of elective procedure (in this case an inguinal hernia) which it is usually wise to preserve for a professional rainy day.[63] A receptionist was specifically allocated to the department and the old system of entering the particulars of the patients' diagnosis and treatment in a ledger was replaced by individual casualty record cards. The start of the National Health Service in 1948 did not cause any obvious or immediate change though the senior casualty officer of the time was convinced the department would be stormed by the citizenry of Aberdeen on the first day and resigned himself to martyrdom. Nothing happened so he survived to become an orthopaedic surgeon instead.[64]

1952–1978

In 1952 David Proctor, senior casualty officer then in post, was persuaded to stay for an indefinite period and his presence ushered in more effective development of a coherent casualty department. It had become obvious that the department needed more space and resources. On the one hand it was beginning to gain the confidence of the community and was no longer regarded as the haven of last resort. On the other hand the better quality of service of itself required more elaborate quarters – but there was no one to speak for it. The registrars came down in turn from Foresterhill for three months at a time and still regarded it, as well as calling it, Outer Siberia. However, there were exceptions and as Sandy Michie remembers the road to upgrading was not always smooth. '. . .Bill Shiach (recently retired as a consultant surgeon in Gisbourne, South Island, New Zealand) wanted to discuss matters with me and see if a few improvements could be made. At that time they had only one set of instruments to be used and I suggested to Bill that three would be better – one on the boil, one in use and one being cleaned up – so I promised to see what I could do, although supplies of instruments at that time were very dificult to obtain. In the afternoon I was back up in my office when Sister Stopani – who had been a ward sister when I was in clinical practice at the ARI and was now the formidable sister in charge of the casualty – rang up. She knew me very well: if I was a good boy I was Sandy Michie; if I was a naughty boy I was Dr Michie. So the voice on the phone said, "I hear you've been re-organizing the casualty department Dr Michie." "Oh, come off it Sister", I said, "not re-organizing, just trying to make some minor improvement." "Well", she intoned, "I just want you to know that I have worked with Sir Henry (Gray) and with Sir John (Marnoch) and with Sir James (Learmonth), and not one of these eminent gentlemen could use more than one scalpel in one hand at one time." And down went the phone with a bang.'

Nevertheless the way to create a workable casualty department was gradually opening up. There was no question of new building at this time and the solution had to be made by re-allocating existing accommodation which became possible when what had been the medical block on the other side of the road became vacant after many years of assorted use. To it moved the out-patient departments for medicine, dermatology and ENT as well as the VD Department. Gynaecological out-patients remained on the first floor of the existing building and the surgical out-patients facilities were relocated on the south side of the main hall. The consequence was that the whole of the northern half of the ground floor became available for the casualty department.

It should not be assumed that this re-shuffle was easily achieved. Most of the senior hospital staff of the day had no interest in the department and inevitably their juniors assumed the same stance. It was the 'administration' – regarded with little favour by clinicians – that was most supportive. The medical superintendent, Dr A.M. Michie, by persuasion and argument – often, as those who remember those days attest, in a most audible form – converted the chairman of the General Hospitals Board of Management to the cause. There was encouragement at a higher level from the chairman of the Regional Hospital Board, May Baird,[65] and from her senior administrative medical officer, Denys Beddard.[66] It is not too much to suggest that their advocacy assured the future of what was to become the accident and emergency service.

The years from 1952 that had been spent in the restricted space of the old department were an excellent stimulus to planning for the future. Three basic requirements were identified: a 24 hour service; full-time dedicated X-ray cover; and short-stay observation beds. The 24 hour service would replace the split one using Woolmanhill during the day and Foresterhill at night, and which was becoming increasingly unsatisfactory and irritating. The advantages of having a service on one site both to the public and all the emergency services was obvious (what was perhaps less clear was that the clinical supervision existing during the day at Woolmanhill could not be applied to the night service because those dealing with the casualties owed their primary allegiance elsewhere and were often locked in to the treatment of in-patients). A full-time X-ray service reserved for the department was essential. The ancient X-ray apparatus which occupied a room at the south end of the waiting hall was available from 9 a.m. to 5 p.m. from Monday to Friday and from 9 a.m. to 1 p.m. on Saturday. Should a patient require an X-ray outwith these hours, he or she had to be sent to Foresterhill where some member of the medical staff would, *en passant*, see and report on the films and then if admission was not obviously required, either send the patient back to Woolmanhill for treatment or dispatch the victim home. Not surprisingly those working at Woolmanhill developed a high degree of clinical acumen in order to avoid referral to Foresterhill. David Proctor recalls 'the possibility of litigation was regarded as nothing compared to that of telephone abuse from those colleagues at Foresterhill to whom requests were made for assistance'.

The third requirement was a capability to admit patients for observation. Many who had sustained a head injury and been briefly unconscious had to be referred to surgical wards at Foresterhill for observation, and there were other examples of the use of beds there for short-term patients who did not necessarily need full in-patient facilities. To provide 'holding' beds would remove the need for routine transfer and thus free beds at Foresterhill for alternative use. The duration of stay was set at 72 hours; any extension beyond this time would invite inappropriate admission and cause undue distraction for the staff and improper use of resources in casualty.

There was an additional problem. The limited space in the existing department and an increasing number of patients together resulted in frequently unacceptable waiting times (Plate 40). While it was not possible to make precise predictions of new patient attendances, what could be defined was the number of patients who would return. An appointment system and a separate accommodation for such patients was initiated to reduce waiting time for both old and new.

The re-organized department opened in 1958 (Plate 41). It occupied over half of the ground floor. There was a larger area for the examination and treatment of new patients with curtained cubicles for those who required privacy and chairs for those who did not. There were as before two entrances: one was by the main door where the reception office and waiting room were situated; the other gave direct entry to part of the new patient areas which was furnished and equipped for the initial reception and care of major injuries. From here there was direct access to the new X-ray area. Patients referred for non-urgent X-ray followed another route via the waiting hall where changing cubicles were available. Anyone coming through the 'ambulance doors' had to be seen at once although they did not necessarily have an urgent problem; indeed there could be occasions when a patient coming through the non-urgent entry was in greater need of attention. However, the system provided a rough initial triage and was not too difficult to remember by those involved.

The development produced two rooms in which X-rays could be taken plus an adjacent reporting room, an office and a room for storing films. The days of wet films were ended by the introduction of an automatic processing machine – a boon to those who remembered the earlier days of 'wet plates.' The machine was far from the neat and speedy apparatus of the late 1980s; rather it was a massive piece of equipment known affectionately as 'Andromeda'. It was prone to lapse on occasions into frenzies of cannibalism which resulted in the eventual illumination of black confetti which could influence even the most hardened and parsimonious radiographer to accept that the films might better be repeated. An excellent full-time service was provided and, in what are now regarded as 'unsocial' hours, a radiographer was always on call and had the use of a bedroom provided in the building.

There were two operating theatres. One, the so-called 'septic' theatre, was used for the operative treatment of all infected conditions. The 'clean' theatre was

Plate 40 Waiting at Woolmanhill in the 1950s.

Plate 41 The East extension at Woolmanhill (Sim's Square) which was completed in 1912 but is now demolished. The view is from the south-west. The ground floor contained the accident and emergency and out-patient department from 1912–74.

not used routinely for such procedures as simple suturing and the like which could be carried out in the cubicles but was reserved for procedures requiring a greater degree of assurance of lack of contamination. Two rooms were allocated to post-operative recovery.

For the first time there was a reception office. Unfortunately it was not staffed at night so that nurses still had to waste their valuable time in carrying out documentation. Another innovation was a plaster room accompanied by the even more valuable provision of a plaster orderly, although when even this allocation was doubled there was no night-service. However, it reduced the time that had to be spent at the end of the day by casualty officers in picking plaster fragments off their persons.

Staffing from 1958

During the planning stage there had been considerable apprehension over provision of medical staff for the extensive activity and responsibilities of the new department. There had to be an increase in numbers and in tiers of responsibility in order that effective cover could be maintained. By great good fortune, the general practitioner vocational training scheme was being set up at this time and included six months of casualty training which ensured six post-registration (that is qualified for more than a year) senior house officers every six months. The work study unit at Grampian Health Board was consulted and produced a scheme which ensured both adequate cover and reasonable off duty. Two bedrooms for doctors on night-duty were provided and there was a somewhat inadequate common room for medical staff. The remaining medical establishment consisted of three senior house officers who had at least two years post-graduate experience; they lived out and provided cover by rotation. Finally there was the senior casualty officer.

The junior medical staff establishment proved adequate but there were significant fluctuations of activity because of the twice yearly change of general practitioner vocational trainees. The senior house officers were appointed on a yearly basis and staggered dates of taking up their duties reduced the chances of all three changing at once. But it could happen and there were horrendous occasions when they and all the junior staff were new at the same time. A nucleus of permanent staff was always needed to mitigate this problem as well as that of rotas: therefore each afternoon from Monday to Friday one of the five general practitioners, all of whom had worked in the department for at least six months and who had subsequently accepted part-time appointment, was on duty. The arrangement not only helped to achieve a continuity of patient care but also provided a valuable source of learning for the trainee general practitioners. The senior staff was augmented by the appointment of a medical assistant in 1966. The senior casualty officer post had been elevated to consultant status in 1963 and a second consultant was appointed in 1977. A senior registrar post was also established in 1974.

The work of the department 1958–1979

For the next 20 years after its re-organization at Woolmanhill the department worked well. The 24 hour service was adequate but required constant surveillance in case it came to be regarded as a convenient alternative to other sources of medical care. It was essential carefully to define the functions of the department and to emphasize that they could not be efficiently fulfilled if staff and resources were to be distracted by inappropriate attendances and referrals. As anticipated, the short stay beds protected the wards at Foresterhill. A new problem associated with this was self-poisoning which inescapably moulded the department into a poisons centre. The close co-operation given by the toxicological service at the City Hospital laboratories and by the psychiatric service ensured effective supervision and subsequent care for the many patients admitted. These needs, together with the other conditions which required short-term treatment and observation, resulted in a high bed occupancy though this was restrained by the rigid rules with regard to segregation of males and females which were then in force (see also p.20).

The move to Foresterhill

Inevitably and like its predecessors, the accommodation of the department became ever more inadequate for the changing times and demands. Remoteness from specialist units at Foresterhill was latterly unacceptable and helicopter landings direct at Foresterhill were becoming more frequent (Plate 42). Fortunately the master development plan for the Foresterhill site had taken account of this and, whether by accident or good fortune, had also appreciated that the city had moved westward, so that it was obviously wrong for patients who had sustained major injuries to come from that direction towards the congested old centre for a direct referral first to Woolmanhill. Side-wards in the orthopaedic department at Foresterhill had already been modified as an 'accident unit' and acted as a primary reception point as required. This arrangement was facilitated by the radio link that had been installed in the mid-1960s to permit direct communication with emergency services. Another increasing problem resulted from the traffic congestion in the Woolmanhill area which, especially at peak times, prevented ready access for ambulances.

1978–1991

Though the above-mentioned considerations of isolation, population shift and traffic congestion added weight to a move this had, as has previously been noted, been envisaged since the formulation of the site plan in 1957–8. Twenty years seems a long time to move from concept to reality but this is what it took, and the new accident and emergency department (the term A & E replaced casualty or 'cas' at the time of the move in 1974) was planned as part of Phase II for the ground floor (basement of the previous phase in view of the sloping site).

Plate 42 2 July 1956. The first patient to be taken by helicopter to Foresterhill was a 15-year-old boy with a crushed limb on a German trawler. The aircraft is a Westland Sikorsky Dragonfly S51 from RNAS Lossiemouth. The head porter is Alexander Petrie.

As before there would be two entrances. One for non-urgent patients would permit registration at a large reception office with adjacent separate waiting rooms for first-time attenders and returnees. The other was reserved for ambulance patients and would provide immediate entry to a resuscitation area or could be used as access to cubicles for less urgent patients. Two theatres were incorporated, each with an anaesthetic room and with common pre-operative and recovery rooms. The short stay ward again had 10 beds available but they were now organized for more effective use in that six were single rooms plus a four-bedded area. Some fresh concepts were introduced. A large fracture clinic area with some cubicles would, combined with a plaster application area and adjacent to the X-ray facilities, provide good facilities for the treatment of bone and joint injuries. A waiting area for patients who required ambulance transport to their homes was provided near the ambulance entry – a simple but effective device to subdivide the patients. However, the most important innovation was efficient resuscitation facilities.

The accommodation considered sufficient in the Scottish Home and Health Department planning notes was judged by those on the ground and experienced in the field as quite inadequate. This was the only occasion on which significant disagreement occurred between those in Aberdeen and the 'central' planners. Local influence, spearheaded mainly by David Proctor as senior casualty consultant, was successful in resolving this issue in favour of the professionals who had to use the department, and the arrangements now permit the simultaneous resuscitation of several patients. The new department was upgraded in every other respect. Accommodation for medical and nursing staff was increased and improved, and offices were provided for senior medical and nursing staff.

The move took place in 1978. A new consultant was appointed when the last of the original senior casualty officers retired in 1984. A third post with a principal commitment to the casualty department at the Royal Aberdeen Children's Hospital was filled in 1988. After years of prevarication, and as a result of continued pleading by the A & E department, based on their practical experience of air/sea rescue and their understanding of the problems posed in the north-east of Scotland both by the climate and by the offshore industry, a helipad was provided nearby in the hospital grounds. It is a feature of A & E departments that they are ever sensitive to social change so that its members were quickly aware of the problems that it would pose. Even with the vast increase in offshore activity, no undue patient delay has resulted and the department was able to respond adequately to the Piper Alpha disaster in 1988 (Plate 43).

The less easily defined consequences of the adaptation required to unaccustomed work requirements and to prosperity remain the cause in the early 1990s of a wide range of attendances. More than granite quarrying or the fishing industry ever did, oil has changed the community. As ever the department has had no choice but to change also; this it has quickly and effectively been able to do.

DENTISTRY AND MAXILLO-FACIAL ORAL SURGERY

It is noteworthy that the first dental surgeon, William Williamson,[67] was appointed to the staff of the Infirmary as early as 1862 and was almost certainly the first dental surgeon to attain consultant status in a teaching hospital in Scotland and undoubtedly the first dental surgeon to give a university lecture.[68] He was followed by his son, also William.[69] A different dynasty then took over with James Crombie[70] in charge until 1932 and his son Hugh[71] thereafter until the beginning of the 1960s. Hugh Crombie was a pioneer of the integration of dentistry with maxillo-facial surgery and worked with James Philip in this field. However, the discipline finally got properly underway and began to receive national recognition with the tenure of Hugh Crombie's successor, Peter Clarke, who not only increased the range of operative interventions but also organized regular postgraduate courses for dentists. How eventually the disciplines of dentistry, maxillo-facial surgery, plastic surgery, ear, nose and throat surgery, and oncology will align in Aberdeen is over the horizon of this history but, if parallels are to be entertained, there will be greater integration as the needs of

Plate 43 Piper Alpha 1988. Urgency and experience are more apparent than in Plate 42 but the intravenous apparatus can still come adrift (right foreground).

the various specialities and the constraints of finance make regional and supra-regional centres of co-operation between disciplines inevitable.

ORTHOPAEDICS

The only surgical speciality apart from ophthalmology and ear, nose and throat (see p.115) to achieve anything approaching full status in Aberdeen before World War II and the subsequent introduction of the National Health Service was orthopaedic surgery.

On the 13 December 1934 the medical services committee of the board of management recommended that an orthopaedic department be created, with up to a maximum of six beds in ward 14, on the understanding that these would be used for general surgery when not required for orthopaedic patients. Before this time, patients with skeletal problems were treated in general surgical wards. Their numbers were, however, small. In 1910 for instance, the number of deformities treated was only 15, the number of patients with joint conditions other than tuberculosis 52, and of tuberculous disease of bones and joints 70. There were 11 cases of internal derangement of the knee. One hundred and eight patients with fractures were treated as in-patients. In 1917 the numbers of all these conditions was not materially different.

Alexander Mitchell[72] was the first surgeon in charge and gave up his general surgical duties at Ward 2 Woolmanhill immediately before the orthopaedic department opened at Foresterhill in 1936; his place was taken by Sydney G. Davidson. Mitchell's interest in orthopaedics was possibly connected with the fact that he himself was crippled as a result of septic arthritis of the hip in infancy. He was, however, a very hardy man. He rode his horse, 'Redwing', in all weathers and on one occasion in the severe winter of 1944, when the roads were blocked by snow, he went on horseback from Old Rayne to the assistance of Dr Sutherland at the Fyvie Cottage Hospital (a direct distance of about eight miles over the hill or 11 around it). As he trotted off home again in a snow storm he was likened by Dr Sutherland to Oates of the ill-fated Antarctic expedition, about whom Captain Scott said: 'There goes a very gallant gentleman'.

Alec Rennie, Mitchell's successor after 1946 recalls: 'I can remember the Department in 1937. Trauma was mainly treated in general surgical wards. Only residual deformities, non-union and upper femoral fractures were referred to the orthopaedic department. Out-patient clinics, held in the small night-casualty room, took place twice a week for about an hour and a half. The then senior anaesthetist once asked me in the operating theatre: "Do you think that there will ever be a living here for a specialized orthopaedic surgeon?"'.

Mitchell was the mainstay of the department until the end of World War II and even thereafter continued to be active as a consultant at Stracathro until 1948, and at peripheral clinics until 1950. During the early years he had to exercise (as Rennie put it) 'a good deal of forebearance' as only one surgeon (James Learmonth) was prepared even to recognize fractures of the femoral neck as orthopaedic. However, his restraint paid off and the fact that orthopaedics blossomed was due largely to his attitude of scrupulous fairness and to the respect with which he was regarded by his general surgical colleagues.

In consequence on Rennie's return as a consultant orthopaedic surgeon in 1946 after war service, centred on the Middle East, the work of the department had grown very considerably but the facilities at the Infirmary had not kept pace, the increase being mainly accommodated at Stracathro. The Cripples Welfare Association, based on the Infirmary, had started peripheral clinics throughout the region. The clinics at the Infirmary were held in a shed immediately to the east of the Special Block where the East Block now stands. It had the impressive title of Passive Air Defence and was used to house fire extinguishers necessary to counter the air blitz. It was roomy but draughty. There was an appreciable space between the wall head and the roof, sufficient in the severe winter of 1947 to admit an occasional flurry of snow. A semblance of privacy was provided by portable screens between the emergency beds used as examination couches, but in a high wind these could blow down on patients and staff alike.

Then in 1948 came the NHS and with it a considerable expansion. Two further consultant surgeons (Neil Hendry and George Hay[73]) were appointed and a new out-patient department opened. At this time acute bony injuries were still being treated by general surgeons who, in Aberdeen as elsewhere, resisted until 1953 the proposal to transfer this responsibility to the orthopaedic department. In that year the notional number of beds was increased to 65, in a ward on the ground floor of the surgical block which had an annual average bed occupancy of about 108 per cent.

Expansion of the consultant staff continued (Tom Carr in 1954, Alex Adam in 1956, Ian Mackenzie[74] in 1960 and John Gibson in 1965). As Chapter 5 on post-war planning and building recounts, the pressure on all surgical beds at Foresterhill led to a scheme being drawn up for development and re-deployment in 1958–9. As a consequence, the orthopaedic department expanded in 1965 to the first floor of the surgical block at Foresterhill, retaining also half of the ground floor. The need for the care of accidents, and the difficulties imposed by accident and emergency (A&E) still being at Woolmanhill, had already led to two rooms being designated as an in-patient accident centre. The following year (1966), the remaining ground floor area became a rehabilitation unit for upper femoral fractures. In 1976 Ken Mills came to ARI as a consultant having been previously a senior lecturer in Dundee and before that a registrar in Aberdeen.

Over the years the nature of orthopaedic surgery has much changed. The emphasis in acute work is increasingly on the treatment of trauma. At the ARI this service was transformed by the transfer of the casualty department from Woolmanhill to the accident and emergency department at Foresterhill bringing into close proximity the out-patient and short stay departments with the accident centre in the orthopaedic department and more recently with the intensive care department (see p.173). Daily fracture clinics, which in 1989 dealt with some 5,000 new cases, are held by orthopaedic surgeons in the A&E department.

Now (1990) the department's beds at Foresterhill number 72, housed in the 'old' surgical block and devoted entirely to the treatment of trauma. Elective in-patient orthopaedic treatment has been transferred to Woodend Hospital which recently has absorbed the workload previously handled at Stracathro Hospital and which will, in the near future, be furnished with such facilities as to make it a centre of excellence.

Within the discipline the individual surgeons (of which there are now 10) have tended to develop important sub-specialities. First came a hand clinic (Tom Carr); next a service for amputees (George Hay); then the back clinic (Neil Hendry); and finally there was development in the surgical treatment of rheumatoid arthritis (John Gibson). The first total hip arthroplasty in the region was done by Alex Adam in 1967. When the merits of this, at first seemingly unlikely procedure, became obvious it was performed in increasing numbers by others so that by 1989 the total number of hip replacements was around 600.

Finally, academic growth has accompanied that of service delivery. In 1969 the need for formal postgraduate training in orthopaedics was acknowledged nationally and the Aberdeen department was one of the first in the UK to be recognized for the training of orthopaedic senior registrars. Alec Rennie was appointed to a personal chair in 1971 with the hope that by 1976 this would be replaced by a full time university chair. However, that objective was prevented by the financial stringency then prevailing and it was not until 1990 that Richard Porter was appointed to the Sir Harry Platt chair of orthopaedics, financed by Action for the Crippled Child for the first three years and thereafter by the university. This was a most welcome, if overdue, development. Rennie's only lingering regret is that the chair did not mark the name of Naughton Dunn[75] – Aberdeen graduate and orthopaedic surgeon of international repute – under whom he had trained.

Parallel with the formal recognition of orthopaedics within the university was an increasing flow of research and publication. By 1990 past and present members had published, or had accepted for publication, some 80 papers covering almost every aspect of orthopaedic surgery. The association with A&E has also produced a bestseller by Ken Mills, Graham Page and Richard Morton entitled *A Colour Atlas of Accidents and Emergencies*.

10

Post World War II Specialities

CARDIOLOGY, CARDIOTHORACIC SURGERY AND THORACIC MEDICINE

Though this is a history of the Aberdeen Royal Infirmary, it is impossible to record its involvement with the specialities concerned with the heart unless the net is cast a little wider. What follows is an account of how cardiology and cardiac surgery came about in Aberdeen as a whole and eventually, as part of the grand design for hospital services to which reference recurs throughout this book, ended up concentrated in the ARI on the Foresterhill site.

Early cardiology

Until the latter part of the l9th century, patients with heart disease were relatively rarely identified as such. This is reflected in their rarity in the records of the Infirmary though the diagnosis of 'dropsy' presumably included many with congestive cardiac failure. By the late 1880s, however, valvular heart disease begins to appear in the list of diagnoses and in 1898 no less than 14 different combinations of mitral and aortic stenosis are entered, suggesting the presence of an unidentified physician on the staff with more than average expertise with the stethoscope or a more than average imagination. Such observational precision thereafter disappears from the records until 1915 after which several categories of heart valve and other disease are recorded consistently. Two major arrhythmias, atrial fibrillation and heart block, are first recorded during World War I, as is hypertension. Electrocardiography (ECG), which was to play such an important part in the development of cardiology, had its origins in 1887 from the work of Augustus Désiré Waller (1856–1922), an Aberdeen graduate who at that time held the chair of physiology at St Mary's Hospital Medical School. He initially recorded electrical impulses which originated from the heart of his pet bulldog but went on to demonstrate the same effects in man.[1] The technique was soon taken up clinically by Einthoven[2] and others and introduced into Aberdeen at the Royal Infirmary by W.F. Croll,[3] who held the post of assistant physician at the ARI from 1912 to 1921 and of physician from 1922 to 1935. He possessed what was then the only ECG apparatus in Aberdeen and Sir James Howie[4] who worked as his house physician in 1931 recalls that Croll was recognized as 'the' heart specialist. In the early days the approach to electrocardiography was fairly primitive. The patients had to go to the machine, which was massive, and older physicians well remember seeing patients for ECG sitting with their arms and legs immersed in troughs of tepid saline.

The electrocardiography department

This was created by and around Croll who was succeeded by R.J. Duthie,[5] previously appointed assistant physician in charge of the department. On the move to Foresterhill, the ECG equipment – such as it was – came to be based in ward 1 (the professorial medical unit) on the ground floor of the medical block and Duthie, now assistant physician to A.W. Hendry[6] in ward 2, had access to it – an unusual arrangement in those days. It was not until 1948, when Duthie stepped up to physician in charge of ward 3 (in succession to John Craig[7] who had been appointed to the chair of child health), that Duthie and Professor R.S. Aitken[8] did an exchange, ward 3 moving to the ground floor and ward 1 to the area vacated. The wards had to retain their numbers because at that time the filing and storage of case records was at ward level.

The development of thoracic surgery

In the meantime and during the aftermath of World War II, thoracic surgery, which would in this country provide the basis for the development of cardiac surgery, was developing in Aberdeen. As in other parts of the country it was driven by the large amount of tuberculosis present in the community at the end of the war and which was yet to yield to chemotherapy. Surgical management of the disease was becoming technically possible through the development of anaesthetic techniques: the endotracheal tube pioneered by Magill and Macintosh; and intermittent positive pressure ventilation of the lungs made feasible by the introduction of neuromuscular blocking drugs. Before this, collapse therapy to rest the lung was achieved either temporarily by artifical pneumothorax or more permanently by extrapleural thoracoplasty.

The latter had been pioneered in Aberdeen by William Anderson[9] who had had extensive experience of chest injuries and their management in World War I but who by the end of World War II was unable to cope with the increasing numbers of patients. Many of those from Aberdeen who required surgery were in consequence being sent to the Brompton Hospital in London and also elsewhere.

The British Red Cross Society (BRCS) had in 1945 purchased and extended the Tor-na-Dee Sanatorium primarily for the treatment of service personnel who had contracted pulmonary tuberculosis during the war. F.J. Sambrook Gowar came to a joint appointment as thoracic surgeon there and at Woodend Hospital in 1946.

He was also at the same time made assistant thoracic surgeon to the Royal Infirmary and lecturer in thoracic surgery in the university. The BRCS had been the driving force behind this new appointment which followed meetings between them, representatives of the university and the Infirmary, and the medical officer of health for Aberdeen. Initially the great bulk of the work was done at Tor-na-Dee as Gowar recalls:[10] 'Tor-na-Dee housed about 70 patients in single rooms; a small washroom on the second floor was converted for use as an operating theatre (known to the staff as the "cupboard") until a modern theatre was built and opened in 1950.

The physician superintendent was Robert Keers,[11] a Belfast man who had suffered from pulmonary tuberculosis and had earned an international reputation for himself and Tor-na-Dee in the treatment of the disease. Anaesthesia was initially in the hands of Howard Wilson,[12] who had made a special study of thoracic anaesthesia in London with Ivan Magill and in Oxford with Sir Robert Macintosh. As the workload increased he was joined by others, notably A.W. Raffan, the late Lawson Davidson[13] and R.G. Milne. Local anaesthesia was still used for both thoracoplasty and bronchoscopy. There was a steady increase in major surgery from 16 thoracoplasties and 27 adhesion sections in the first eight months to 77 thoracoplasties, four resections and 46 adhesion sections during 1949'.

As the scourge of tuberculosis receded and service personnel became less in number, the BRCS eventually handed over Tor-na-Dee to the National Health Service on 1 April 1955 and the focus of thoracic surgery gradually moved to Woodend. At first there were no beds designated for the speciality but the general surgeons of the day (Sydney Davidson and Norman Logie) allowed the use of the few single rooms in their ward (ward 7) for patients with tuberculosis and other septic thoracic conditions. Subsequently a Thoracic Surgery Unit with 36 beds was established in the Emergency Medical Service Annex at Woodend.

The advance of technical cardiology and the beginning of cardiac surgery

The major advance in cardiology, which would impinge also on surgery, was the introduction of cardiac catheterization. The technique was first deployed in the Royal Infirmary in 1952 when the three-bedded side ward in ward 3 was equipped with an X-ray table and fluoroscope screen. There was a tall glass manometer to record pressures and a Scholander apparatus to measure oxygen saturation, though as the years passed more sophisticated equipment was eventually installed. Patients who required surgery – at that time limited to the relief of valvular stenosis and the closure of atrial septal defects – could then be referred to the thoracic unit at Woodend, where in 1953 Peter Brunnen was appointed as a second consultant after having trained in closed cardiac surgery with Lord Brock at Guy's Hospital in London.

In the Woodend unit a close relationship with the tuberculosis physicians (Douglas Bell,[14] Robert Fraser and Anna Mason) had also developed and this contributed to the subsequent collaboration between thoracic medicine physicians and thoracic surgeons in the treatment of pulmonary disease. When Duthie had to retire through ill health in 1959, he was replaced as physician in charge of ward 3 by T.N. Morgan.[15] This created a vacancy for a consultant in the linked ward at Woodend and to this D.S. Short was appointed although the ECG department remained in ward 3 ARI. The work of both the cardiology and cardiothoracic surgical units continued with an ever-increasing clinical load at Woodend throughout the 1950s, and included patients from the northern region who required surgical care.

J.K. Finlayson – a doctor who was trained also in engineering, hydraulics and electronics – became a second consultant in 1964: the post was specified as a general physician with an interest in respiratory medicine although his subsequent career was more to the benefit of local cardiology.

The return to Foresterhill

Cardiology and cardiothoracic surgery again become directly part of the story of the Aberdeen Royal Infirmary when Phase I was planned and built, Brunnen serving on the Professional Planning Committee for the development (Chapter 5). Both disciplines moved to Foresterhill in 1966, cardiothoracic surgery to ward 15 south with 30 beds still under the charge of Sister Taylor who had been the ward sister at Woodend, and cardiology and ECG in adjacent accommodation in ward 15 north. The move opened up new possibilities for co-operation and development. The two units were close together for the first time; cardiac catheterization was now carried out in purpose designed accommodation in the X-ray department (Chapter 12); and there could be a better liaison with the respiratory function laboratory which was adjacent to the ward though C.D. Needham, who had become the chief medical consultant to the thoracic surgeons in the later years at Woodend, continued to assess clinically all patients admitted for major surgery.

The proximity of both units – now in the ARI – to other hospitals on the Foresterhill site was a rational step forward, reducing staff travelling time particularly to the Children's Hospital.

Cardioversion and pacing

Before these physical moves had taken place, new therapeutic techniques were becoming available to the cardiologist. The first in the early 1960s was countershock (cardioversion) in the management of arrhythmias. The representative of an American firm which manufactured one of the early machines came to demonstrate its capabilities. That evening a patient developed an intractable arrhythmia. The salesman was located and alerted by a message flashed on the screen of the cinema he was attending. The patient was successfully shocked back into sinus rhythm and eventually discharged. As a consequence, the first synchronized defibrillator was purchased but – the reader will almost certainly say 'inevitably' – the Board chose not the machine that had performed so well but a cheaper British alternative.

Plate 44 John MacWilliam. Honorary physiologist to the Royal Infirmary. The first to describe ventricular fibrillation and the possibilities for cardiac pacing.

The second was cardiac pacing which was introduced into Aberdeen in 1964 initially for the treatment of complete heart block and later for some other arrhythmias. It had had a long gestation period in the city because in 1889 John A. MacWilliam (Plate 44), then professor of physiology in the university and a designated member of the Aberdeen Royal Infirmary staff, first suggested that ventricular fibrillation might be a cause of sudden death and that electrical stimulation might be used to maintain heart rhythm in bradycardia.[16]

From the outset this was a joint development between cardiology and cardiothoracic surgery and ultimately a separate out-patient pacemaker clinic became necessary.

Coronary care

With the move back to Foresterhill and the growing feeling amongst cardiologists that early deaths from myocardial infarction could be reduced by intensive care, the setting up of a coronary care unit (CCU) began first to be mooted. Studies of the case load suggested that a unit of 12 beds should be sufficient to cope with patients up to the age of 65 suspected of having had an acute episode. The cost of such a unit was estimated at around £85,000 and, in late 1968, a donation for that amount was received from Dr John F. Hall, of the building firm of Alexander Hall and Sons, who had for so long been associated with the Royal Infirmary.

Construction was undertaken in early 1969 on a site adjacent to ward 3 with an opening date planned, as one cardiologist recalls, rather ominously for 1 April 1969. This did, indeed, prove to be a fool's estimate because enough trained nursing staff could not be found and the CCU was first used to accommodate day surgical patients. It was not until August 1971 that half of the CCU was opened and it took several years before all of the beds could be 'reclaimed' for their original purpose. The bringing into action of the CCU was associated with the appointment of a third consultant physician, Alasdair Kenmure from Glasgow, who was given special responsibility for this task as the first full-time cardiologist.

The recent years in cardiology

The expansion of dialysis for chronic renal failure in the 1970s had en-croached on the cardiac department in ward 15 north. So in 1975 a further re-shuffle took place: a new cardiac department was built beside ward 3 and the CCU with an inter-connecting corridor. It was not until 1977 when W.R. Gauld, who had succeeded as physician in charge on T.N. Morgan's untimely death in 1969, retired that all the physicians with an interest in cardiology moved completely from Woodend, so that by the 1980s all beds and facilities were at last concentrated on one site. Once more the long-term vision of the creators of Foresterhill had achieved fruition. Technical innovations in cardiology continued with the development in 1973 through co-operation with the department of medical physics of a 'telelink', which enabled the transmission of an ECG of a patient many miles from Aberdeen over the telephone system to the cardiac department for immediate interpretation. Equipment was installed at Kirkwall, Lerwick, Banff, Fraserburgh, Peterhead and Turriff and the system remains in use up to the time of writing. All the technical advances – in diagnostic cardiac catheterization, pacing and telephone links – were facilitated by Finlayson's special interests.

The introduction of coronary artery bypass surgery, the history of which is traced below, greatly increased the need for high quality angiography which was initially undertaken by Kenmure and Peter Ward of the department of radiodiagnosis. This service, along with echocardiography and Doppler imaging, isotope scanning, graded exercise testing and 24 hour ECG monitoring, were advances that the department took into its activities with a gradual increase in the number of supporting technical staff from one in 1949 to 15 at the present time. In 1983 Short retired and was replaced by Kevin Jennings, a London graduate latterly trained in Newcastle; two years later Stephen Walton, a Manchester graduate came to Aberdeen from London, on the retiral of Finlayson.

More recently balloon dilatation of coronary artery stenosis has become available for selected patients as a cardiological procedure but pre-supposes the presence of a surgical service to correct a complete occlusion.

The growth of cardiac surgery

As has already been mentioned, the 'state of the art' in 1953 was closed cardiac surgery during which the circulation remained intact or was briefly arrested under hypothermia. Heart–lung bypass techniques began in the United States in 1954 (though much pioneering work had been done in the United Kingdom) but did not reach Aberdeen, mainly for political and economic reasons, until 1974.

Regional perfusion had been used on a trial basis in 1961 for chemotherapy in the surgical unit and, in the late 1960s, Andrew Foote, then senior lecturer in the department of surgery, had collaborated with the neurosurgeons in the use of bypass and hypothermia in an attempt to improve operating conditions for the treatment of intracranial aneurysms. However, these early efforts were prone to complications and did not improve results. Foote, with encouragement from Professor George Smith, then spent six months in Toronto, where he studied the latest surgical techniques in coronary artery surgery and heart–lung bypass; he also visited various centres in the United States including the Cleveland Clinic, where coronary artery surgery had begun in 1968. On his return, and after much experimental work from 1972 onwards, the first cardio-pulmonary bypass procedure (for a coronary artery vein graft) was done in March 1974. The following year Gowar retired and was replaced by Foote, who continued with his interest in coronary artery surgery as well as in thoracic surgery.

In spite of these developments in Aberdeen, a committee chaired by Professor Sir Andrew Watt Kay, who held the Regius chair of surgery at the Western Infirmary in Glasgow concluded in 1977,[17] that all cardiac surgery in Scotland should be carried out in three units: two in Glasgow and one in Edinburgh, and that this should be centrally funded on a so-called 'supraregional' basis – though it conceded that coronary artery surgery could continue in Aberdeen if the board agreed to finance it out of its own funds. In the same year as the Kay report, Peter Brunnen retired and was succeeded by John Cockburn, who had been trained and accredited in cardiothoracic surgery in London and in Southampton, and who was ultimately to introduce valve replacement surgery in Aberdeen in 1979.

Though there was continued national scepticism amongst senior members of the cardiac surgical profession, including a gloomy view from an Edinburgh adviser on a local appointments committee in 1975 that there was 'no future in coronary artery surgery',[18] there was a universal increase in the number of patients being referred for this operation. However, during this period a great deal of debate continued about the 'viability' of small units for cardiac surgery, in terms of both the professional consequences for mortality and morbidity, and the costs incurred per bypass procedure. Though no one doubted the efficiency of open heart surgery in the hands of the surgeons at the ARI, the chief administrative medical officer of the day (W. Bruce Howie[19]) acting on behalf of the Grampian Health Board, issued a directive that, for economic reasons, no further valve surgery was to be carried out in Aberdeen.

A heated and prolonged debate followed and was reported in the local press over many months. On one occasion an unidentified hospital spokesman added his own comment that it might be better for patients to go to established units than to take 'pot luck' in Aberdeen Royal Infirmary where smallish numbers of procedures were being done.[20] The result of this was a letter published the following day from Howie stating that the board's implication that the standard of heart surgery in Aberdeen was lower than elsewhere in Scotland was not intended; an apology was made to the medical staff concerned.

The subject was discussed in the House of Commons[21] and perhaps the local climax was a public debate in the Aberdeen Music Hall on 30 May 1980. Subsequently, and not without further controversy, though the board did not lift its ban on valve surgery, it agreed to a review after a two year period during which time coronary artery bypass grafting only was permitted. The result of the review was that in 1982 a full case mix for open heart surgery was achieved with a limit of 50 operations a year. This frugal approach, although well-meaning and intended to conserve funds for other specialities, was unlikely to influence the body of opinion which still existed against small units such as the one in Aberdeen. Over the next few years the controversy over the restriction on numbers continued and a campaign to become a recognized cardiac centre was mounted by the cardiac surgeons, their sympathizers on the board and health council, members of Parliament and former patients. A petition to the secretary of state for Scotland was organized by a grateful patient[22] and presented along with a statistical analysis of the patients that had been treated.

Many obstacles had still to be overcome on the way to full status as an open heart surgery unit, including the view which emanated from Dundee that a cardiac centre north of the Tay should be located at Stracathro Hospital and serviced by visiting consultants from both Dundee and Aberdeen. Perhaps the most telling argument was the continuing success of the ARI unit which, despite 'small' numbers, was achieving good results for the complete range of open heart surgery. Finally, in 1988, logic and common sense prevailed. Following a review by the National Specialist Advisory Committee, the unit at the Aberdeen Royal Infirmary was declared the fourth national and centrally funded centre for cardiac surgery in Scotland. As a consequence the number of cardiac operations rapidly increased to 150 per annum and justified the appointment in 1989 of a third cardiac surgeon (R.R. Jeffrey) who had been trained in Edinburgh and Liverpool. The unit can now look forward to a more certain future and will in all probability provide a service for the north of Scotland as a whole.

The evolution of thoracic medicine

This account has so far concentrated on the medicine and surgery of the heart. With the conquest of tuberculosis, thoracic specialists were confronted with new problems such as smoking-related diseases – chronic bronchitis and bronchial carcinoma – and a rising tide of morbidity from asthma.

K.N.V. Palmer[23] had developed a strong academic interest in asthma and the investigation of new agents for its treatment. He introduced new measurement techniques during the 1960s and this led to his founding the pulmonary function laboratory in 1968. He started an asthma clinic, and fostered the careers of a new generation of thoracic physicians.

Increasing integration of thoracic medicine into general medicine was to follow the appointments of James Friend in 1973 and Joe Legge in 1977, with thoracic medical beds opening in Foresterhill in 1980. Expertise in fibreoptic bronchoscopy led to another important service development and a close working partnership shared with the thoracic surgeons. In 1986 an ever-expanding workload led to the appointment of a third consultant, J. Graham Douglas from Edinburgh.

Envoi

As in other parts of the United Kingdom, the growth of cardiology, cardiothoracic surgery and thoracic medicine in Aberdeen required the dedication of a great number of men and women, many of whom must go without mention. However, looking back, the ground work of R.J. Duthie will long be remembered and also that of Sambrook Gowar who brought expertise in thoracic surgery that was to create a unit which would in time, and not without difficulty, develop into a successful centre first for thoracic surgery and later, through the efforts of many others, for cardiac surgery. David Short who had played an important part in the teaching of cardiology in Aberdeen was appointed physician to the Queen in Scotland and a personal clinical professor in the university shortly before his retirement.

DIABETES AND METABOLIC MEDICINE

Before insulin was discovered in 1922[24] by workers in Toronto (amongst whom was the Aberdonian, J.J.R. Macleod[25]), diabetes mellitus in its more severe forms was a uniformly fatal disorder. Dietary management was the only approach available and some patients (who are now recognized as having type II disease[26]) might respond, but for the young with insulin dependent (type I) diabetes, death was only postponed and usually not for long. Reference to the old hospital records shows that rigorous dietary treatment was being used in Aberdeen in the early 1900s with morphine elixir as a supplement to relieve suffering. In 1906, Thomas Fraser[27] in association with a friend the zoologist, John Rennie,[28] tried a new approach and were tantalizingly close to success. Von Mering and Minkowski[29] had shown that complete extirpation of the pancreas in the dog led rapidly to the development of severe and ultimately fatal diabetes. At this time the first hormones, chemical messengers in the blood, were being isolated and belief soon hardened that the islets of Langerhans in the pancreas probably produced some substance to control the metabolism of sugar, and that this was lacking in diabetics. Rennie discovered that certain bony fishes (teleosts) had islets which made up a separate structure lying away from the main pancreatic digestive gland. He and Fraser obtained this tissue from angler fish (*Lophius piscatorius*) bought at the local fish merchant and fed boiled or raw extracts of it to four diabetics without, however, any clinical improvement. They went on to prepare a filtered extract which they injected into one patient with some clinical improvement but there was no objective evidence that they had influenced the course of the disease by changes in urine volume and sugar content, and they were forced to abandon their experiments because of toxic effects.[30] Later Macleod, established that the material they had used was indeed rich in insulin[31] but the two pioneers had lacked the necessary experience in the techniques of extraction which was to be the key to success.

Review of the admission books for the period 1900–17[32] shows only 191 admissions for diabetes during those years, the assumption being that many patients in the community were not referred because there was no effective treatment. One hundred and eleven (58 per cent) were discharged 'relieved', almost all of them in the older age groups where some response to dietary treatment would be expected. Forty-seven (24 per cent) were 'unrelieved' and 33 (18 per cent) died.

Insulin revolutionized diabetic care. By the end of 1922, hundreds of patients had been treated in North America and their lives saved. Its introduction into Britain, however, was slow. The early reports from Toronto seem to have passed unnoticed. Soon, J.J.R. Macleod offered the Medical Research Council the British patent rights on insulin but officials there were cautious in their approach and it was not until late in 1922 that reports of the discovery appeared in the *British Medical Journal*.[33,34] However, by 1923 the hormone had become more readily available and the first patient in Scotland was treated in the summer of that year.[35] The first use of insulin in Aberdeen has proved impossible to trace. Certainly from May 1923 there was an upsurge of admissions for diabetes with a total for the year of 43 and of 50 in 1924. Many of these were in younger age groups than before and, except for two patients who died with complicated problems, all were discharged 'relieved'. In the hospital's annual report for 1923[36] it was noted that £200 had been spent on insulin and that expenditure would increase. By 1929, 113 patients were recorded as having received the hormone and were requiring constant supervision. To meet the need, Ashley Mackintosh, at that time professor of medicine, was able to persuade the university to create a lectureship in clinical chemistry within the department of medicine. Alexander Lyall[37] was invited to apply and was appointed in 1926.

Lyall, who in the mould of the day had initially no access to beds, was often asked by other physicians to advise on diabetic patients and to arrange subsequent follow-up and supervision. Within the year there was in conse-quence an embryonic clinic for diabetes and the number of patients steadily grew so that, by 1932, the first qualified dietician was appointed and other medical assistants recruited.[38] By now the clinic was accruing about 150 patients every year and its needs were recognized in planning the move to Foresterhill. Stanley Davidson[39] instigated a special metabolic ward on the second top floor of the medical block (ward 4 at the time and now ward 27/28) which was occupied in 1938. There Lyall had access initially to only eight of the 32 beds but, with the passage of time, he gradually exerted squatter's rights and in particular was able gently to displace David Campbell,[40] the professor of materia medica whose interests were more in the fields of education and medical administration.

The ward included a special diet kitchen and also had two adjacent rooms of about 14 square metres. One was Lyall's and there he consulted from behind an oakwood roll top desk which he himself had provided.[41] The other was a clinical laboratory where patients were weighed and their urine and blood tested. Here Sister Thomson[42] ruled supreme, loved by her patients but held in terrified awe by junior members of the medical staff. Throughout the subsequent years to Lyall's retirement the service gradually extended, mainly through his drive and enthusiasm, to take in the supervision of diabetes in pregnancy and the training of district nurses in diabetic management. His work in establishing clinical chemistry in the Aberdeen Royal Infirmary which was intimately bound up with the management of diabetes is recounted in Chapter 13.

In 1961 direction of the diabetic clinic passed to John Stowers who was appointed to the new post of consultant in diabetes and endocrinology. He initiated several changes and innovations. A formal appointments system began; the dietetic service in Aberdeen which had lapsed was re-introduced; and ultimately, in conjunction with Alastair Macgregor[43] (David Campbell's successor in the chair of materia medica), a dietician's training course was instituted at the School of Domestic Science (the Robert Gordon Institute of Technology, see also p.207) .

As the years went by, more staff were needed[44] and the diabetic service also became part of the rotating registrar training in medicine so that, by 1990, five of these had taken up consultant posts at home or overseas in diabetology.[45] Subsequently a senior registrar post was established and has likewise proved a source of future specialists in the field.[46] A new post of consultant in metabolic diseases was created in 1968[47] and a joint endocrine clinic began in 1974. The continued growth in patient numbers resulted in a move in 1963 to more spacious premises on the first floor of the Mount Stephen pavilion at Woolmanhill.[48] Even this was not to prove adequate and a further shift was undertaken in 1974 to purpose designed accommodation in what had been the eye department at Woolmanhill.

John Stowers retired in 1984 and was succeeded by Donald Pearson. As with all other like departments, expansion of secretarial, technical and computer facilities has continued and, in common with work in the field elsewhere, Aberdeen has come a long way since 1922. The clinic currently has 265 patients who have been in attendance for over 30 years, of whom 68 have put in more than 40 years, and six over 50. The longest survivor would bring a smile to the face of Sandy Lyall, though the clinic cannot take too much credit for the success. It is appropriate that this account should end with his story.

J.M. had just celebrated his twenty-first birthday when, in late 1928, diabetes was diagnosed by Lyall. He was admitted under a physician who at his bedside told a group of students: 'this is a hopeless case; there is no cure; the young man will spend the rest of his life in and out of hospital,' – words vividly remembered more than 60 years on. A young medical student of the day, James Howie, found the patient later in the night, awake and, with good reason, upset. It is the patient's recollection that Howie said, referring to the physician, 'b. . . .y fool, don't worry we'll work it out together' – and they did with the additional help of another clinical student.[49]

Not well pleased with this unfortunate hospital experience, the patient attended the clinic for only a short period and thereafter, helped by a succession of interested general practitioners, looked after himself. Michael Williams encountered him when he attended the eye department because of cataract and glaucoma in 1990, 62 years after the diagnosis had been made.

HAEMATOLOGY

The recognition of haematology as a distinct speciality began during the tenure of the chair of medicine by Stanley Davidson[50] when clinical studies on the pathogenesis and natural history of iron deficiency anaemia were carried out by Harold Fullerton[51] in the department. During his subsequent tenure of the Regius chair in the department of medicine, Fullerton fostered the establishment of the first haematology laboratory and initiated a routine laboratory service to Aberdeen Royal Infirmary from the department. This developed rapidly in the late 1950s and early 1960s as the complexity of laboratory investigation of haematological disorders increased. The first appointment specific to haematology was that of Audrey Dawson, who became Lecturer in Haematology in the department in 1963. She took over supervision of the laboratory service and also initiated and established the clinical service in haematology and oncology for Aberdeen Royal Infirmary, the Children's and the Maternity Hospitals. Organizational running of the haematology laboratory was transferred to the department of pathology in 1969, Dawson continuing to manage it from there.

In 1973 a second consultant post was established in the medical school laboratory and Ron Davidson who had created a haematological laboratory at the City Hospital, moved to join Dawson. Since then Dawson has concentrated on the rapidly expanding clinical end of the service while Davidson has supervised the development of the laboratory aspects.

Haematology in Aberdeen has shared in the world-wide growth of the discipline as it has moved into the fields of chemotherapy of malignant disease – both solid growths and haematological ones – and into disorders of coagulation. This expansion has also necessitated a great increase in the number and complexity of laboratory investigations. Computerization of laboratory management has taken place and the City laboratory moved to a combined organization on the Foresterhill campus in 1989.

NEUROLOGY AND NEUROSURGERY

Neurosurgery and neurology were both post-war developments with the first preceding the second by some years. Before 1948, W.C. Wilson had undertaken a limited range of neurosurgical procedures but, as a former colleague of Norman

Dott[52] in Edinburgh, he appreciated the need for a neurosurgical service for the North East and Northern regions and, in April 1948, secured the appointment of Martin Nichols[53] as a specialist in neurosurgery to the Aberdeen Hospitals. In his first year Nichols created a small team including R.J.A. Fraser, who had had previous experience of neurosurgery in the western desert and Cairo, Margaret Thomson, as a nursing sister, and Evelyn Craig as a secretary. Along with Nichols, Robert Fraser and Evelyn Craig were to spend the rest of their professional lives in the unit, both retiring in 1982.

There was initially no other junior medical staff and the high standards of nursing care typically associated with neurosurgery – half hourly charts of temperature pulse rate, arterial pressure and level of consciousness, plus the maintenance of a clear airway and nasogastric feeding – were new and alien to the nursing administration. However, Margaret Thomson overcame these problems and created an excellent nursing service in both wards and operating theatres so that she was promoted to departmental sister, leaving in 1967 to become at first matron of Morningfield Hospital and later matron of the Glasgow Royal Infirmary. The medical staff slowly increased. First a house officer in the early 1950s and ultimately a second in the mid-1960s. In 1956 Robert Fraser became a consultant and soon after there were two registrars, one a rotating and one a career post.

Space was always a problem as the clinical involvement of the unit increased. Initially Wilson allocated two four-bed wards and three side rooms in his professorial unit (ward 8) along with one of the two attached operating theatres. By 1960, as a consequence of the move of ophthalmology to Woodend, neurosurgery was able to occupy ward 11 on the top floor of the surgical block, the available space being increased by southward extensions at either end. This brought the total beds in the ARI up to 32 and there was also a sitting room for ambulant patients. The operating theatre at this level was converted into a room for cerebral angiography and air contrast studies. A notable feature of the unit and one ahead of its time, was the use of colour in the decoration, particularly the curtains and the sitting room where pictures were also displayed. There was a setback in this regard when the next move occurred and all wall decorations were strictly forbidden. However, as is described on p.7, a more enlightened attitude now prevails. Ward 11 was to be the unit's home for the next 20 years after which it moved to ward 40 of Phase II, where the planned accommodation for both neurosurgery and neurology included a neuro-radiological diagnostic service and suitable offices. The care of patients with respiratory problems – common in neurosurgery – had been met in 1964 by putting one of the four-bed wards aside for intensive therapy and respiratory support; this arrangement was perforce continued in Phase II with a six-bed unit which also provided frequently for patients from other specialities.

From its inception the unit was never short of work. The extensive area which was served, necessitated peripheral clinics and in-patient facilities, particularly at Stracathro where there was also a regular operating session every week. More beds were obtained first in ward 7 at Woodend and then in the ENT ward 12 at ARI. In spite of this it was often necessary to return patients to their ward of origin at an early stage to relieve bed shortages. The pattern of clinical activity followed that of the development of neurosurgery throughout the country, though in the early days it was distressing to find patients with progressive lesions such as cord compression arriving too late for effective treatment. However, the active educational programme that both the neurosurgeons and the neurologists pursued has made all in the regions more aware of what can be offered. Prefrontal leucotomy was still extensively used for psychiatric treatment at the time the neurosurgical unit opened and continued to be done for some years. Surgery on the peripheral nerves – trigeminal neuralgia, lumbar ganglionectomy, operations for thoracic outlet syndrome and extensive sympathetic denervations for hypertension all fell within the initial surgical ambit.[54] Stereotactic surgery for Parkinsonism and pituitary ablation for advanced breast cancer were also part of the repetoire until therapeutic change and fashion rendered them obsolete. At all times there was a steady flow of head injuries and intracranial tumours though only those who required surgery or specialized care could be admitted to the unit. Brain abscess was initially a considerable commitment but has now become rare.

It early became apparent that a large number of patients being seen by the surgeons had neurological problems that did not require surgery and that there was a need for the development of neurology as a speciality. Harold Fullerton[55] recognized this but, in the restricted circumstances of the post-war period, it was not until 1965 that the first senior lecturer/consultant post in neurology was created within the department of medicine. Allan Downie became its first occupant, and recalls: 'I was very aware that I was to be the first physician to concern himself solely with the subject and not be a 'physician with an interest' which had been the predominant pattern in Aberdeen and, with few exceptions, throughout the United Kingdom. Though I also realized that my own interest had been fostered both by serving as a house surgeon in the neurosurgical unit and by working as a registrar with one such physician, T.N. Morgan,[56] I had no idea how far back in time the involvement of the North-East of Scotland with the practice of neurology extended. As early as the last quarter of the 19th century, Sir David Ferrier,[57] a native of Balgownie had migrated to London to the Hospital for Nervous Diseases (Queen's Square). Ashley Mackintosh[58] who held the chair of medicine at Aberdeen from 1912–29, was for upwards of three years, Ferrier's assistant and, in Mackintosh's words, was to remain his 'dearest medical friend and master until his death.' Mackintosh in turn influenced many younger men to turn towards neurology both in Aberdeen and elsewhere, among whom were Alexander Greig Anderson,[59] A.W. Hendry[60] and John Craig.[61] Initially the senior lecturer was dependent upon both the department of medicine and neurosurgery for both staff and facilities. A second consultant post was created in 1972 and reflected the growth in work. At first the beds were located in both the professorial medical unit and the neurosurgical ward but with the move to Phase II they were all consolidated with the neurosurgeons to form a comprehensive unit with facilities for electro-encephalography, electromyography and neuro-radiology. The development of magnetic resonance imaging is considered on p.193.

Two of the founders of the speciality of neurological science in Aberdeen may fittingly have the last words. Robert Fraser writes: 'By the time the original consultants had retired we were well established in modern accommodation, with the facilities and staff to give an excellent service to the people of the area served and to continue to advance patient care' and Dr Downie comments: 'I would like to think that the local enthusiasm for neurology, which began with Sir David Ferrier and passed to Sir Ashley Mackintosh, and thence to a group of Aberdeen physicians, and so to me will continue through the present generation of neurologists and to their students of present and future generations'.

PLASTIC AND RECONSTRUCTIVE SURGERY

As with some other technical specialities, plastic surgery emerged as a full speciality in Aberdeen only some time after World War II. It seems almost certain however, from the records of conditions treated by surgery at the ARI, that many operations, which would now be regarded as plastic in nature, were performed there during the latter half of the 19th century and subsequently. One name of particular note is that of John Wolfe[62] an ophthalmic surgeon who worked in Aberdeen from 1863–8. He is immortalized eponymously for the Wolfe graft – the transfer of full thickness skin from behind the ear which he used to re-surface defects of the eyelids. The technique remains in use to this day.

In Aberdeen and throughout the country, and in spite of the fact that plastic surgery had become a specialized discipline in the hands of such as Harold Gillies during World War I, the majority of plastic surgical procedures continued to be done by surgeons who practised general surgery. Nevertheless there was an interest in Aberdeen in skin injury and replacement through the work of W.C. Wilson which had begun in Edinburgh in the 1930s and was continued both there and in Aberdeen by Andrew Wilkinson until his departure to the chair of paediatric surgery in Great Ormond Street, London. Furthermore J.F. Philip's appointment in 1948 as a surgeon with a special interest in oncology (see p.161) led to the development of reconstructive surgery for head and neck tumours and the use of skin transfer techniques for the cutaneous malignancies which were largely under his care.

In 1952 an Aberdeen graduate and senior registrar in general surgery Francis L.F. Innes[63] took a particular interest in the reconstructive surgery of children and was seconded for a year to work under A.B. Wallace[64] in Edinburgh. On his return all the cleft lip and palate work and most other paediatric plastic procedures fell to him, but a consultant post was not established perhaps because, as we have seen elsewhere in this history, resources remained very restricted. Innes left in 1954 to join Professor Kilner at Oxford, subsequently moving to a consultant post at Norwich. During the rest of the 1950s and most of the 1960s and, in spite of the fact that by the beginning of this decade almost all other hospital boards in the United Kingdom had established departments of plastic surgery, the majority of the work continued to be done by general surgeons, although some patients with complicated deformities and severe burns were transferred to Edinburgh.

At last in 1969 the North-East Regional Hospital Board found space in its development programme for the speciality and I.F.K. Muir, then a consultant at the North West Metropolitan Regional Plastic Surgery Centre at Northwood and the West Middlesex Hospital, took up the post of consultant. Adult beds were intitially provided at Woodend and the Children's Hospital but the adult side of the work moved in 1986 to ward 39 at the Royal Infirmary. Muir had a special interest in burns and had written a standard work on the subject.[65] His expertise centred particularly on the use of modern air-conditioning methods to provide the optimal environment for healing. A room in ward 5 at Woodend was adapted for this purpose and the work carried out there formed the basis of the new burns unit in the ARI.

In recent years the advance of techniques in reconstruction immediately or very early after acute non-burn injury, increasingly required co-operation between plastic and orthopaedic surgeons in the management of injuries of the limbs. The irregular occurrence of injury, often in what it is now fashionable to call 'unsocial hours' made such collaborative work impossible for one plastic surgeon and therefore in 1978, C.R.W. Rayner, who had been a senior registrar in Manchester, was appointed as the second consultant. It then became possible to establish a service with the orthopaedic surgeons (R.B. Chesney being most involved) for the treatment of all serious hand injuries. This work, with the continued innovations in reconstruction and the use of micro-surgical techniques, has become the basis of the rapid reconstruction in a single stage of many defects of the head, neck and limbs.

Muir retired in 1986 having seen the establishment of a vigorous department in his speciality and was succeeded by O.M. Fenton. The department continues to conduct an active research programme which includes work on the healing of burns and other wounds, scar formation, aspects of cleft lip and palate repair and of the management of hand injuries.

At the time of writing in 1991 both Rayner and Fenton have resigned to take up posts in Birmingham and Wakefield respectively; Muir has come out of retirement to supervise the work of the department during the period of re-appointments.

PSYCHOLOGICAL MEDICINE

Psychological medicine had but a brief life within the curtilage of the Aberdeen Royal Infirmary. In the account of the early days of the institution (Chapter 2) we have seen how primitive were the arrangements for the care of the mentally ill. Thereafter patients with mental disorders were hived off into separate accommodation outwith the Infirmary until, in 1937, Alexander Greig Anderson[66] invited T.A. Ross[67] to address the faculty of medicine on the need to introduce teaching of neurotic and psychosomatic conditions to medical students. The outcome, through a financial initiative from John Alexander Ross,[68] was the setting up of the Crombie-Ross lectureship in psychopathology of which the first (and only) incumbent was Dr Douglas MacCalman.[69]

With his appointment was combined that of physician in psychological medicine in the Royal Infirmary with emphasis on out-patient consultation and liaison with general practitioners – truly a first generation liaison psychiatrist. A few in-patient beds were made available in Dr A.G. Anderson's ward (ward 3) and later these were supplemented during the war by facilities in the emergency bed service at Woodend.

After the war, Ross made a further substantial contribution to the university in order to found a chair of mental health of which, in 1946, MacCalman was the first incumbent. The department grew slowly in size[70] but MacCalman moved on to Leeds in 1948. The department within the Infirmary was not looked upon as of high priority and as Malcom Millar recalls[71] the chairman of the hospital board (J.C. Duffus[72]) was fond of saying that mental illness was 'Region's problem, not ours.'

Endless streams of patients of every type and severity turned up at out-patients from 9 a.m. to 6 p.m. without appointment. Eventually a disused hut that had been Stanley Davidson's[73] research unit was acquired and a new entrance at 89 John Street gave it a life of its own. A generous grant of £100 was provided by the board of management and furniture was acquired mainly from the major second-hand emporium of the time.[74]

The ensuing years saw a satisfactory appointments system established and by 1953 ten in-patient beds were allocated to the department. However, by 1959 it was clear that any plan for a fully effective psychiatric service and teaching centre on the Foresterhill campus were unlikely to come to fruition in the foreseeable future. This view and the increasing changes in the management of the mentally ill which were incorporated in the Mental Health Acts of 1959 and 1960 led to re-organization with the closure of the department of psychological medicine in the Royal Infirmary and the opening of the Ross Clinic within the grounds of nearby Royal Cornhill Hospital.

RADIUM, X-RAY THERAPY AND ONCOLOGY

Radium in Aberdeen

The possibility of treating malignant disease by disrupting cell division using ionizing radiation was recognized not long after Roentgen discovered X-rays in 1895 and the Curies isolated radium in 1898. Two methods thus became available: natural sources of radiation such as radium and its fission product radon; and X-rays derived from generators. Radium was introduced first. It was not surprisingly regarded as the province of those who were already using diagnostic X-rays. In 1910 John R. Levack, whose work in that field is recounted

in detail in Chapter 12, had his request for a supply of radium at a cost first of
£88 but finally of £150 'deferred' by the Directors of the ARI.[75] This decision was
apparently based on the opinion of representatives of Dundee Royal Infirmary
who, while admitting their lack of personal experience, felt that the results of
treatment with radium were uncertain.

After World War I, a national effort initially centred on the exploitation of
radium and undertaken by the Medical Research Council (MRC), which had
been founded in 1913, was mounted to deliver, on loan as it were, radium –
usually in the form of one of its salts – to selected centres throughout the United
Kingdom. Aberdeen received its first allocation in 1922 when, as related in
Chapter 9, it began to be used for the treatment of cancer of the uterus.

The national administrative organization changed over the years and, in 1929,
the MRC demitted its responsibility to the National Radium Commission (NRC)
to secure the custody, distribution and use of radium purchased by the Radium
Trust (itself a quasi-independent body) using a fund subscribed partly by the
public and partly derived from the Treasury.[76] The Royal Infirmary, because it
was a teaching hospital and associated with the medical faculty of the University,
was accorded the status of a National Radium Centre. The Commission was
finally dissolved at the time of the inception of the Health Service in 1948.

By 1926 the Aberdeen Royal Infirmary held 200 mg of radium and received a
further 'loan' of 250 mg. Shortly afterwards, 500 mg of radium salt was made
available to the Department of Natural Philosophy (Physics) at Marischal College
for the production of radon. The latter is a radioactive gas formed as the outcome
of the decay of radium; it has a short half life (4 days) and itself decays through a
complex series of steps to non-radioactive lead. It is in consequence suited to
implantation in the form of seeds or pellets and was amongst the first forms of
regional therapy.

Everyone was aware of the hazards of potent radioactive sources and from the
outset a strict regimen of control – not as we shall see always completely
successful – was put in place. John Cruickshank,[77] who had come to Aberdeen
from Dumfries to the Georgina MacRobert[78] lectureship in malignant disease in
the Department of Pathology and was to go on to hold the chair of Bacteriology
(see Chapter 13), was charged in May 1922 by the medical committee of the Royal
Infirmary with the custody and administrative control of the radium. He was
given the title of 'radium officer' reporting to a 'radium committee.' The latter
was strengthened in 1930 by the creation of a joint radium committee, composed
of members of the board of directors of the Infirmary and of the faculty of
medicine. The Infirmary radium committee met for the last time in March 1938
but the joint committee continued to function up to the time that the Radium
Commission was dissolved.

When the joint committee was formed, W.G. Evans[79] was appointed
MacRobert lecturer in malignant disease at the University and director of radium
therapy and research at the Infirmary, a post which he held until 1939. At about
the same time, H.D. Griffith[80] of the Natural Philosophy Department became
Aberdeen's first medical physicist (see also Chapter 14) and in 1935 he took on
the post of honorary physicist to the X-ray department working out of a small

laboratory just off the main corridor of the building. He was to play a vital part in the development of radiotherapy before, during and after the years of World War II, especially in relation to radiation protection (see Chapter 12), the design and installation of equipment and the control of dose. He set up a plant to produce radon seeds and along with Evans devised a radium 'bomb' which, when loaded with radium and radon, could deliver a dose of irradiation to a depth of 6 cm below the surface. Although this was not the first such apparatus in Britain, it was nevertheless at the time, a very significant achievement. Indeed, the events of the 1930s heralded the start in Aberdeen of the discipline of radiotherapy separate from that of radiodiagnosis though, until after the war and the start of the NHS, therapy with radium remained in the hands of the 'radium officer' while the use of X-rays for treatment was undertaken by the senior radiologist. With the departure of Evans in 1939, the funds available for the MacRobert lectureship were transferred to pure research and James Philip was appointed surgeon in charge of radium therapy and to 'work in close co-operation with the radiologist in charge of the X-ray department.[81] This was the beginning of an even more integrated approach to the management of malignant disease to which this account will return.

At the outbreak of World War II in 1939, the radium stock at the Royal Infirmary had increased by a further loan from the Radium Commission to about 2 g plus about 0.75 g held at Marischal College for the production of radon. The exigencies of war made it impossible for a centre to use the element unless it could be removed from patients and put 50 feet underground in safe storage within ten minutes of the sounding of an air-raid warning. Such a stringent limit was not possible at Foresterhill, where treatment was now centred, in view of the short period of grace and the fact that the water table at Foresterhill was believed to be only 10–15 feet below the surface (see also Chapter 5). The radium salt in solution at Marischal was therefore dried out and transferred to a quarry at Cove (Plate 45);[82] throughout the war years, the small plant set up there supplied the requirements not only of Aberdeen but also of Edinburgh, Glasgow and Newcastle. The clinical use of radium was adapted to radon deployed in needles and containers, loaded to the strengths required with the gas in glass capillaries. This work was not undertaken, however, without damage over the years to the fingers and nails of the University staff involved.[83] The radium stock was stored in a borehole in the Rubislaw granite quarry where as Griffith pointed out[84] there was enough material which, if it had been dispersed by a direct hit from a bomb, would have endangered, if not ended, the lives of 20,000 people. The bore hole 12 feet deep and eight inches in diameter was 50 feet above the floor level of the quarry in a granite cliff which formed one of the 'benches' used to extract the stone. A German bomb did fall on the quarry floor but produced an insignificant effect on the bore hole, so confirming the faith of the locals in the safety of the storage place. For very special patients a small quantity of radium was stored in a concrete protected safe in the hospital at Torphins.

These seemingly obsessive precautions were characteristic of the first half century of use of radium and led as a whole to a good safety record. On only four occasions was any radium lost. The first in April 1932 when two needles went

Plate 45 The radiation 'laboratory' at Cove.

missing and were never recovered. The second in November of the same year when five needles disappeared. The third in the late 1940s when a 50 mg tube of radium was withdrawn by a disturbed gynaecological patient and flushed down the toilet; in spite of an extensive search through all the sewage outfall from Foresterhill to the Bay of Nigg, this radium is for ever lost. And finally in the 1950s, a 50 mg tube of radon was inadvertently destroyed in the hospital incinerator at Woodend without, as far as is known, producing a nuclear disaster.

The organization of radiation in the management of malignant disease and the rise of oncology

Ever since the ARI had become a National Radium Centre, annual reports had been submitted to the National Radium Commission of the patients treated, dosage, techniques and survival rates, but the Commission's promise to publish the results with perhaps some general guidance on the most effective methods of treatment was never fulfilled. Though having failed in this regard, the Commission in 1942 announced its intention of extending its remit to cover the whole field of malignant disease[85] and through the pages of the *Lancet*[86] in 1944 emphasized its right to organize registration of all patients with cancer who were treated under schemes within the Cancer Act. Further attempts at centralization continued with the NRC stating in 1945 – again in the *Lancet*[87] – that 'it is generally recognized that all hospitals, voluntary and otherwise will have to be planned. Each will have its place in a well arranged scheme, each doing the work allotted to it and which it undertakes to do, and not doing work for which it is not intended'.

In 1946 Aberdeen reacted against these trends and policies and the joint radium committee, at the instigation of the directors of the Infirmary, informed the Commission that it repudiated many of its statements.[88] The Committee further noted that the NRC might try to apply financial and material sanctions so as to obtain a stranglehold on treatment. With the growth of radiotherapy, it was felt that the Commission's vested interest in radium was likely to be disadvantageous if not disastrous.

Fortunately the matter was resolved when the NRC was wound up with the inception of the Health Service. Aberdeen was then free to develop its own policy in relation to all aspects of cancer control. Already, as we have seen, a clinician had been appointed as radium officer,and in 1949 James Philip also became adviser to the Regional Hospital Board on both radiotherapy and the treatment of malignant disease in general. Following this the Board agreed to the creation of a post in radiotherapy alone[89] but it was not until 1950 that David Levack was able to relinquish radiotherapy to Ernest Ridley[90] who became consultant in charge of radiotherapy.

These changes formed the nucleus around which Oncology developed and in this field Aberdeen can claim to have been the first centre in Scotland and, as far as can be ascertained, the first in Britain to put this concept into practice. The word was, however, not part of the medical vocabulary until at least 10 to 15 years had elapsed from the foundation of the malignant diseases unit in the ARI. It is on record that in 1972 the Standing Cancer Committee in Scotland urged – through the Department of Health – the other Scottish health regions to establish a cancer organization similar to that which had been in existence in Aberdeen for the previous 20 years.[91]

The need for such a service first became apparent from a report published in 1949 on the outcome of treatment of malignant disease at the ARI between 1930 and 1943.[92] Up to that time there had been no treatment policy defined by discussions between the various disciplines involved in diagnosis, treatment and follow-up nor was there any registration scheme for cancer. As elsewhere surgical and medical services were organized on a unit basis: each surgical or medical ward (a firm in English terms) was a self-contained unit with a 'chief,' an assistant and a resident medical officer. The treatment given to any patient with cancer under their care depended mainly on the views and experience of the senior member. This situation had been aggravated rather than helped by the introduction of radium and X-ray therapy whose use remained, until l950, in the charge of separate disciplines. Fragmentation of this kind resulted in unsatisfactory treatment reinforced by the common view that those specializing in the treatment of malignancy, other than surgeons and physicians, should only be asked to deal with advanced disease.

As a result of long planning and consultation by both the administrative and the medical staff of the Aberdeen hospitals and the faculty of medicine, the malignant diseases unit came into being in 1950. It was responsible to the regional malignant diseases committee which was created by the regional board and had a remit to keep under review all matters pertaining to the Board's cancer services and to advise accordingly. This unit formed the basis for the establishment of a department of oncology in the 1970s.

The unit's tasks were:

1. All the radiotherapy for the region including consultation.
2. Elective surgery for malignant disease in patients referred by consultants and, in selected instances, by general practitioners.
3. The chemotherapy of cancer which at that time was just beginning with derivatives of nitrogen mustard. As practice changed, new agents such as methotrexate and 5-fluorouracil were assessed including their use in combination with surgery and radiotherapy in the treatment of advanced cancer mainly of the head and neck and of the breast.
4. Registration and follow-up of all patients with cancer in the region. As the technology developed, computerized records were kept outwith the system of national registration.
5. The preparation of reports and the organization of staff meetings for definition of treatment policies.
6. The creation of joint diagnostic and follow-up clinics in the Royal Infirmary with the departments of gynaecology, neurosurgery, ENT, dermatology and thoracic surgery. There was also a subsidiary joint clinic for the reticuloses.
7. Peripheral diagnostic and follow-up clinics set up in Elgin, Buckie, Fraserburgh, Banff, Peterhead and Huntly.
8. The teaching of undergraduates, postgraduates, nurses and health visitors.

The Unit obtained 30 beds and occasionally used others for patients undergoing radiotherapy. For many years it was staffed by two consultant surgeons, one consultant radiotherapist, one-part time radiotherapist and one-part time medical assistant who looked after the registration records. There was also a full-time physicist who held a joint appointment with the university department of medical physics (now the department of biomedical physics, and bio-engineering, see p.191). Though not officially on the staff, a consultant haematologist worked with the unit. Surgical registrars had the opportunity of attachment during their training and a general practitioner was later appointed to work on a sessional basis. Adequate secretarial staff was gradually acquired for all the multifarious duties of registration, organizing clinics and the preparation of reports.[93]

In 1957 a fundamental change of policy in the treatment of malignant disease began to overtake the views previously promulgated by the Department of Health. Up to that time the primary objective had been to ensure that effective treatment was available for every patient; however, this did not imply that the management of malignancy should be regarded as a speciality in its own right either by the establishment of special centres or by clinical and educational activities. The wind of change which now blew was towards such a speciality – a widely ranging discipline under the comprehensive title of Oncology. The need now perceived was to concentrate in selected places the facilities and special expertise needed for all aspects of the control of malignant disease. Control embodies the principles of prevention, detection, treatment and after care including rehabilitation, and should also include research as well as an involvement in registration and statistical analysis. The existing Aberdeen unit had already met all these principles and was thus a prototype for the new concept of oncology. Though it was not a large national centre as envisaged by the World Health Organisation, it served a recognizable and largely self-contained geographical area and, where need be, was nationally orientated. It had always agreed that national treatment centres for rare tumours are essential as are research centres staffed by highly trained personnel and containing facilities which could not be made available on a regional basis. The Aberdeen unit at the ARI also presaged the concept of a team with which other individuals and groups could interact. Though in the early days of clinical oncology it had been envisaged that one individual might have therapeutic expertise across a wide field, it soon became clear – as had been recognized in the North-East for quite some time – that many different skills were required. With the promise of chemotherapy, physicians world-wide were beginning to develop the speciality of medical oncology, and this became established in Aberdeen in 1978 when Dr Andrew Hutcheon was appointed to develop the non-surgical care of solid tumours and to augment the efforts of those working with haematological malignancies.

Initially split between Woodend and the ARI, the activities of medical oncology are now concentrated in ward 46 (in-patients) which has special facilities for immunocompromised patients and the department of clinical oncology (out-patients). Medical oncology's role is often to integrate the various aspects of care. All aspects of oncology are united by the Grampian oncology research project which is co-ordinated from a clinical trials office in the ARI.

Accommodation and equipment in the post-war years

RADIUM

For many years radium, which produces penetrating gamma rays, continued to be used under conditions hazardous to those who had to handle it. Its last use, in the intracavity therapy of cervical cancer, was eventually replaced by caesium-137 in 1980. Further developments took place thereafter with 'afterloading' techniques to allow the insertion of hollow applicators which are positioned under X-ray control and then filled with the radioactive source. A further refinement to reduce exposure of clinicians and nurses, was the introduction of a computer-controlled remote loading device (the Selectron) in 1989. Iridium wire replaced the local use of radium in other solid tumours.

X-RAY THERAPY

When the move to Foresterhill took place in 1936, the new X-ray department (see Chapter 4) contained a 100 kV therapy machine for superficial treatment and also a 250 kV unit. These continued to serve the region until 1950 when an additional 250 kV machine was acquired. The physical separation of radiodiagnosis from radiotherapy came about in 1963 with a new purpose-built department, largely created by Ernest Ridley, which also contained a cobalt unit. The steady increase in workload required the addition of a further cobalt unit in 1975 and a simulator suite in 1976. For technical reasons in therapy it is often necessary to immobilize the patient, and for this purpose a 'mould room' extension was built and became operational in the late 1970s. The original cobalt unit was also replaced in the last year of that decade. Though a linear accelerator was considered, it was rejected on financial grounds and also because only a low-energy machine would have been possible in the existing room. Nevertheless the idea was resurrected in the mid-1980s when the second cobalt unit was to be replaced and a further extension was built for this purpose.

RHEUMATOLOGY AND PHYSIOTHERAPY

Stanley Davidson[94] had intimated his intention of concentrating at least part of his efforts as the first full-time professor of medicine on the problems posed by rheumatic disorders (p.86). He may not have been thinking entirely of problems in joints because during the 1930s acute rheumatism with its disastrous effects on the heart was still a common disease. Nevertheless he appointed J.J.R. Duthie as a clinical assistant in the Department of Medicine with a special interest in the subject; subsequent developments in Aberdeen were delayed when the latter moved with Davidson to Edinburgh and went on to a distinguished career (including a personal chair in Rheumatology) in the field of joint disease. The war also intervened and it was not until it ended that further thought could be given to the needs of the speciality. Patients continued to be admitted to general medical beds but in 1945 a Department of Rheumatic Diseases was established by Professor Aitken.[95] Beds were made available at Stracathro and in 1946 a rheumatic out-patient clinic was set up in relation to the orthopaedic out-patient facilities at Foresterhill.[96] Logie Bain[97] – somewhat to his surprise – became consultant in charge of this development and in 1957 accommodation for his patients was found in the City Hospital. He became responsible for Physical Medicine at Woolmanhill which he directed until 1979.

Long before these events, however, the Infirmary had been involved in the care of what might be called the 'diseases of physique' – aches and pains related to the joints and related structures such as muscles, ligaments and connective tissue. Towards the close of the 19th century there was great enthusiasm for massage as a therapeutic measure though there was but a thin dividing line between its use for treatment and for pleasure.[98] To remedy this a Society of

Trained Masseuses was announced in 1895[99] with its own rules of professional conduct. It flourished and subsequently became the 'Incorporated Society of Trained Masseuses' with legal and public status as a professional organization. At about this time the Infirmary employed one masseuse whose salary was £55 per annum, though she secured a rise of £5 in 1898.

In common with other developments of that time and since, there were many cross-links between emerging specialities and what was to become physio-therapy was inextricably linked with 'medical electricity' the history of which is recounted on p.175. Electrical treatment, presumably by galvanic stimulation of muscles, had been introduced in the 18th century and a machine for the purpose had existed in the Infirmary at least from 1781.[100] Such treatment received a boost from the introduction of other applications of physics. It would appear that the masseuse continued her association with the Electric Department throughout the first quarter of the 20th century. By 1929 we learn of the inclusion in the plans for the Foresterhill complex (see p.50) of an 'Electric Department for X-ray, Radiant Heat, Deep Therapy and Massage'. The statement reflects the view of the day that X-rays had a therapeutic role other than in the management of malignant disease – one that was to persist for perhaps a further decade. In common with the other plans for Foresterhill there were changes and modifications, and the department eventually ended up in proximity to the new X-ray department (see p.177). The management of rheumatic disorders was also obviously being recognized with, in 1934, plans being considered for the provision of 'facilities for the treatment of chronic rheumatic diseases by means of special baths and massage'.[101]

Further sources of pressure to expand the work of experts in massage and manipulation was the institution of the Orthopaedic Department in 1937 (see p.138) and the impressive development of rehabilitation made necessary by World War II. The profession of physiotherapy was beginning to emerge and the word is mentioned for the first time by the governors of the Infirmary in 1942[102] which coincided with the adoption by the professional body of the title Chartered Society of Physiotherapists. There was agreement in principle for the appointment of 'one or two' physiotherapists but suitable candidates were not forthcoming. The governors continued to record the need for an expansion of facilities over the next few years while at the same time noting that they were unable to do anything about it. Nevertheless the title Physiotherapy Department is recorded for the first time in the annual report for 1945.[103]

The last report of the governors, before the NHS was established, again recognized that more facilities for physiotherapy were needed and that recruitment was a problem which would only be solved with the establishment of a 'School for the training of Physiotherapists'.[104] It was to be another 14 years, and in spite of the appointment of Margot Martin in 1949 with the specific objective of creating a school,[105] before that objective was achieved. In 1962 the school opened in the Simpson Building at Woolmanhill[106] above a new out-patient Physiotherapy Department which was itself adjacent to the Department of Physical Medicine now being run by Logie Bain and Hubert Balch.[107] Meantime, in 1950 the Bon Accord Baths were opened in an effort to deal with the pressure of accommodation at the Infirmary and the lack of facilities for hydrotherapy; they also served as an extra out-patient department. They functioned well, and are remembered by many staff with affection, until it was possible to re-organize in 1962.

Though formal growth and recognition continued to be difficult throughout the first decade of the NHS, the staff did increase so that by 1952 there were 13 – a superintendent and 12 'assistants' – though turnover was rapid and the numbers actually in post were sometimes as low as five. From 1962 onwards the more ready supply of qualified staff from the School was able to meet increased demand. The department at Foresterhill lost some of its old geographical allegiance to X-ray in 1979 when new accommodation was commissioned in the sub-basement of Phase II though the old premises including the gymnasium continue in use.

Although now independent, rheumatology and physiotherapy were by no means mutually exclusive in their early development at ARI; rheumatology has become an established speciality within general medicine and at the time of writing there are three consultants[108] based for in-patient purposes at the City Hospital.

11

Anaesthesia

There had been many surgical operations at Woolmanhill before inhalational anaesthesia with ether was first used in 1847 on a 15-year-old boy for the amputation of a scrofulous leg.[1] The newspaper report of this procedure regarded it as a triumphant success, recording in particular how the patient had slept peacefully throughout. Nevertheless there was continued controversy over the merits of anaesthesia and William Keith,[2] who carried out this procedure, still preferred, 15 years later, to have his patients bound to the table after a glass of whisky and a prayer. To a certain extent this was because a great deal had to be learned about the administration of ether and the alternative chloroform, also introduced in 1847, and initially regarded as a perfect anaesthetic, was soon to be feared as a result of occasional unexpected deaths of apparently healthy individuals during induction. Keith was aware of this from personal experience (see Chapter 7), and the antagonism he expressed was a significant setback for anaesthesia in the small community of Aberdeen because of his influence, national reputation and senior status. However, the manifest benefits of general anaesthesia were probably behind an attempt in 1856 to nominate a person to administer chloroform and be responsible for patients, but the proposal was rejected by the surgeons' committee which maintained that no incident with chloroform had occurred in Aberdeen and that it was the operating surgeon's responsibility to delegate its administration to an assistant under his immediate supervision.[3] In 1871 such an incident did take place and resulted in death.[4] The hospital committee then formally recognized the post of staff chloroformist and nominated Alexander Dyce Davidson[5] (Plate 46) to the post. His deputy was Alexander Ogston[6] destined later to become Regius professor of surgery. Dyce Davidson moved on to his ultimate career in ophthalmology in 1875 and was replaced by a succession of individuals (see Table IV) until in 1895 the term anaesthetist was substituted for chloroformist, coincident with the appointment of J.J.Y. Dalgarno to the combined post of anaesthetist and medical electrician.[7] His responsibilities included the increasing number of electrical accumulators used to power hospital lighting and faradic apparatus. As recounted in Chapter 12, these duties were not long compatible with the growth of knowledge in the field of radiology and physics and what was to become radiodiagnosis parted company with anaesthesia within two years. The anaesthetists, with the

Plate 46 Alexander Dyce Davidson, first staff chloroformist at ARI. This memorial medallion is in the entrance hall of the 1936 building at Foresterhill.

exception of Dalgarno who was a general practitioner, continued to look upon their appointment as a stepping stone to a post as assistant physician or surgeon, for example, MacKenzie Booth,[8] but after 1910 and the appointment of James Robertson[9] all were general practitioners apart from William Anderson[10] and Robert Richards.[11]

Robertson, John Johnston[12] and Alexander Ogston[13] were founder members of the Scottish Society of Anaesthetists formed in 1914 to 'promote the study of the service and practice of anaesthetics, its proper teaching and the conservation and advancement of the interests of anaesthetists', objectives no doubt prompted by the poor status of anaesthetists at this time. As an example, it was only when Ogston retired in 1929 that he was granted consultant status and thereafter the medical committee decreed that the senior – but only the senior – anaesthetist should have the same status as surgeons and physicians. In this, as in other fields, the surgeons were intent on maintaining their controlling influence; a cynic might remark that they were the source and in control of income from private practice.

Change was soon to come as the skills of anaesthesia advanced. Soon after Ogston retired, Ross Mackenzie[14] took what was a bold decision to relinquish his general practice and concentrate solely on anaesthesia and an honorary hospital appointment. He was probably the first to work full time as an anaesthetist in Scotland and one of the first few in Britain. Appropriately he was co-opted in 1931 as one of the 12 founder members of the Council of the Association of Anaesthetists of Great Britain and Ireland and, when he became senior anaesthetist at the Royal Infirmary, he persuaded the governors of the day to appoint a full-time resident anaesthetist.[15] The responsibilities of this individual were to be available for all emergencies and to help out in the morning elective

Table IV Early anaesthetists at Aberdeen Royal Infirmary

Alexander Dyce Davidson	Resigned as chloroformist	1875
Patrick Blaikie Smith	Chloroformist	1875–86
James MacKenzie Booth	Chloroformist	1886–90
George Maitland Edmond	Chloroformist	1890–6
John James Young Dalgarno	Assistant anaesthetist	1895–6
	Anaesthetist and medical electrician	1896–7
	Anaesthetist	1897–1910
Alexander Rudolph Galloway	Assistant anaesthetist and assistant medical electrician	1896–7
Henry McIlree Williamson Gray	Assistant anaesthetist	1897–8
William Robinson Pirie	Assitant Anaesthetist	1898–1908
Thomas Fraser	2nd assistant anaesthetist	1904–10
Arthur Wellesley Falconer	3rd assistant anaesthetist	1909–10
	Anaesthetist	1910–12
James Robertson	Assistant anaesthetist	1910–18
John Johnston	Assistant anaesthetist	1910–29
	Anaesthetist	1929–37
	Hon. consulting anaesthetist	1937–62
Alexander Ogston	Anaesthetist	1912–29
	Hon. consulting anaesthetist	1929–40
William Anderson	Assistant anaesthetist	1913–9
James Ross MacKenzie	Assistant anaesthetist	1919–37
	Anaesthetist	1937–46
	Hon. consulting anaesthetist	1946–63
Robert Richards	Assistant anaesthetist	1919–22
Thomas Ogilvie Robson	Assistant anaesthetist	1922–48
	Consultant anaesthetist	1948–53
James Smith Stewart	Assistant anaesthetist	1926–61
Thomas James Chalmers MacDonald	Assistant anaesthetist	1929–48
	Consultant anaesthetist	1948–64
John William Levack	Assistant anaesthetist	1937–66

operating lists which were still normally undertaken by general practitioners with honorary appointments.

Ogston, who as a student had been taught by MacWilliam, the professor of physiology, was impressed by the latter's demonstration[16] of an association between chloroform inhalation and ventricular fibrillation in animals. He knew also of Blaikie Smith's[17] advocacy of the safety of ether which had led to the design of one of the earliest temperature compensated ether inhalers[18] in a bid to facilitate and promote the use of that agent. Ogston acknowledged these men and perpetuated and taught the use of ether[19] at a time when the Scottish doctrine of the use of chloroform was, as a consequence of the influence of the Edinburgh school, widely followed. The mask that he devised (Plate 47)[13] was so popular locally that when house officers who had been burdened with the responsibility of emergency anaesthetics in Aberdeen went further afield, they invariably took one with them so that Ogston's invention was introduced to many hospitals in London and elsewhere.

Towards the end of his career, Johnston described his experience of over 300 injections of the first of a new generation of anaesthetics – the intravenous agent evipan (hexobarbitone) sodium.[20] He was proud of his complete lack of mortality although he described one who had 'returned from the dead' – 600 mg of evipan had been administered and the surgeon was about to enucleate an eye when the

Plate 47 Ogston's wire frame mask for open ether anaesthesia. (a) Wire frame mask;
(b) mask with gauze only before towel is pinned around the upright struts to
form a chimney; (c) mask fully draped and ready for use.

breathing became shallower and apparently ceased and the pulse was
imperceptible. In spite of resuscitation for 45 minutes, no heart sounds could be
heard and the jaw was bandaged for the patient's transfer to the mortuary.
Fortunately he was kept a little longer in the operating theatre and presently a
nurse noted some slight movement of the jaw, a faint pulse in the neck and
occasional slight movements of the chest. Further resuscitation was successful. In
retrospect and quite strangely, the assumption of the death of this patient
undergoing an eye operation had been based on respiratory depression and an
imperceptible pulse and not on 'rail-roading' of the corpuscles in the retinal
arteries which had been first described as a sign of death by the Aberdeen
ophthalmologist Usher.[21]

The Health Service

During the first year of the NHS the consultant establishments of all departments
around the country were reviewed and anaesthesia in Aberdeen fared rather
badly, being restricted to four appointments – T.O. Robson,[22] T.J.C. Mac-
Donald,[23] H.B. Wilson[24] and Rosalind Milne. In 1951 the complement was
increased by the promotion of J.W.L. Bain[25] and A.W. Raffan from senior
hospital medical officer to consultant. Wilson, who had largely created the
organization of anaesthesia into a speciality in Aberdeen after his appointment
as regional director in 1954, died unexpectedly in 1958 and was succeeded by
Norman Rollason.[26] With the help of his colleagues Rollason set about acquiring
the increasingly technical anaesthetic equipment and also set up workshop and
laboratory space in a small area alongside the rotunda at Foresterhill, where
maintenance of equipment and research could be undertaken. He strove – with
the support of Martin Nichols[27] and the medical superintendent Sandy Michie –
for a respiratory unit against considerable opposition from various clinicians and
administrators. At one stage it was suggested to Rollason that his persistence
might cost him his career but he persevered at the committee table with
admirable tenacity.

Since those days, anaesthesia has expanded steadily in Aberdeen and the department is now, in terms of medical staff, the biggest in the Infirmary, albeit that it provides a service far beyond the walls of that institution. It has branched out into other fields amongst the most of important of which is intensive care.

Intensive care

In the early 1960s, as a result of developments in technology and advances in cardio-respiratory science, and in the understanding of shock and renal function, it became apparent that survival was possible in critical illness where previously death was accepted as inevitable. Consistently good results were only achieved by treating such patients in units where the necessary nursing and medical expertise were concentrated and constantly available. These became known as intensive therapy units (ITUs) and brought together groups which had been pioneering advances in, for example, renal failure, trauma management and post-operative respiratory failure.[28] Rollason's respiratory unit was set up in 1964 (in ward 11, see p.155) and offered a valuable service for the needs of neurosurgery but was also of great potential use for the general management of the seriously ill. The planning for the professorial unit had foreseen this in the Phase I design (see p.69) but such an isolated unit was doomed at an early stage because of lack of funds and nursing staff and the need to concentrate skills and, in particular, constant respiratory support controlled by an anaesthetist. The respiratory unit continued for some years to labour under the need to accept a task for which it was totally unsuited both structurally and in the provision of nursing staff. Complex surgical problems with their invariably associated sepsis caused an unacceptable risk for the other patients within the unit.

Though all this was well known, no provision was made in the original plans for Phase II but intervention from the anaesthetic department[29] ensured that an ITU would be incorporated. The advice proferred (probably then ahead of its time) to create an open plan area was over-ruled on bacteriological grounds[30] and the legacy of this is structural, including the triple glazing to reduce noise from the hospital loading and service bays directly underneath. This timely development was dealt a demoralizing blow in 1975 when the opening of the ITU had to be deferred for 13 years because of lack of funds, insufficient numbers of nurses and perhaps – some would say – by the direction of the Health Board's priorities elsewhere to the opening of a psychogeriatric assessment unit. As a result the original respiratory unit moved in 1981 with neurosurgery to the new ward 40 in Phase II. No progress had been made in separating different types of patients. By this time anaesthetists had evolved as the responsible clinicians for the day to day running of the ITU and, although there had been early recommendations that trainees from several disciplines should work there, this was never followed through.[31] Anaesthetists and their trainees have continued to provide resident staff cover and the department of anaesthetics has borne the overall responsibility for the ITU.

Eventually the five bed unit of Phase II (originally planned as 10 beds) opened in 1983. Expansion to eight beds took place in 1988 and the unit now serves the ARI and the Children's Hospital, including the growing need of the cardiac surgeons (see p.150). As we write, a new specialized cardiac ITU is under development and will allow the general ITU to fulfil the function for which it was intended 15 years ago.

12

Diagnostic Radiology and Radiography

From Roentgen to real time

The momentous discovery of a new kind of ray by Roentgen on 8 November 1895 was reported in January 1896.[1] The popular press made fun of it; the initial reaction of the *Lancet* was one of ridicule[2] which changed quickly to enthusiastic support once the editors had been given a 'live' demonstration by an electrical engineer.[3] Thereafter articles on X-rays were given pride of place in both the *Lancet* and the *British Medical Journal* when pioneers began to report their experience.

The first Aberdeen radiologists and the establishment of the department

Several medical graduates were quick to appreciate the clinical value of Roentgen's discovery. The first was James McKenzie Davidson[4] who had begun his professional career as an ophthalmologist. He had an absorbing interest in physics, especially light and electricity and was probably the first man in Scotland to produce photographs using X-rays. His contribution to the localization of foreign bodies in the eye is recounted in Chapter 9. By 1897 he had decided that his future lay in radiology and, after he had departed for London in 1897, he became Britain's leading radiologist of the day during the first decade of the 20th century.

An 'electrical department' had existed in the Infirmary for a number of years before Roentgen's discovery and provided treatment with ultra-violet and infra-red lamps, galvanism, faradism and massage. Alexander MacGregor,[5] who had previously been assistant to the professor of medicine, was until 1895 the medical electrician – a title which reflected his therapeutic role rather than his knowledge of electromagnetism. He resigned, however, after an unsuccessful application for the chair of medicine.

The confused state of the disciplines that were ultimately to become anaesthesia, diagnostic radiology and bio-engineering is reflected in the observation that initially MacGregor's job was to be discontinued but that, after this had been blocked by the professors of medicine and surgery, a committee recommended that a combined appointment of 'chloroformist and electrician' be created.[6] Two individuals were appointed – J.J.Y. Dalgarno[7] and A.R. Galloway.[8] Not surprisingly this arrangement did not work and the committee then appointed John Levack[9] as medical electrician, leaving Galloway to pursue the practice of anaesthetics. This move paved the way for the establishment of a proper X-ray department at the Royal Infirmary.

Levack had already installed X-ray equipment in his house in Golden Square and proved to be a radiologist of distinction. He had a close working relationship with McKenzie Davidson and a common interest in the advancement of the new science. As early as 1896 he arranged for undergraduates in medicine to receive instruction in the work of the department. This contribution led to his appointment in 1919 as a lecturer in radiology and electrotherapeutics, a post he held until 1931. He effectively created the department at the ARI and was prominent both in X-ray diagnosis and in the use of radium and X-rays in therapy (see also p.159).

The workload caused by the diverse functions in electrical treatments and the growing demand for skiagrams (radiographs) and procedures done under the fluorescent screen, prompted Levack to make regular submissions to the directors for increases in space, equipment and staff. In 1905 an assistant medical electrician, Clifford T. Bell,[10] was appointed but this post seems to have lapsed after 1918. By 1931 when Levack retired and was succeeded for a short time as radiologist in charge by Middleton Connon,[11] the department at Woolmanhill, housed in a single room, was completely unable to cope. A second X-ray room was added and it was agreed that ultra-violet treatment should be transferred to a custom-built hut 'between the massage room in the surgical block and the boiler house'.

Two years later the staff establishment was increased by the appointments of an assistant radiologist, David P. Levack,[12] an assistant radiographer and two pupil radiographers. The extent of the department's work at this time is made clear from a table published in the annual report of the directors for 1933.[13]

The move to Foresterhill was now beginning to take shape (see Chapter 4). The X-ray department, which incorporated the radium dispensary and equipment for radiotherapy, was to be in the special diseases block, the building of which was due to begin in 1934. The original plans were changed, however, as the radiologists recommended that out-patient examinations should be at Foresterhill. Though this had some merit in the existing circumstances, it resulted in the Foresterhill department being too small to meet the unforeseen increase in demand for diagnostic services and unable to expand further because it was surrounded on three sides by established departments.

1935 – a critical year

Two important events took place in 1935. First, John Blewett,[14] an Australian, was appointed as whole-time head of the department with David Levack continuing as his assistant. Second, Harry Griffith,[15] a senior lecturer in the university department of physics, was appointed honorary physicist to the X-ray department. His contribution to personnel monitoring is considered later. Blewett describes his advent and the conditions in the department at the time in the following words: 'I was appointed to the hospital young and inexperienced, but my subject was very little older than I was and in much the same state of development. . . .Our activities were generally confined to cellars or more remote parts of the hospital building and there we laboured amid open high tension wiring, electrical coronal discharge – most spectacular in damp weather – and dank tanks of photographic solution. Such was the X-ray department at Woolmanhill. . .'

Foresterhill

Things were to improve for a while with the move but the planning constraints soon led to demands outstripping the resources of the department. Blewett comments on the equipment: 'For the new Infirmary, I was instructed to install the best type of electrical equipment. . .It required all the strength of Aberdonian character to face the bill, but in the end we had a department that if it did not equal in luxury those of the Swedes or the science of the Germans. . . at least we were equal to anything else in Scotland. The full installation reached the enormous sum I believe of £10,000. . .' And on the workings of the department: 'We were limited by development, photographic methods were manually performed, acres of film were processed daily, clinicians demanded films and information sooner than we were able to provide them. . .'

From this time Blewett ran the department but after David Levack was called to war service in 1939 he did so single handed until help arrived in the person of John Innes[16] who appeared, Blewett records, out of a 'blue haze' created by a small pipe which 'seemed part of his personality'. Innes was assistant radiologist until he moved in 1945 to a similar post in the Glasgow Royal Infirmary and was replaced by Sandy Bain who went on to become consultant radiologist to the Inverness Royal Infirmary.[17]

Monitoring radiation exposure in department personnel

In the years before World War II, Harry Griffith, who was amongst the first to take up medical physics as a specialist subject (see Chapter 14), and Blewett developed the photographic monitoring of radiation exposure of department staff now so familiar to all who work in places where radiation is a hazard.[18] The system was taken up nationally within a few years. Griffith also took on the supervision of the installation and the technical performance of all equipment that used ionizing radiation.

The advent of the NHS

Many events followed the 'appointed day' of 5 July 1948. First a separation of diagnosis from treatment was set in train and is described in Chapter 10 (Radium, Radiotherapy and Oncology). Second a major consequence of the introduction of the NHS was the progressive increase in the number of referrals to out-patient clinics which had enormous 'knock-on' effects for radiodiagnosis. At Woolmanhill, immediate services were needed for out-patient clinics and casualty patients; at Foresterhill 'booked' examinations both from out-patient clinics and directly from general practitioners mushroomed, as did the in-patient load.

Nine years into the health service, 22,000 patients were examined by a staff of three radiographers at Woolmanhill where a new 'clinics unit' had been established, while at Foresterhill seven radiographers coped with 32,000. It was no mean task to maintain an efficient service for a major teaching hospital operating on a split site.

Twenty years on, the Foresterhill department had grown to four X-ray rooms but the facilities for patients and staff were limited in the extreme. Anyone undergoing a barium study and requiring a lavatory urgently had, if that next to the screening rooms was engaged, to face the indignity of a trip to the far end of a crowded waiting room where there was a single toilet with walls that did not reach the ceiling and equipped with the loudest flush system in the hospital (see also p.60).

The cramped office provided minimal space for the filing of films and report cards. The director had a small office to himself; two others served as reporting rooms, the first occupied by three consultants and the second by a senior hospital medical officer and three other junior members of staff (Plate 48).

Still 'in the dark'

Even in the late 1950s the simple fluorescent screen was the only method by which physiological activity and the flow of contrast medium could be observed (Plate 49). The light emitted from the screen was of such low intensity that 'screening' had to be conducted in total darkness with the radiologist adapting his eyes to the dark for 15 minutes beforehand. Any inadvertent turning on of the room lights ruined this and proceedings had to be suspended. On many occasions such would happen and a typical occurrence in Aberdeen[19] was when the door was flung open flooding the room with light and revealing a large group of people. The account goes on: 'the leader of the group shouted "Hello, Hello, is anyone there?" I managed to limit myself to one "Hello" followed by "what (expletive deleted) do you want?" A brief period of silence was followed by the reply "I'm looking for the head physiographer". It ultimately transpired that this meant Dr Levack. While the title used was perhaps not surprising in view of my chief's many responsibilities, it was clear that this official visiting group had little knowledge of the workings of their X-ray department.'

These clumsy arrangements came to an end when the therapeutic X-ray equipment was moved out into the new radiotherapy department in 1964 (see p.166). A new 'barium suite' with a group of toilets-cum-cubicles giving direct

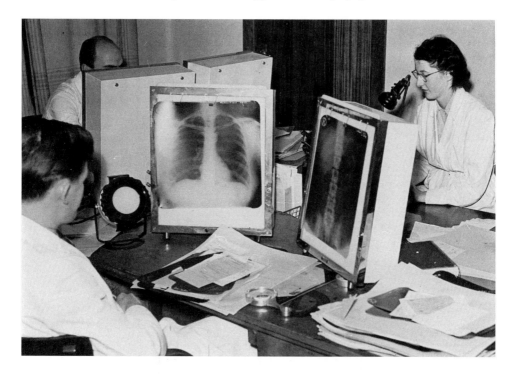

Plate 48 Cramped working and poor facilities. The old X-ray reporting room.

access to the screening room was introduced, a design which was so successful that it was incorporated into Phase I. The installation of image intensification to the barium suite, coupled with cine-radiography and ultimately TV imaging and tape recording, meant that screening could be done in well-illuminated surroundings. At the same time the introduction of automatic film processing machines made it possible to reduce the size of the huge darkroom[20] and to dispense with the massive tanks of developer and fixer solutions. Films were delivered within a few minutes into an adjacent, well-illuminated 'viewing room'.

From the late 1950s on procedural difficulties were nevertheless beginning to be compounded by the demand for new and time-consuming techniques such as angiography on in-patients, which had to be carried out in a department daily besieged by out-patients. The only solution at the time was to establish satellite areas: one in a room adjacent to the department for cardiac catheterization and angiography in general (see Chapter 10, Cardiology, Cardiothoracic Surgery and Thoracic Medicine); and another on the top floor of the original surgical block for neuroradiology (see Chapter 10, Neurology and Neurosurgery).

Clinical subspecialities within radiology – developments in the 1960s

By 1956 the consultant staff had risen to three and specialist interests began to emerge. Robert McKail[21] worked in close association with the neurosurgeons and

Plate 49 Low technology and high risk. Screening the chest before image-intensification. The radiologist is David P. Levack.

the thoracic surgeons who at that time were still at Woodend. Archibald Stewart[22] had a primary interest in paediatrics but worked out of the original Foresterhill department after the opening of Phase I (see below) to continue a service in obstetric radiology from, as he put it, the 'bottom end'. Lewis Gillanders (1958–88) took over peripheral angiography which had been begun by George Mavor[23] and extended this to selective imaging of the abdominal organs.

The need for consultant staff continued to increase during the 1960s and Peter Ward in 1963 undertook responsibility for bronchography at the ARI and gastrointestinal investigations at Woodend. James Palmer (1964–7) was a further accretion to the establishment[24] as was Sandy MacDonald in the same year. The latter took over neuro-radiology from McKail and was to play an important role in the initial development of nuclear medicine, ultrasound and mammography for breast cancer screening. Also during the 1960s, clinical conferences between individual units and clinical teams became a regular feature and created close working relationships with the professorial surgical unit, the department of materia medica, the neurosurgeons and the urologists.

Lymphography was introduced by Ronald Mahaffy in 1965 on his appointment to a consultant post. For some years (1968–78), Michael Allen looked after the out-patient department and City Hospital as well as acting as visiting radiologist to Banff and the Outer Islands.

Into Phase I at last

The planning of Phase I is dealt with in Chapter 5 and the new in-patient department housed there opened in 1966. The original department now became the out-patient department which dealt with all other requests. The in-patient department had four separate rooms, together with an X-ray theatre designed originally for cardiac catheterization (see p.71), angiography and other procedures that needed aseptic conditions. There was a large film store next to the office and the luxury of individual offices for consultants and the superintendent radiographer. In addition there was accommodation for registrars and nursing staff, and a staff room with a small kitchen attached. The growing need for conference facilities was met by two rooms with banks of viewing boxes and the entrance bay included an enormous waiting area designed to accommodate bed-fast patients. In later years this large space became invaluable for housing new imaging equipment.

Capitalizing on technical advance

From the opening of the new facilities in 1966, the story of imaging in Aberdeen is one of continuing expansion. Ultrasound examination of obstetric patients began in the Maternity Hospital in 1967 under a grant from the MRC to Professor Ian MacGillivray and Professor John Mallard of the department of bio-medical physics and bio-engineering (see p.193) and their original machine was transferred to the in-patient X-ray department in 1969. The explosive growth of this form of imaging in both general and cardiological applications required the appointment in 1975 of two additional consultants (Tony Bayliss and Jamie Weir).

At the same time as these changes in practice, which would lead to the discontinuation of obstetric radiology in 1970, were taking place, computerized radiological scanning was being developed. A head scanner was installed in the in-patient X-ray department in 1976 but the Health Board's plan to purchase a whole body scanner in 1980 came to grief on financial grounds. Nevertheless, the community came to the rescue: at this time there was a public appeal to secure equipment for the laser treatment of cancer of the uterine cervix and donations had poured in to the Aberdeen Journals offices at such a rate that the target was exceeded within weeks (see p.128). The surplus money was diverted towards a scanner and the cost of the machine (£300,000) was achieved within six months. The scanner was in place in 1981 with the costs of a radiographer and secretarial

Table V Department of Radiology, Aberdeen Royal Infirmary. Workloads for 1990 in terms of patient attendances

Foresterhill		Woolmanhill
In-patients	56 654	
Out-patients	25 671	5 396
Neuroradiology	965	
Head scan	3 522	Accident and Emergency Department
Computed tomography body scan	2 043	
Ultrasound scan	10 232	46 840

Table VI Department of Radiology, Aberdeen Royal Infirmary. Staff complement: Foresterhill (In-patient/Out-patient Departments) 1990

Radiologists		Radiographers	
Consultants	12	Area adviser	1
Senior registrars	3	Superintendent	1
Registrars	10	Radiographers	35
		Darkroom technician	8
Secretarial staff	6		
		Nurses	
Office staff		Sister	1
General administrator	1	Staff nurse	5
HCO	1	SEN	1
Other	12	EN	10
Accountant (P/T)	1	N/Auxiliary	1
		ODO	2
Porters	15		
		X-ray Department, Woolmanhill	
A and E X-ray Department		Superintendent radiographer	1
Superintendent radiographer	1	Radiographer (P/T)	1
Radiographer (W/T & P/T)	10	Darkroom technician	1
Darkroom technician	3		

W/T, whole time.
P/T, part time.

staff met by the Health Board.[25] Many other technical advances have been introduced in the department over the years. Guided biopsy, operative intervention to dilate diseased arteries (angioplasty) and percutaneous drainage procedures are all part of the Foresterhill department in the late 1980s and advances in digital imaging, the transmission and storage of information and the computerization of records are on course for the 1990s. The department was considerably involved with the creation of the breast screening centre (for the early detection of breast cancer) now sited next to the Health Centre at Foresterhill and with a mobile unit to cover the remainder of Grampian, Orkney and Shetland. The unit began operation in 1990 and three consultant radiologists and four radiographers from the department are involved.

The singular interactive role of the ARI department of radiology and the university department of bio-medical physics and bio-engineering in the development of isotope and magnetic resonance imaging is recounted in Chapter 14.

The workload and the staffing of the department for 1990 are shown in Tables V and VI.

Education

It was recognized early that no department can survive and develop without a sustained educational programme. In 1948 an arrangement was made with the University of Edinburgh for a trainee at senior house officer level who had received a year of theoretical and practical training to be seconded to Aberdeen for 12 months.[26] A senior registrar post was created in the same year.[27] By 1958 the staff at the ARI comprised a senior hospital medical officer,[28] a senior registrar,[29] one registrar and one senior house officer.

Though this arrangement prospered it was clear that what was needed to redress the imbalance between the number of consultants and those in training was a full in-house postgraduate training programme which would also help to rectify the national shortfall of consultants in the discipline. Fortunately the late 1960s was a period of growth in the Health Service and by 1967 a two year course of training leading to a university diploma in medical radiodiagnosis was established.[30] The formal component was taught jointly with medical physics and the school of radiography (see below). In the first year there were three students and, though one withdrew, the other two completed the course and went on to become senior registrars.[31]

By 1990 a total of 30 who took the diploma had become consultants, 21 within the UK or the Republic of Ireland and the remainder overseas. Some were appointed to Aberdeen.[32]

This highly successful academic programme was recognized by the award to Lewis Gillanders in 1977 of a personal chair in radiology, by the creation of a senior lectureship in 1980[33] and the appointment of a technician with special responsibility for teaching material. This initial mini-academic unit has developed further and though, after the senior lecturer went to a consultant post in 1985, the funds were frozen, by 1988 an academic department of radiology was funded by the Roland Sutton Academic Trust in recognition of his family's generous donation. Throughout all this period, members of the staff were active nationally in a bewildering variety of roles, and in 1991 Dr Jamie Weir was invited by the university to follow Lewis Gillanders as a personal clinical professor.

Envoi

Lewis Gillanders who was the architect of modern radiology in Aberdeen writes:[34] '. . .Radiology is now blessed with extremely effective imaging systems developed as a result of the inventiveness and endeavour of many medical and para-medical professionals, scientists and engineers. Job satisfaction for radiologists has. . .increased by the more frequent patient contact required. . . For me it has been a fascinating experience and a privilege to have played a part in shaping a comprehensive, efficient and caring radiology service. All those with whom I have been associated have adhered to that aim and I believe Grampian can be proud of the quality of its regional service based on the Aberdeen Royal Infirmary'.

The School of Radiography

As the previous pages recount, the use of radiography was beginning to take hold in Aberdeen at the end of the l9th century and it is thought that the first diagnostic film was exposed at Woolmanhill in 1902. Until 1921 all the steps of such procedures were carried out by the medical staff – John Levack,[35] later joined by Frederick Philip.[36] In that year the first radiographer was appointed, William Cairns,[37] an ex-staff sergeant from the RAMC who had learnt his skills in World War I with gas tubes, induction coils and glass plates. Dr Blewett describes him: 'Surely he was one of the most constant and dedicated servants of the hospital. His voice still rings in my ears to this day as, with sergeant major overtones, he demanded holding a dripping wet film, "who done that?"'.

The first student radiographer[38] began training in 1930 and was followed by three others in 1931.[39] There were no specific entry qualifications and students sat the national examinations when they felt ready to do so. It was not until the advent of Blewett and the opening of the new department at Foresterhill in 1936 that the idea of a school for radiographers was born. What Blewett remembers as 'young ladies with a vocation' were to be supplanted by the new profession of radiography.

By this time the Society of Radiographers[40] had become that profession's representative body and, in association with the British Institute of Radiology, had produced a syllabus for the training of radiographers. Entry qualifications were also set by the society. The Royal Infirmary was approved as a training centre in 1937 with the consultant in charge of the department of radiology as director and the superintendent radiographer as tutor.[41] These arrangements persisted for 33 years[42] with the student intake eventually rising to 16 but were supplanted on the recommendation of the Society of Radiographers by an organization in which a teacher principal came to have the sole responsibility.[43]

In subsequent years and in parallel with the developments in radiodiagnosis, the school has continued to expand. Initially housed in the main Infirmary above the administrative quarters adjacent to the Rotunda, it moved in 1986 to more extensive premises next to the nursing college on the south fringe of the Foresterhill campus three years after the course had increased in duration from two to three years. Training for the higher diploma in radiography was introduced and Aberdeen had the singular record of having all five initial candidates pass at the first attempt against a national success rate of only l0 per cent. In 1990 training for the diploma in ultrasound was introduced and the school became a department within the Centre for Professions Allied to Medicine at the Robert Gordon Institute of Technology. It now comprises a director (Donald Graham), a senior lecturer (Christine Cockburn), one full- and one part-time lecturer, and similar numbers of clinical tutors. Degree courses are being developed and a BSc in radiography has been provisionally initiated for 1992.

13

Pathology, Bacteriology and Clinical Biochemistry

The development of laboratory services for medicine at the ARI must be seen against the background of two routes to association between laboratory scientists and clinicians in great teaching hospitals. Down one path, laboratories evolve from a need seen for their services by clinicians plus the development of knowledge in general, and of expertise by scientists and practitioners in particular. Down the other, while these needs may be similarly perceived, the presence or the creation of an academic department within the university, whose main role is to teach and advance the understanding of its subject, provides a centre which can also provide the day to day needs essential to the care of patients. The first has tended to be the model in England, the second in Scotland but there is no uniformity, and combinations of the two exist. Such blends will be found in the pages that follow.

In the history of applied medical science, pathology precedes bacteriology. The inspection of the dead with the naked eye dates from the earliest times. After the microscope's invention and, as surgery advanced, tissues from the living also became available and began to give a firm and systematic scientific foundation to the subject of 'morbid anatomy', especially from the work of the continental pathologists culminating in that of Virchov (1821–1902) and his many pupils, and also of clinicians such as Hunter and Paget. Regrettably, little written evidence survives about the early days of the Royal Infirmary but the Simpson Building (see Chapter 3) which dates from 1840 appears to have had a small post-mortem theatre with an adjacent 'dead house' (the predecessor of today's mortuary) at its north-east corner.

The lack of knowledge of the nature of transmissable disease – the science of bacteriology – is evident from the juxtaposition of the kitchen and meat house to this building. The plan shows this construction not to be symmetrical with the form of Alexander Simpson's design and it may have been an addition at the time the fever block was added. In that block, one storey up from the post-mortem theatre was the pathological museum with a laboratory little larger than a cupboard.

The earliest individual who is referred to as a pathologist was Robert Beveridge[1] who held the post from 1863–9. When he died in 1887 his will left funds to provide a legacy to be given to a teacher of pathology, to endow prizes in the subject, to defray the expenses of a museum in the Infirmary and, by a codicil which attested to his foresight, for money to encourage pathological research by the newly founded Erasmus Wilson chair of pathology.

The endowment for the chair was achieved by William Pirrie who was professor of surgery between 1839 and 1883.[2] It was first occupied by D.J. Hamilton[3] in 1882. He was to introduce not only the dynamic and enthusiastic teaching of pathology but also that of systematic and practical bacteriology which at the time was beginning to emerge as a sub-discipline of pathology. Before this event, however, James Rodger[4] succeeded Beveridge as pathologist to the Royal Infirmary. As the Erasmus Wilson Chair was being established, Rodger reported that the number of autopsies varied between 50 and 80 a year and that voluntary classes were attended by 10 to 26 students. The museum had 30–40 permanent specimens but he complained that those which were dried suffered greatly from mould in the winter and those that were wet could be damaged by drying out. To this teaching resource, in spite of its state, Hamilton was anxious to have access but Rodger was not willing to surrender his privileges and possession. Touchy and delicate negotiations are recorded in the minutes of the museum committee with, on the one hand, Rodger using the matter to obtain for himself a full physicianship and, on the other hand, though this is less obvious, Hamilton working towards the appointment of honorary pathologist to the ARI which he achieved in 1887.

Hamilton came to Aberdeen as both an accomplished histopathologist and a skilled bacteriologist. He proceeded to teach both and to set up practical classes in the latter – it is surmised that he was the first in the country to do so. Though it can be argued from a historical perspective that bacteriological studies in Aberdeen preceded Hamilton's appointment with the work in the 1870s of Ogston (see Chapter 7) on the pathogenesis of wound infection, this was applied research, albeit of profound importance, and did nothing to provide a diagnostic service. How quickly the expertise Hamilton developed in his student and postgraduate classes became available to the Royal Infirmary cannot be stated with certainty. However, he is known to have co-operated from the outset with Matthew Hay, for by 1894 the facilities of the pathology department were available to the medical officer of health (MOH) to examine 'throat brushings from suspected cases of diphtheria' obtained from patients of general practitioners in Aberdeen and a number of surrounding burghs.

By 1896 sputum could be examined for tubercle bacilli and the bacteriological diagnosis of typhoid and cholera be made. Though the prime bacteriological focus of Hamilton's department continued to centre on the work of the MOH, George M. Duncan[5] was appointed assistant to the professor in 1898 and began to carry out both routine pathological and bacteriological work at the Infirmary. He was formally made a university lecturer in 1905 while continuing to carry out work in the Infirmary. After war service he returned to the Infirmary staff as clinical pathologist and bacteriologist and remained a source of 'good, straightforward and common sense advice' until his death in 1935.

During the last years of the 19th century and in the first decade of the 20th it is clear that Hay, along with Hamilton, was thinking of setting up a municipal laboratory to co-ordinate bacteriological investigations and to meet the challenge of any emerging need such as the tracing of an epidemic and the routine examination of water. However, nothing formal was done. Hamilton retired in 1907 to be replaced by his former assistant George Dean[6] who was also prominent in the field of bacteriology. At this time the hospital board, though it accepted Dean as pathologist, was seeing the need for a 'paid official who might be assigned certain of the duties performed by the pathologist'.[7] The point was raised again by Dean in 1914[8] but he died in the same year and when his successor Theodore Shennan,[9] a bacteriologist from Edinburgh, took over, the board confirmed the appointment but again with the understanding that it might eventually have its own man in post. By this time there was a shift away from the view that a pathologist can also be a bacteriologist while at the same time there was a growing clinical need for bacteriological expertise. Shennan was primarily a histopathologist with an interest in bacteriology. Here then was the start of the separation of the two disciplines. The war intervened but by 1919 it was decided to make alterations at the Infirmary to enable a laboratory to be built.

The commitment of the university to a joint development was recognized by a contribution of £500 from its funds on the understanding that facilities would be available within the laboratory for research and the instruction of students in clinical pathology. The laboratory provided quarters for Dr Duncan. At the same time Matthew Hay's ideas came to partial fruition – though they also created fission – when the municipal authorities set up a separate bacteriological laboratory at the City Hospital. This, under its director John Smith,[10] opened its doors in 1920 to receive specimens from the municipal hospitals, from general practitioners in Aberdeen and the north-east and to serve the Public Health Authority. It is, at the time of writing, still functioning but will soon amalgamate with the university laboratory at Foresterhill so ultimately bringing to a successful conclusion the vision of Hay and Hamilton.

Pathology and bacteriology were about to go their separate ways both academically and in the Royal Infirmary. In 1926 John Cruickshank,[11] primarily trained as a pathologist but who had been reader in bacteriology since 1923, became the first professor of that subject in Aberdeen. The microbial work from the ARI continued to be handled in his new department's cramped space at Marischal by G.M. Duncan, but on his death the hospital and university court jointly considered the future of bacteriological services and it was agreed that the temporary arrangements would continue until the developments were complete at Foresterhill. Thereafter the laboratory services in both fields would be provided on a permanent basis from quarters in the medical school. The groundwork for this had been set in 1929 when it was agreed that professors in such subjects as pathology and bacteriology would be *ex officio* members of the honorary medical staff of the hospital. As for pathology, Shennan had served the Royal Infirmary with distinction until his retirement in 1936 and his successor J.S. Young[12] supervised the transfer of what had now become a separate department from Woolmanhill/Marischal to a purpose-designed area for both clinical service and research at Foresterhill. It is recorded that the whole of the department's impedimenta filled but a single packing case.

The subsequent years have seen the firm consolidation of the link between the service laboratories, embedded in the school, with the clinicians in the Infirmary and other hospitals on the Foresterhill site. The proximity of the laboratories has led to productive interaction which was pioneered by Cruickshank in bacteriology and Young in pathology and continued by their successors Alexander Macdonald (bacteriology, 1954–78), A.R. Currie (pathology, 1962–72) and A.L. Stalker (pathology, 1972–82[13]). Perhaps one of the most generally influential fields in which this co-operation took place was the work of the department of bacteriology in the design of Phase I when Ogston's interests once more came to the fore. This exciting period is recounted in Chapter 5.

The foregoing has concentrated on pathology and bacteriology. However, the 1920s saw the rapid emergence of the speciality variously known as clinical chemistry, clinical biochemistry and chemical pathology. Much of this was initially centred on the management of diabetes but gradually the field widened until there was scarcely a disease or a management problem in which chemical estimations of body fluids or excreta was not involved. Alexander Lyall[14] was already active in the field of diabetes and in 1925 the university took the initiative and established a department of clinical chemistry with him as part-time lecturer. His staff was a single apprentice technician and his budget £500 a year. At the same time as this appointment he achieved beds in the Infirmary specializing in diabetes and endocrinology (for an account of his contributions in the clinical field, see p.152). For 35 years he successfully straddled the complementary interests of laboratory and clinical medicine. After a ward round he would return to his department – initially at Woolmanhill and after the move to Foresterhill in the university building there, where he spent the rest of the morning doing basal metabolic rates (at that time a favoured method of detecting thyrotoxicosis) while at the same time, manipulating stopcocks and manometers, he would see visitors, dictate letters and deal with departmental problems. Many members of his staff moved on to important appointments elsewhere.[15]

At the time of Lyall's retirement, the growing importance of the field of clinical chemistry lead John Young and May Baird to press for a chair of chemical pathology. Universities were still in a phase of expansion and in 1962 Sam Frazer was appointed to the chair having trained with one of the doyens of chemical pathology in Scotland, C.P. Stewart in Edinburgh.[16] Frazer contributed much to the intellectual and professional life of the Infirmary[17] but on his retirement in 1983 it was not possible, because of academic financial restrictions, to maintain the chair, and Dr Iain Ross, a senior lecturer, was given charge. Later in 1987 the university department and the NHS department at the City Hospital, which had given a similar service to that provided by the bacteriological laboratory there, were amalgamated to form a new department of clinical biochemistry at Foresterhill (currently sited in the link building). This grouping now provides a comprehensive service for the whole of the north-east of Scotland and has created one of the largest laboratories in the United Kingdom with unprecedented resources in its field. Once again the foresight of those who planned concentration on the Foresterhill site has achieved fulfilment for the goal of a regional centre serving all those in the north-east and the north of Scotland.

14

Physics Related to Medicine

Medical physics began to be established in the l9th century, much influenced by a Scottish physician, Neil Arnott.[1] He was educated at Aberdeen Grammar School and Marischal College where he graduated MA and MD and then migrated to London where he had a busy practice and, in his spare time, gave courses of lectures in natural philosophy and on medical physics. These were popular and formed the basis of his textbook, *Elements of Physics*, published in 1827. He drew freely on anatomy, physiology and medical practice to illuminate the ideas and methods of physics.

Arnott's ideas of physics as applied to medicine can be said to have returned to Aberdeen and the Royal Infirmary with the appointment in 1923 of G.P. Thomson as professor of natural philosophy at Marischal College.[2] He brought with him Harry Griffith, one of his research students; to him went the task of teaching the first MB physics course, a responsibility he continued until he died in 1964.[3] Such an association led naturally to his being consulted by clinicians on specific problems and his flair for building his own equipment to tackle new problems, laid the foundations of a firm collaboration between the university department and the hospital. As recounted in Chapter 12, the provision of support for the developing disciplines of radiology and radiotherapy was to the fore. He became honorary physicist to the X-ray department in 1935 and was latterly assisted by G.E. Swindell.[4]

The inception of the National Health Service led to the formation of regional radiotherapy centres (see Chapter 10). In Aberdeen Duncan Lindsay, who had developed an important technique for optimal radiotherapy,[5] replaced Swindell. He and Griffith had to spend much of their time teaching medical students and 4th year honours physics and were only able to allocate what was left over to Foresterhill. Here their work was recognized by an arrangement for joint salaries, between the NHS and the university, and by two part-timers – a technician and a secretary. The routine essentials of physics in relation to radiotherapy were dealt with but they did not take part in individual treatment planning or radiation protection.

At the same time as the scope and efficacy of radiotherapy was being extended, advances in the biological and medical use of radioactive isotopes, which had been foreseen before the war but became possible because of the development of the nuclear reactor, were creating a burst of scientific development, mainly centred on the use of isotopes as tracers, though their 'targeted' use for treatment in areas in the body where they were concentrated was soon to follow.[6]

The first applied advance was in thyroid disorders when, in the late 1940s, iodine-131 became available from the reactor at Harwell. A laboratory to support this work was set up in the new extension for radiotherapy in 1956 after the arrival of Tom Buchanan as senior lecturer in medical physics in 1954. The clinical use of iodine in both diagnosis and therapy was expanded with the appointment in 1962 of Professor Alastair Macgregor[7] to succeed Sir David Campbell. This work was the start of a nuclear medicine service which in 1991 provides 19 different radionuclide tests from the same but expanded premises.

The growing importance of medical physics was recognized by the creation of a new department in 1963 behind the medical school which superseded the four rooms in the Infirmary and a single laboratory in the medical school building. This became the medical physics headquarters and brought together not only all the medical physicists,[8] who were now much in demand for radioisotope work and to sustain the legal requirements which related to radiation protection, but also the mechanical workshop which had been set up at Woolmanhill.[9] An electronic equipment development laboratory became possible to replace the *ad hoc* arrangements in the mechanical workshop.[10]

The mid-1960s was the time of the Robbins-inspired expansion of the universities and, following the death of Harry Griffith in 1964, medical physics became a full university department to be headed by an established professor. Folklore has it that an arrangement was reached over a glass of sherry in the board room of the health authority between the university Principal[11] and the chairman of the board[12] that the staff would be university employees but that all costs would be shared on an equal basis. Similar arrangements were reached for other university departments which provided laboratory services to the board, but for medical physics this decision made possible the creation of a team of physicists, engineers, mechanical assistants and students, which gave a surge to research and development in Aberdeen over the next quarter of a century.

Isotopes were now beginning to be used not only for the purposes indicated above but also for imaging by equipment that could pick up their emissions. The first isotope scanner in Europe had been built by John Mallard at the Hammersmith Hospital in 1957–8 and he brought it with him to Aberdeen on his appointment to the chair and began a scanning service with iodine-131 for the thyroid and brain, and gold-198 colloid for the liver. Dr Sandy MacDonald of the department of radiology at Foresterhill took on this field from the clinical aspect which, in combination with the diagnostic work that had begun in the radiotherapy department, laid the foundation of present day nuclear medicine in Aberdeen.

Also in Professor Mallard's luggage was the first gamma camera in Europe.[13] It was soon replaced by one of the early commercial versions built by the Edinburgh Company, Nuclear Enterprises Ltd.[14] With the help of Dr Peter

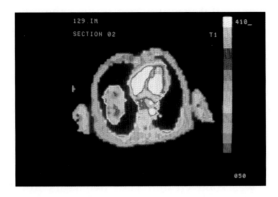

Plate 50 The first human pathological NMR image. On 29 August 1980 at Aberdeen
   Royal Infirmary this first NMR image was made at the level of T9 in a patient
   with a primary oesophageal tumour. It can be seen lying between the aorta and
   the heart; the liver (yellow) contains two metastases (red). Blood within the
   ventricles of the heart appears white and is demonstrated without the use of
   augmenting contrast medium as would have been the case if X-ray computed
   tomography were used.

Undrill, who had joined the department as a computer expert, it was connected
to a small computer (DEC PDP8/I) to begin modern digital imaging.[15]

Computer developments also made it possible to develop and use in Aberdeen
the technique of radioisotope tomography now known as single photon emission
computed tomography (SPECT). The first such scanner outside the USA (ASS –
Aberdeen Section Scanner[16]) gave improved contrast between tumour tissue and
the normal, and it and the gamma camera version which was built during the
1970s were the method of choice in Aberdeen for the diagnosis of brain tumours
until they were replaced with computerized X-ray tomography (CT scanning) in
1975.

Two other advances in imaging have dominated the interaction between
medical physicists and the clinicans of the ARI. First the introduction of
ultrasound, initially into the Maternity Hospital and subsequently into the
department of radiodiagnosis, was the outcome of a grant to medical physics and
Professor I. MacGillivray (obstetrics and gynaecology) for the purchase of a
scanner.

Second was the development of magnetic resonance imaging (MRI) based on
the phenomenon known as nuclear magnetic resonance[17] by the Aberdeen
department. From the confirmation that this could detect differences between
disease and normal tissues through obtaining the crude image of a mouse,[18] it
led to the climax of the world's first image of a patient (who had cancer of the
oesophagus and deposits in bone and liver) on 26 August 1980 produced by the
whole body imager, which had been painstakingly built in the department (Plate
50).

Workers in Nottingham University had at the same time built a brain scanner
but the Aberdeen instrument was larger and capable of imaging all regions of the

body. From September 1980 it was used for routine clinical diagnostic work and so established Aberdeen Royal Infirmary as the first hospital in the world to offer MRI as a regular service. Collaboration with clinicians[19] led on to several other 'firsts' in imaging and a second version of the scanner constructed with funding from Japan was installed in the ARI in March 1983 to be replaced in 1991 by a Siemens instrument.

The development of MRI was seized upon by the world of radiology and commerce with both hands, and vast sums were poured into its development. It was hailed as 'the biggest breakthrough since diagnostic X-rays' and found to be the choice for many diagnostic investigations because of the large contrast on the images between different soft tissues. An international industry worth a billion pounds per annum was soon created and, five years from the first image in Aberdeen, many hundreds of imagers were in use in the United States, Japan and Germany. In the whole UK there were only 10 and the one in Aberdeen was, to quote John Mallard its pioneer, as 'out of date as an abacus'. The only consolation was that the patents on NMR gave a financial life-line to the department during the years of national cut-backs in the late 1980s.

The interaction of the physics department with the Infirmary has continued over the years with extensions on the Foresterhill site – first a single storey in 1969 and then a three storey one in the late 1970s. The formation of a cyclotron unit in old buildings behind Woodend laid the groundwork for extensions of both biological research and further development of clinical PET imaging. There have been many developments in education in the field and new clinical applications of physics will doubtless lead to a continuing close relationship between the Royal Infirmary and the department of physics which is now appropriately styled 'bio-medical physics, and bio-engineering'.

15

Blood Transfusion

On the 3 April 1919 Henry Gray back from World War I described the enormous benefits of blood transfusion that he had witnessed while working as a battle surgeon in France.[1] In some casualty clearing stations during the last year of the war as many as 30–40 transfusions might be given in a day and a soldier 'lying blanched like a corpse and with sunken features almost unrecognizable by his friends would, within a few minutes from the beginning of the transfusion, have his ashy complexion replaced by a fine pink flush, his face and eyes fill out and his breathing and movements become strong'.

Gray's experience spoke for itself but for the next nine years only occasional transfusions from relatives or friends were done in the city, and it was not until 1928 that the Honorary Staff of the Infirmary considered the establishment of a Blood Transfusion Service. Terms and conditions were established the following year and received publicity in the local press.[2] Volunteers between the ages of 20 and 40 were sought and would be given a general medical examination by a member of the Infirmary staff and have a blood sample tested. A donor would not be called more often than once in three months and it was laid down that 'the operation of transfusion shall be carried out by a member of the honorary surgical staff and not by a clinical assistant or resident.'[3] Six years later there were 34 citizens on the donor panel and 32 transfusions had been given during that year.[4] One unidentified donor had given blood nine times.

The Scottish National Blood Transfusion Service

After the Munich crisis when war seemed imminent, the Department of Health set up a Blood Transfusion Committee for Scotland under the chairmanship of Sir John Fraser, professor of surgery in Edinburgh, which advised that a national service[5] should be established dependent on volunteer donors organized regionally with blood banks in the principal centres of population of which Aberdeen was one. Representatives of the directors and staff of the the Infirmary attended a meeting convened by the Lord Provost and agreed to cooperate with the public health authorities and the university to formulate a scheme for Aberdeen and the North-East. John Cruickshank[6] undertook to provide a blood bank in the Department of Bacteriology and the regional service was formed under his directorship. More than 1,300 donors were enrolled and on the day war was declared (3 September 1939) the collection team was engaged in its first session at the Infirmary.

From the outset the service was based on Foresterhill where the university provided accommodation for the organizing secretary and her staff, and for the laboratory services. Banks were also established in Elgin, Orkney and Shetland. After the NHS was established, the administration of the service remained with the Scottish National Blood Transfusion Assoiciation, now wholly funded by the Department of Health, but since 1974 the service in Scotland has been part of the Common Services Agency of the Scottish Health Service.

New regional centre

Though the university continued until some time after the war to house the service in the medical school it needed more space and, as is recounted on p.56, a new department was opened in 1956 in the east wing development of the Infirmary. A full-time director was appointed (John Campbell[7]). The accommodation had been planned for one medical officer but such was the expansion of the service that within a year there were three. Expansion has continued so that now three of the four floors of the wing are occupied by the service and a new purpose-built department elsewhere on the Foresterhill site is being constructed.

Expansion of work

The functions of the service have widened to provide immunohaematological services. First, the Rh testing of all pregnant women to detect those likely to have infants affected with haemolytic disease of the newborn. Second, when the prevention of this disease became possible the necessary prophylaxis was introduced. Third, investigation of patients suspected of suffering from auto-immune haemolytic anaemias. Fourth, the assessment of immunodeficiency. In 1972 a tissue typing service was set up with organ transplantation and disease diagnosis. In 1989 a regional bone bank was established – one of the first in the country. Testing for diseases transmissible by blood and some of its products also became extensive. Syphilis had long been looked for in donations and samples from ante-natal patients, but now all donations are also tested for the viruses of hepatitis B and C and for the human immunodeficiency viruses 1 and 2 (HIV). Nearly 35,000 donations of whole blood are collected and processed each year but, because the demand for Factor VIII is greater than these can provide, fresh plasma equivalent to a further 6,000 donations is obtained by plasmapheresis.

Thus a service which began with the object of replacing lost blood has evolved into a department of transfusion medicine.

16

Pharmacy

By the time the Aberdeen Infirmary came into being in 1742, pharmacy had already a long history. It would seem that the use of medicaments to cure or alleviate disease has, as far back as knowledge goes, always had a substantial role. Formal study of the effects of plants, fruits and roots, based mostly on trial and error, dates at least from Roman times and the first pharmacopoeia, with 250 entries, was the work of Scribonius Largus in AD 40. He was personal physician to Claudius (Emperor of Rome AD 41–54) who put in train the definitive Roman conquest of Britain. Though, as with medicine as a whole, pharmacy stagnated with the Galenism of the so-called Dark Ages, it flourished in the subsequent Renaissance so that the pharmacopoeia of Scribonius was printed largely unaltered in 1528. Local records show that at least 16 apothecaries or druggists were in business when the Infirmary opened in 1742.

It was initially a physician to the Infirmary who was responsible for the supply of drugs (see p.28). He had new pharmacopoeias to help him: that of London had been published in 1618; the Edinburgh in 1694; and the Irish in 1793. However, a druggist was appointed in 1796. Other physicians to the Infirmary also combined the role of doctor and dispenser; it is known, for example, that George French (1765–1833, see p.29) had an apothecary's shop in the Upperkirkgate 'provided with an assortment of the most reputed patent medicines and several perfumery articles'. There seems also to have been a shop within the Infirmary from the late 18th century at least until 1838. What one citizen thought of the proprietor and his shop was mentioned in an open letter of 1834 concerned primarily with the state of the Infirmary (see also p.24): '. . .one of the fraternity that put up serpents in large bottles, and glasses filled with red and blue liquids in their windows in order to allure customers to the shop and profess to give good advice gratis, to their patients on condition that they will swallow indifferent medicine at a trifle above prime cost'.[1]

At that time new regulations were introduced. The appointed apothecary was bound by the same residential rules as the house surgeon, namely to reside in the hospital and not to be absent at any time except with leave from the committee of management or the medical officer. He became formally responsible for the storage and preparation of medicines in which task he was assisted by four students. In addition he had charge of 'wines, spirits and porter

Plate 51 Dispensing in the 1950s. The screw closured bottles are presumably medicaments.

belonging to the house'. The uncertain professional standing of the apothecary is indicated by the fact that his role could be combined with that of house surgeon. It was not until the Infirmary extended in 1840 that a dispensary was included in the structure. In the meantime the physicians of the Royal Infirmary had published their own pharmacopoeia in 1826, the Pharmaceutical Society had been founded in 1841 and in 1843 gained its Royal Charter; the tide of Victorian science and medicine was beginning to flow. The ARI produced a new pharmacopoeia in 1868 which was in line with the British version. Nevertheless the dispensary remained in but a single room even in the Foresterhill development of 1937.

Relocation there followed and by the end of World War II the pharmacy occupied two rooms of modest dimensions, one off the main corridor of the hospital, the other off the basement or service corridor. There were but two staff (Plate 51) Jack Fraser and an assistant.[2] Relocation took place to the new east wing in 1957. During the 1950s the functions of the pharmacy began to take in such matters as sterile production, the preparation of intravenous solutions and the supply of radioisotopes for clinical use. It became clear that a purpose-designed area should be included in the Phase II development. The long gestation period of this enterprise (see p.73) rendered obsolete even the forward looking plans (which in the tradition of the 1838 regulations were rumoured to include a still for the production of a single malt whisky) that had been produced and much change was required before the new pharmacy department opened in 1977. At that time, however, it fully satisfied all the criteria for a teaching hospital pharmacy and in consequence Aberdeen was invited to join the Association of Teaching Hospital Pharmacists.

At the time of writing, the advantages of scale have led to the department becoming responsible for drug and medication services for all hospitals in the NE Region including Orkney and Shetland as well as to HM Prisons at Craiginches and Peterhead.

17

Medical Records – Past and Present

As remarks in the opening chapters of this account attest, it was the habit of 18th and 19th century physicians to record information about patients in case-books and admission and discharge registers. The first case-book available is for 1743 where the history of the patient on admission is recorded on one page and subsequent events are kept in the form of a daily journal, which listed the condition and progress of all on that day. Of greatest interest is that the register contained information using a widespread convention of the time – 'cured', 'recovered so as to follow their usual business', 'incurable', 'dead' or 'dismissed after trial'. The number of patients in each category was calculated at the end of the year and such measures of outcome therefore exist for the Aberdeen Royal Infirmary for 250 years. Similar records were retained and are available (with but a few gaps) until 1954. The case-books unfortunately stop in 1807 and all 19th century case-notes were destroyed as part of the paper salvage campaign in World War II. Thus it is not certain when the use of separate case-notes for each patient began but in 1886 the medical staff were considering the format of case-sheets as opposed to case-books and photographs around the same time show individual charts at the end of each bed.

During the first half of the 20th century notes were maintained at ward level, filed in chronological order of admission usually bound by year in the surgical wards and stored in boxes in the medical wards. At the start of the National Health Service in 1948 it had been realized that there was an advantage in having all the records referring to a patient in one folder. In April 1949 the Board of Management for the Aberdeen General Hospitals had intended moving slowly towards the creation of a complete central records and registration system involving additional clerical staff. As is so common in other parts of this history, initial steps in that scheme had to be deferred. The Board recorded its regret but it appeared to them that there was no alternative in 'view of the large cuts in expenditure for the year 1949–50'.

The financial situation must have improved by 1954 because at this time the first Group Medical Records Officer was appointed.[1] Additional staff was still a problem and in 1955 the Board reported that '. . .any developments within hospital groups would require to be made as the result of savings in other directions and that necessary monies to finance the salaries of two clerks could be found without asking for an additional allowance from the Regional Hospital Board'. This seems to have been done and was also accompanied by improvement in the design of recording systems and record sheets. James Crooks[2] and Roy Weir[3] were particularly active in creating new forms during the next decade including the Drug Prescription Sheet and Drug Recording Sheet which are now used widely throughout this country. Thus, when the Scottish Home and Health Department reported on 'Standardization of Hospital Medical Records' in 1973 most of the recommended forms were those currently in use in the Aberdeen hospitals.[4]

By 1972 the storage problem associated with increasingly bulky case folders was giving rise to concern. Not only was more written at each admission but also the changing nature of medical care with an increased prevalence of chronic illness, repeated admissions and long-term surveillance swelled the case folder. The present record (1975)[5] was designed to meet these problems.

The extent and value of microfilming had been debated extensively over many years. As early as 1959 the medical records sub-committee noted that 'storage space was left (i.e. remained) for approximately three years. . . . The question of microfilming should be discussed with the Medical Staff Committee'. By 1961 the matter had become urgent and the records sub-committee recommended that 'medical records be kept in their original form for a period of six years and that thereafter they may be microfilmed and destroyed'. The Regional Board in 1962 approved the appointment of an additional clerk for this work. However, little was done and in 1964 the Board 'now felt that some measure of selection was required in selecting the records to be microfilmed'. So they referred the policy to the recently created medical records liaison committee and purchased two additional rows of steel shelving for storage space. The debate has gone on since with a lull when extra storage space became available with the opening of Phase II. It is only in the past three years that a significant quantity of microfilming and editing of old notes has taken place.

Another long-standing debate has centred around the location of waiting lists, traditionally held and maintained at ward level. In 1961 the medical records officer thought that a centralized list should be established but no further action is recorded. It is only now, when computers make a centralized list readily available at unit level, that it seems a solution to this debate may be at hand.

There are now 76 records staff employed for the Royal Infirmary and its associated out-patient clinics. The use of computers has in some ways revolutionized the Records Office, especially with the introduction of the patient administration system (PAS) in 1989. It is now easier to identify patients correctly and locate their records (using the bar-code system – another Aberdeen initiative[6]). However, computers have yet to have an effect on reducing the quantity of paper held in case note folders. Clinical computer systems such as the patient record system (PRS) and microcomputers, useful as they are in facilitating patient care, have still some way to go before they can replace the traditional case-notes. Aberdeen received a substantial grant from the central audit funds to develop techniques of audit, particularly in relation to the Department of Anaesthesia, and at the time of writing considerable advances have been made.

18

Human Services

FROM ALMONERS TO SOCIAL WORKERS

Hospital almoners were trained to provide a social service to hospitals, the first being appointed in 1895 to the Royal Free Hospital in London. The Hospital Almoners' Council was formed in 1906, responsible for the selection and training of almoners, and in 1922 this became the Institute of Hospital Almoners. The service gradually developed over the years following World War I and was extended to many hospitals in the country.

In Aberdeen the Board decided to create an Almoners Department in 1937 and the first appointment was made in 1938[1] with her responsibilities defined as '. . . co-operating with the medical staff by obtaining all information with regard to patients' home life etc. likely to be of help in their treatment; endeavouring to remove any personal or home difficulties which may be associated with their illness and may tend to retard recovery and by co-operating in after care arrangements so as to ensure that patients obtain the fullest benefit from their stay in hospital. It will also be the responsibility of the almoners to ensure that patients are not allowed to take advantage of the charitable services of the Infirmary if they can afford to pay for their treatment privately, and to see that patients who have received treatment make a contribution towards the cost of such amount as in the opinion of the almoner, their circumstances justify'. These words give a flavour of how the voluntary system approached the deserving and not so deserving poor.

The social services still endeavour to 'remove any personal or home difficulties' – that much has not changed in its remit over the years. Fortunately the problem of collecting money ended with the advent of the National Health Service in 1948.

The era of the hospital almoner came to an end in the late 1950s replaced by the medical social worker directly responsible to the Infirmary and employed by the health boards. These medical social workers provided the social work service until in May 1975 new national legislation brought about a major change. 'Regionalization' led to the hospital medical social workers being transferred to the local authority social work departments. At this time a working party was set up to consider the practical arrangements for the provision of social work services by the local authority to the health service. Its report in 1976 recommended that wherever appropriate, hospital based services should be developed – a conclusion based on the fact that the majority of the patients in hospitals who needed social work help were not already known to social workers based in the community. The importance of multidisciplinary team work was also stressed in the belief that a flexible collaborative approach to patient care should be developed in which the contribution of each discipline is understood and acknowledged by those who come into contact with the patient.

So, from 1975, the social work service to the Royal Infirmary was provided, as elsewhere, by the Regional Council, the Health Board's contribution being the provision of secretarial staff and office accommodation, an arrangement which continues to the present day. Social workers in the hospital lost their 'medical' prefix.

In the days of the hospital almoner it was an all female profession. This has changed over the years, although hospital-based social work still attracts more female than male staff. It is a small group of professional people who operate within a large complex organization and its responsibilities have grown with social change so that in 1990 over 1,200 patients were referred to it. This is double the numbers compared to a decade ago.

CHAPLAINCY

There is a long Christian tradition of caring for the sick. Indeed, both in the UK and in many other countries, the original hospitals were Christian foundations. This is reflected in the name of many of the oldest ones such as St Thomas' and St Bartholomew's. So, when in 1739, the Royal Infirmary was conceived, there is no doubt that part of the impulse was the belief that 'taking care of and providing for the sick, the diseased, and the infirm poor is the Christian and necessary duty'.[2] From the start and indeed right up to 1948, when the hospitals were taken over by the State, the churches contributed largely to the maintenance of the Infirmary. As mentioned earlier in this history, for over 150 years the annual church collections remained one of the most important sources of revenue for the Infirmary.

The early years of spiritual ministration to the sick – or the lack of it – have been recounted in Chapter 3. When the Rev. J. Massie was appointed as chaplain in 1853 his salary is recorded as £150 per annum for full-time service. In 1865 we read of him expressing concern about the poor attendance at the regular Sunday services. These were held at 3.30 p.m. and he discussed with the medical superintendent and the matron whether a more convenient time could be found. In fact it could not. The superintendent explained: 'A few patients are on foot before 11, but the patients are not generally so. From 11 to noon is the busiest hour of the day, patients and servants being then engaged preparing for the visit of the medical officers, in whose occupation the House may be said to be from 12 till 2 o'clock'. The matron concurred. In the following year a Bible Woman was appointed to visit the hospital for the purpose of reading to the patients. She was expected to attend the services as often as possible, bringing with her such patients as were willing to come.

After World War I, in the planning that took place for the move to Foresterhill, no provision was made for a chapel in the new Royal Infirmary. The only accommodation available for religious purposes was a chaplain's office and an interview room near the main 'rotunda' entrance. With the coming of the National Health Service in 1948 it was laid down that chaplains were to be appointed wherever there were 750 patients of one denomination. The appointment was to be made by the appropriate church authority in consultation with the Board of Management and remuneration paid to the church authority by the Board. A church of Scotland chaplain was appointed under these terms but applications by Episcopalian, Roman Catholic and Baptist bodies were rejected. The Rev. James Youngson who had been appointed in 1945 continued in post for a number of years in spite of poor health from a chest condition.

The 1960s saw a revival of the Sunday services. On the initiative of some members of the medical staff, a regular service, which proved popular, was started in a lecture theatre. Patients unable to walk were pushed there in wheel-chairs by medical students and staff. On one Sunday a month the service was conducted by the chaplain; on the others by members of the medical staff. On an occasion, which was to have far-reaching consequences, the Moderator of the Aberdeen presbytery was passing the door of the lecture theatre just before the service began. He looked in and saw the auditorium packed with almost 100 people and enquired what was going on. When he realized the situation he decided to support a proposal for the inclusion of a commodious chapel in the plans of Phase II which were being drawn at the time. As a result the Infirmary was provided with its first purpose-built chapel dedicated in June 1977. Weekly services are carried out there to this day, conducted jointly by the chaplain and members of the medical staff with a medical student usually playing the organ. Groups from city churches convey patients to and from the chapel.

The appointment of the Rev. Alan Swinton in 1971 signalled a considerable expansion in the work of the chaplaincy, with short services being broadcast to the wards at the start of each week-day. He was also appointed as a recognized teacher in bio-ethics. After the Piper Alpha oil platform explosion in 1988,[3] the support of the chaplain's department was invaluable. All the relatives of those involved were referred to him. He ministered, jointly with a team of psychiatrists and social workers, to those admitted for treatment – mainly with severe burns – and to members of staff. Following this, a second chaplain was appointed.

DIETETICS

Food was an essential part of medical management in the 18th century and we have already seen on p.30 some details of the hospital diet of the time. The year

1800 was a bad one for farmers in the North-East. Wheat and barley crops failed which meant that the housekeeper in the Royal Infirmary had to find other sources of supply. This led to a review of 'state of the diets' and three levels of meals were devised consisting of oatmeal, porridge, sowens[4], milk, various vegetable broths, biscuits, oatcakes and wheaten bread. Beef, cooked in the broth was served only to soldiers. The hospital brewed its own ale which was the preferred liquid because water supplies were often contaminated. Wine was used as a sedative before and after surgery until it became too expensive during the Napoleonic Wars (approximately 1803–14) and porter[5] replaced it. By 1804 each patient had a diet ticket attached to his bed indicating low, middle or full diet and the fluids to be given as prescribed by the physician.

On her return from the Crimea in 1860 Florence Nightingale published *Notes on Nursing*.[6] Two chapters were devoted to the provision of food and she stated that 'the science and art of feeding is an essential part of nursing'. This view was – with good reason – to persist until the early 1950s of this century. By 1875 nurses in the Royal Infirmary had joined the physicians in producing a 'revised dietary table' and in the following year beef and egg diets were included.

The first three decades of the 20th century saw an increase in the interaction between nutrition and disease; vitamins were discovered and diabetes came under control with the introduction of insulin. The need for specialist training in applied nutrition became apparent. A signal Scottish event was when Sister Ruth Pybus in the Diabetic Clinic of the Royal Infirmary of Edinburgh was awarded a Rockefeller Travelling Fellowship to study in North America and on her return in 1924 set up the first dietetic department in the United Kingdom. In Aberdeen the first dietitian was appointed in 1932[7] and came from the Royal Infirmary of Edinburgh, where she had trained and later became assistant dietitian. Her duties included attendance at diabetic clinics, lecturing to nurses and being available to all wards between noon and 1 p.m. A passage adjacent to Medical Out-patients at Woolmanhill was converted into her office and a cooker bought so that she could give twice weekly demonstrations to patients and their relations. Her versatility was such that each morning she also worked as an assistant biochemist. In her first full year (1933) she saw 282 new patients of whom 85 had diabetes, 123 were overweight and the others suffered from a variety of disorders. Meanwhile the Infirmary at Foresterhill was nearing completion and there ward 4 was planned for 'metabolic and other diseases requiring special dietary provision'. Just before it opened in 1936, Maisie Thomson[8] was appointed sister dietitian on a salary of £150 a year and remained in that ward (now 28) until her retirement in 1959. Sandy Lyall's role in this ward is recounted on p.152 and the two were a formidable team. Sister Thomson gave demonstrations to patients and their 'carers', lectured to nurses and produced educational displays for patients and staff. She also supplied special dietary foods to all wards requesting them. She was reputed to produce excellent ginger beer and there are memories of exploding bottles in the diet kitchen. To distinguish her from other nurses she chose to wear a white coat and flowing triangular head gear in contrast to the prevailing uniform of the time which included a small cap.

In 1948, while rationing remained in force,[9] a committee was set up to review catering and dietetic arrangements in the hospital. A dietitian was appointed to coordinate food production and to instruct nursing and domestic staff on dietetics and food service. This initiative was short lived following national recommendations that a new position of catering officer be created to relieve hospital matrons of their responsibility in the supply of food. When Sister Thomson retired there was a vacuum which was partly filled by research dietitians from the Department of Obstetrics and Gynaecology and staff from the local authority. A senior dietitian was appointed in 1962.[10]

To meet this somewhat unsatisfactory situation, Alastair Macgregor[11] and John Stowers,[12] frustrated by the lack of dietary care, encouraged Robert Gordon's Institute of Technology (RGIT) to set up a training course which began in 1965. The same year Pat Robertson, newly qualified in Glasgow became the only dietitian in the Royal Infirmary and finance was made available to re-equip and staff the metabolic kitchen and appoint the first diet cook. Two part-time dietitians began work in 1966 and a chief dietitian's post was instituted a year later.[13]

With staffing now established and the supply of future dietitians guaranteed, the discipline began to flourish. Metabolic studies in diabetes, obesity and mineral turnover were carried out – still based on ward 4 – until in 1979 the enlarged department moved to Phase II. Dietary treatment of other diseases such as renal failure led to the creation of specialist dietetic posts to work with such patients so that at the time of writing there are individuals who specialize not only in renal dietetics but also in acute care, diabetes and gastroenterology. In the out-patient clinics, dietitians are on hand for the management of patients with renal disease, diabetes, cancer care, disorders of lipid metabolism and obesity.

Staff from the department have lectured throughout the UK and overseas on nutrition in the care of the seriously ill and on tube feeding. Others have won Churchill and World Health Organisation fellowships and served on national professional committees and multi-disciplinary working groups of the Scottish Home and Health Department. The importance of the profession led it to becoming one for graduates only in 1980; the first were produced in the honours course at RGIT in 1989. In 1971 the Infirmary began to take student dietitians for seven months of practical experience before their state registration and around 130 have trained in the department. There are now nine dietitians, two working part-time, to staff not only the Royal Infirmary but also Woolmanhill, Tor-na-Dee and Roxburghe House. Their importance is indicated by the fact that around 10 per cent of all in-patients are prescribed special diets as part of their treatment.

OCCUPATIONAL THERAPY

Occupational therapy does not have a long association with the Infirmary. Although Aberdeen can lay claim to having engaged the first professional occupational therapist in the country, this was in mental health. In its early days, occupational therapy concentrated on the traditional craft-based activities and provided an opportunity for those patients whose stay was prolonged to maintain mental concentration, stave off depression and, where relevant, to improve their range of movement. The cramped, overcrowded wards restricted the last of these activities.

In the late 1950s the Infirmary's share of the extremely limited number of occupational therapists employed in Aberdeen was one, available every morning, Monday to Friday, the remainder of this person's duties being at Woodend. The base for the therapist was a small room, originally a store, off the medical lecture theatre at the west end of the original hospital. From there everything had to carried to the wards. This was before ready-use kits became available and many hundreds of soft toys and wicker baskets must have found their way from the industrious patients of the Infirmary to all parts of the local and distant community. Much frustration, inconvenience and hilarity ensued during the 1950s and early 1960s as the therapist of the day struggled in this long narrow cupboard of an office to set up equipment and to encourage the exercise of specific joints or muscles. Whilst the lecture threatre offered more space, therapists had to be extremely careful to clear everything away after each session and to sweep up. Consultants were never pleased to find piles of sawdust or other craft debris scattered around their lectern.

By 1965 the hospital management had given in to pressure and the service moved into a larger room near the east end of the hospital where it was possible to specify the layout and include such items as a small cooker. By this time occupational therapists had become recognized for the contribution they could make to promoting independence in the practical skills of life such as dressing, feeding and cooking and also to the assessment of workmanship. Whenever possible patients came to the department rather than therapists going to the wards. Staffing expanded to a full-time therapist and then to a senior and basic grade. The struggle to break free of the image of the 'diversional craft lady' was, however, to continue for several years.

The development of Phases I and II of the Infirmary presented an opportunity for the service to have a say in the planning of purpose-built accommodation, which is now the department in Phase II. By the time this opened the physical seams were bursting, with patients and therapists having initially to programme the use of space and equipment. A less than helpful though well-meaning planner had reduced all the working heights to wheel-chair level and it took some time to have this gesture corrected.

Students have always come from other areas in Scotland such as Edinburgh and Glasgow, and new facilities and pleasant surroundings drew more staff and increased the demand for student places, with some returning to join the service after training. The current busy department, well equipped and contributing to the quality of life of even the most severely disabled, is a far cry from the part-time therapist in a cupboard. Its speed of development over just 30 years is a tribute to its staff.

SPEECH THERAPY

Speech therapy has developed nationally in two distinct ways. Initially the service was mainly for children with speech defects and was the province of teachers of speech and drama. Training schools were to be found in Edinburgh and Glasgow but not Aberdeen, and those who passed through them were also qualified to work with patients who had suffered a head injury or a stroke.[14] After training had been completed, therapists could take one of two pathways – working within the National Health Service or the local Education Authority which provided a service for schools. It was not until 1974 that all therapists were brought into the Health Service.

Before 1963, a loose arrangement existed between the hospitals in the Aberdeen area and the Education Authority, with therapists visiting patients with neurological problems and occasionally on a domiciliary basis. However, a hospital-based service was properly established in that year though it was to suffer from shortage of staff and facilities for some time to come. One appointment was made to the Aberdeen Hospitals, based on Woolmanhill.[15] This meagre full-time cover involved the therapist visiting Foresterhill, the City Hospital, Woodend Hospital and Morningfield. In 1965 difficulties in obtaining a therapist reduced this service until 1974 to a bare minimum with a therapist sporadically working on the wards mostly at the patient's bedside. However, by that year things had begun to improve and there were now the equivalent of two full-time therapists at the Infirmary. In 1978 one individual was assigned fully to the Infirmary giving a service which included the care of neurological and neurosurgical patients. Over the years to 1990 the staff continued to rise. In 1987 an area adviser's post was created, based on the Infirmary and shortly thereafter a chief speech therapist was appointed to manage the service at the Infirmary, Woolmanhill, the City Hospital, Woodend and Morningfield. By this time the total staff was eight with four at Foresterhill. Finally in 1990 a unit therapist was based on the Infirmary so that there is now a total staff of six.

Improvements in accommodation marched with the increased recognition of the importance of the discipline and the growth in staff. As with other services not seen as 'mainline' this had its share of problems, and even with the completion of Phase II, the Infirmary did not have assigned space for the therapists who for a decade had been using the patients' library. In 1978 three rooms were made available on the ground floor and by the middle 1980s additional rooms were in use adjacent to wards 15 and 16 (previously ward 10) in the old surgical block. Now the department is mainly housed adjacent to occupational therapy in Phase II which is a suitable environment for patients from the neurological wards.

19

Education

From the infancy of medicine the hospital on the one hand and the university on the other, were the real starting points of medical science. All progress in knowledge is dependent upon the intimate union of the two – the one cannot do without the other.[1]

Early days

An academic medical presence had existed at King's College since 1505 when James Cumine (Cumyne) was appointed 'mediciner', a title at that institution apparently synonymous with professor and as such making the Aberdeen chair the oldest in Scotland.[2] Funds from such upper Deeside parishes as Glenmuick and Glengairn[3] were earmarked for the support of the appointment so giving it an air of importance. This was not, however, translated into activity in teaching and as late as the second decade of the 19th century a notable Aberdeen historian recorded that its mediciner 'simply refused to lecture.'[4] Marischal also had a chair of medicine from 1700[5] but likewise did not instruct students until the middle of the 18th century. The total absence of commissioners and other external authorities to regulate degrees made the universities intensely parochial. Both staff and students were local, coming mostly from land-owning, farming and professional families. The influence of the artisan and those in trade was minimal, though there were notable exceptions as in the case of James McGrigor.[6] Dynasties were common, some with more to offer than others. The Gregorys were an example of distinction having furnished 14 professors to British universities, four of them mediciners in King's College. But there was much blatant nepotism which did harm. The dead hands of the Bannermans, father and son, spanned 45 years as mediciners at King's.

It is not surprising therefore that the impetus to exploit the Infirmary for apprenticeship training in clinical medicine – then the almost universal method of becoming a practitioner – came from the physicians who worked within its walls rather than from academe. In 1751 they recommended that their students should be admitted as apprentices to the hospital.[7] Four were duly allowed to attend the Infirmary at a fee of one guinea each. In 1754 rules for their conduct

Plate 52 William Livingstone (1760–1822), professor of medicine at Marischal College. Distinguished supporter of medical students and President of the Medico-Chirurgical Society 1791. This portrait by John Moir is in the Medico-Chirurgical Society Hall.

were drawn up.[8] Any apprentice paying one guinea was allowed to dress patients in the last of his three years but could attend for the first two. If he paid two guineas he was permitted to dress for the second and third years. A ticket was issued to those who paid. The apprentice had to be able to give a report on his patients to the physician in charge. These were divided amongst the apprentices and, if the number was insufficient, the students were to take turns. By 1783 it was ordained that, as well as taking down and applying dressings, the student could carry out minor operations such as bleeding and opening abscesses under the direction of the physician. The number of students who paid these fees up to 1774 varied each year from three to 16 so that at one time as many as 48 may have been under instruction.

However, while these practical moves were being taken, and as Malcolm Millar has described in some detail,[2] attempts were being made to establish more formal teaching in the Infirmary. In 1758 John Gregory and David Skene[9] proposed to Marischal College that they should advertise classes for medicine and midwifery; this attempt foundered on personal differences. Nevertheless in 1786 and for two years subsequently, William Livingstone (Plate 52) and George French (Plate 53)[10] – both on the staff of Marischal – advertised a six months course of clinical lectures in the Infirmary. They were to be given once or twice a week and this plan was 'warmly recommended by all members of Marischal and the three medical managers of the Infirmary.'[11] In spite of this endorsement the lectures disappeared after two sessions for reasons that are not clear.

In 1789 the students took matters into their own hands and founded the Medical Society (later the Medico-Chirurgical Society) and established their own course of systematic medical teaching. This, in the course of time was formally transferred to Marischal College. For example, in 1807 Charles Skene – one of the many generations of distinguished doctors in this family – and afterwards

Plate 53 George French (1765–1833), professor of chemistry at Marischal College. This portrait by John Moir is in the Medico-Chirurgical Society Hall.

professor of medicine, was asked to lecture on anatomy.[12] By this time Livingstone was senior physician to the Infirmary and a supporter of the students, not least by providing a meeting place for the society. As an aside it seems that the students of the day were remarkable for their youth and mischievous nature. On one occasion the gardener complained that they pulled up his flowers and other shrubs and would not desist in spite of his efforts to stop them. They were at times a nuisance in the apothecary's shop. In 1800 the managers, noting that some were mere boys, decreed that none under the age of 15 years should get tickets of admission to the Infirmary.[13]

There was formidable reaction against the endeavours of the Society, notably from the professor of chemistry, George French, described by Bulloch as 'a cranky druggist' who owed his success in life largely to his two uncles, Sir William and George Fordyce. Sir William was the wealthiest and most fashionable London physician of his day who actually founded the chair of chemistry to which his nephew was appointed having failed as a doctor in London.[14] Unfortunately he held the chair for 40 years (1793–1833). Formal education within the Infirmary, linked to a university college continued to be frustrated by the internecine academic war between King's and Marischal College. In the late 18th century Scottish degrees were in low repute and there was a market in their distribution.[15] However, as a forerunner – admittedly an ultimately unsuccessful one – to the union of the colleges in 1860, a joint medical school was established in 1818,[16] mainly at the instigation of the authorities at Marischal, which by this time (and presumably as the result of the stimulus of the Society and the proximity of the Infirmary) had lectureships in anatomy, midwifery, surgery and materia medica. This transient trial of co-operation owed more to competition from the Medico-Chirurgical Society (which had acquired its new title in 1811) than to a unified sense of purpose. As such it foundered in 1838 not least in consequence of the King's mediciner's continued refusal to teach.

Thereafter until the union of King's and Marischal, the school based on the latter and backed by the facilities at the Infirmary and its associate, though now separate, general service (Dispensary) was the only one to flourish, driven all the while by the Medico-Chirurgical Society. Though it may be a harsh judgement, the standing and indeed survival of clinical teaching in Aberdeen, at this time and subsequently, owes much more to the Society than, with the exception of a small number of individuals and families, it does to either of the academic institutions in the old town or the new.

All was not, needless to say, rosy. A pamphlet of 1830[17] directed towards the managers of the Infirmary, referred to rumours that the medical staff was to be reduced by one in order to cut expenditure and went on to say that this would: 'ruin the Medical School, deprive the Infirmary of student fees of ten times the amount (saved) and deprive the public of the services of one man who would be all the better able to treat their diseases (in) that he had acquired experience in hospital practice.'

Its author restated the age long perception that those who hold academic office can teach but only from a theoretical basis, not from practical experience: 'A man', the author wrote, 'may harangue from a university chair and suit his cases to his taste for eloquence, but no ignorant man can lecture at the bedside of a patient without being detected.'

At this time such strictures were justified by the failure of academics to practise as well as to teach but gradually, as we shall see, this deficiency was overcome. The author of the pamphlet also re-explained the importance of the Infirmary to the universities: '. . . without the Infirmary, Aberdeen, even with two universities, would be no more a medical school than Oxford, or Cambridge, or St Andrews'.

These financial and educational points were re-iterated in an open letter (dated December 1833) from a self-styled 'benevolent and interested person' whom we have already encountered on p.34.[18] The sub-title was 'With some account of the State of the Medical School (so called)'. This writer, with a percipience which we might associate more with the Universities and Health Service of the 1990s, also called for publication of the financial and clinical statistics of the medical school with comparative figures from Edinburgh, Glasgow and Dundee and petitioned that physicians and surgeons be obliged to give student lectures. He further pointed out that, because of the lack of specialized departments of medicine and surgery in the Infirmary, graduates from Aberdeen could not enter the Royal Navy without spending six months in a London hospital. Perhaps most tellingly he pronounced – after a polemic against arts professors who wanted only to have the medical school 'hang to' the rest of the university – 'Medicine is learned not in the college but in the Infirmary'. He concluded with a series of trenchant instructions to the treasurer.

To balance this 'radical' pamphlet there was in January 1834 a splendid reactionary reply of 28 pages published in the same way, which – once one cuts through its prolixity – denies the opinion that medicine is learnt at the bedside.[19] Perhaps neither author was as well informed as they were endowed with the gift of ornate penmanship.

Costs were also increasing and by 1838 the fees for a student had, under the new regulations of the Infirmary,[20] risen to seven guineas a session which did, however, include a course of lectures in medicine and surgery.

The union and after

The ultimate union of the two university colleges was the outcome of concern throughout Scotland over the state of the involvement of all the universities in medical education. A royal commission to address this subject reported in 1831[21] but legislation was delayed until 1858. Even then there were some who opposed it and Alexander Kilgour[22] in 1855 was apparently maintaining that '. . .a first class man in science does not make a good instructor' so implicitly supporting the view that teaching of medicine should be vested in the Infirmary clinicians.[23] The Act formalized the fusion of the two university colleges and led directly to the geographical concentration of medicine at Marischal. This in turn seemed to act as a catalyst to academic growth so that by the end of the century gaps in academic resource to underpin the curriculum had largely been filled. Chairs existed in botany, chemistry, physics, zoology, geology, anatomy, physiology, medical logic and jurisprudence, public health, materia medica, surgery, pathology, midwifery and medicine. With but minor change, this complement and organization was to serve the medical school and interact with the Infirmary well into the 20th century.

From the union two new degrees were created, the Bachelor of Medicine (MB) and the Master of Surgery (CM), taking the place of the old MD. Gradually the medical degree strengthened itself to a position rivalling the MA in no small measure due to the creation of the General Medical Council in 1858. A diploma in public health was also introduced.

It would appear that, at least on the surface, the integration of education between the medical school and the Infirmary in the second half of the 19th century was relatively smooth. In 1857 William Henderson[24] (lecturer at the time in materia medica) was emphasizing in a commencement address at Marischal the importance of hospital attendance 'which forms a prominent part of the occupation of every student and which is very properly required by all the examining boards'. He was of the opinion that the student should not attend patients in the early stage of his instruction but 'postpone it until he is in some degree qualified to make intelligent use of the cases which present themselves in the wards of the hospital' (by which we must presume he was referring chiefly to the Infirmary). However, this implied, and probably real, separation of academic teaching from clinical apprenticeship that had its legitimate origins in the dominance of the Medico-Chirurgical Society, is reflected in a report of 1864 which stemmed from an Infirmary sub-committee.[25] At that time three courses of lectures were delivered annually, each lasting three months and consisting of two lectures weekly. Lecturers were appointed annually. The courses alternated so that in one year there were two courses of clinical medicine and one of clinical surgery followed the next year by two of surgery and one of medicine. This did not fit with the clinical instruction required for the ordinary diploma (licentiate) of the Edinburgh College of Surgeons, which was one course of six months or two of three months. However, it would seem that a stumbling block to change was the fee which at that time was two guineas for the first course, one guinea for each succeeding course or (and here was a possible bargain) four guineas for a 'perpetual ticket.' These monies were presumably given, at least in part, to the individuals involved but there was a problem in that any one physician or surgeon had difficulty in producing sufficient clinical material from his own resources. Instruction then would tend to become more systematic than practical. The further implication seems to have been that partitioning of fees would follow and be a cause of friction. The sub-committee suggested that the senior physician and surgeon should give one lecture per week while another two physicians and two surgeons should alternate in providing a second lecture, fees to be divided in the ratio of 50 per cent to the seniors and 25 per cent to each of the others. After discussion which involved the leading members of the medical staff, it was resolved 'that the clinical teaching in the hospital should be entrusted to the two senior physicians and the two senior surgeons – each to deliver a lecture weekly, and the fees to be equally divided: that there should be a six months' course of medical and the same of surgical lectures in winter, the fee for which should be three guineas for the first course and two guineas for the second: a three months' course of medical and the same of surgical lectures in summer, at fees – two guineas for the first course and one guinea for the second'. These recommendations were adopted by the next quarterly committee of the hospital.[26]

We do not know much about the teaching that went on in the ARI during the years from the turn of the century until the late 1930s. Individuals stand out and are recorded elsewhere in this history but there was not any great revolution in the teaching of clinical subjects. Clinical professors continued to be part-time (see p.86). During World War I many more women were admitted as undergraduates but their numbers fell again in the 1920s and 1930s.

By 1920 serious thought was being given by the university court, the senatus and the faculty of medicine to the proposal that had arisen for a joint hospital site on the lands of Burnside and Foresterhill (see Chapter 4). Perhaps the impetus for the university's interest came in part from an adverse report by the General Medical Council's inspector which had been considered by the Court in October 1920. The professional examination in midwifery was criticized since 'it could not in the absence of a clinical examination be regarded as sufficient'. McKerron, the professor of midwifery, explained that whilst present conditions existed, it was impossible because of lack of patients.

Up to this time it is obvious that professional examinations in all medical subjects took place in Marischal College and not in any clinical setting. They would, therefore, be largely based on written work. At this same meeting of the court a proposal had been made that there should be a meeting with the clinical teachers and, by January 1921, it was remitted to the faculty of medicine to consider which departments should move to the proposed joint hospital site. However, as early as July 1920, the court was also considering proposals to bring together Aberdeen hospitals and certain departments of the medical school on a common site. In the Minute of 13 July 1920, the principal, Sir George Adam Smith, reported that 'the heads of the institutions expressed general approval of the scheme and deemed it worthy of fullest consideration by the public bodies concerned'. The hand of Matthew Hay – a very senior member of the university and on the court for some years previously – can be detected in this statement.

There is much to be gleaned from university minutes about the slow evaluation of the joint hospital site as seen from the viewpoint of the academics who were to play a crucial part in the years, until it finally came to fruition between 1927 when the Children's Hospital was built and 1938 when the first part of the medical school was created. There are innumerable entries in court minutes on the progress of this highly complex co-ordinated activity. The university was represented either directly or indirectly, by Matthew Hay, John Marnoch, Ashley Mackintosh, James Crombie and Sir Thomas Jaffrey and members of court during this period.[27]

From the beginning it was agreed that all departments would move to Foresterhill except those teaching subjects for the first professional examination in basic biological science; chemistry, physics, botany and zoology. Thus both anatomy and physiology were included with all the clinical subjects though from the outset a priority was clearly indicated for medicine, surgery, midwifery and pathology (including bacteriology). At this time there was controversy over the future of Marischal and it was being rumoured that the university might forsake its down-town college altogether. However, it was emphasized that the need was to get the clinical and related departments close to the hospital development. Even after the first part of the medical school had been opened officially by Lord Dawson of Penn in 1938,[28] there were still court and faculty resolutions that anatomy and physiology must move to Foresterhill if only to make room for expanding departments at Marischal. World War II intervened and these two departments have in 1991 yet to reach Foresterhill.

The contemporary model,[29] (whose front elevation resembles a profile view of a large ship) was followed through into the creation of the building and has a remarkably modern appearance (Plate 54), though its construction of reinforced concrete with granite 'facings' was to cause some trouble in after years when in the 1960s some of the structure became unstable.

The move to Foresterhill was a co-ordinated one and a unique example of co-operation between hospital and university. There appears to have been agreement between the university court and the hospital governors throughout. Through cross-membership and common purpose effective use was made of any resources that could be found. Within this happy environment many distin-guished academics such as Stanley Davidson,[30] and James Learmonth[31] could flourish in their roles both as clinical scientists and clinicians involved in patient care. They tended, perhaps because of the opportunities offered by their

appointments, to move on as opportunity arose. Prominent among those who stayed was David Campbell, who achieved fame as president of the General Medical Council.[32] He had been a persuasive negotiator during the move to Foresterhill and thereafter was a considerable force in integrating academic and other aspirations in the interests of the Royal Infirmary.

After the war there was a social upheaval, which included the formation of the NHS, and which features prominently in other sections of this history. In undergraduate teaching the major change for Foresterhill which developed during the 1960s, was the increase in intake to 135 a year that in turn led to students faring forth to Inverness and Dumfries for their clinical education. Inter-departmental teaching developed to bring in such departments as radiology (see p.180).

For postgraduate education, formalized training programmes developed throughout the country and at Aberdeen, as elsewhere, had to be blended into the staffing requirements of the NHS. Both in this context and generally it was initially possible, given the relatively comfortable relationships between town and gown in Aberdeen, for the Infirmary to interact with the university so that there was always a significant involvement of university staff in patient care, both at the bedside and in the provision of support services. These arrangements were not without their difficulties as the increasing involvement of academics with the care of patients interacted with their other roles. By 1979, over 100 of the 121 medical school staff were theoretically providing clinical services. As important, though equally theoretical, over 300 health service staff were teaching and receiving access to university facilities for scholarship and research. It is probable that this situation was an inevitable consequence of the joint developments of the 1920s. Indeed at the start of the Health Service in 1948, the regional board and the court of the university had agreed to share equally the costs of the existing joint laboratory services. This concept survived into the 1970s but then collapsed, perhaps because of an inability to match clinical initiatives with an increased through-put of students and the demands for more research. An example was the failure of the 'embedded' university departments in Phase II which, because of the inadequacy of funding, had to be given up by the university who moved their much reduced staff back to the medical school, and allowed their purpose-built units to be converted for direct clinical use. Nevertheless the university continued, in the tradition of the close links between teaching and patient care which had existed since the merger of 1858, to be involved in many of the developments on the Foresterhill site and this is apparent from the accounts of the development of specialities and services given in other chapters. Perhaps because of this reasonable and inevitable involvement with patient care, Aberdeen came out badly in a review of research performance carried out by the (then) university grants committee in 1981.[33] The result was the loss of nearly 25 per cent of clinical and support staff. These

---

Plate 54 The Medical School in 1985 from the south. The jutting prow is still clearly visible. The link building is on the left.

disastrous cuts have since been largely remedied and the university members of staff continue to have an impact on clinical care within the Royal Infirmary.

There are no rules with which to make value judgements but most of those who as clinicians with an academic bent can remember the ARI in the post war years would say that their time was happy and made easy by the extent of co-operation between those in primarily hospital service (now the NHS) and those in academic appointments. The needs of service in a tightly organized region made this not only desirable but also achievable.

20

Planning and Development Beyond 1991

A reasonable man adapts himself to the world: the unreasonable one persists in trying to adapt the world to himself. Therefore all progress depends on the unreasonable man.

G.B. Shaw[1]

Throughout this history, boards of management and sundry other bodies have been noted as those who controlled the destiny of the Infirmary. Through the activities of many philanthropic and well-intentioned citizens who seized opportunities to improve care and collected the money necessary, the Infirmary became a force in the community and a means whereby good services were brought to bear. They had perforce to interact with the clinicians who provided the service and who, with the authoritarian tradition of the medical profession, often felt that their word was law when decisions affecting their patients had to be made. In the voluntary system where physicians gave their services free, the contract between them and managers was a delicate one dependent entirely on trust and understanding both of which could be in short supply. A full history of management of the Infirmary within this system which operated until the advent of the National Health Service in 1948 and persisted thereafter in a modified form almost to the present day, would require a volume of its own and in Aberdeen would be a microcosm of what has happened throughout Scotland. Such cannot be pursued here but the impact of national changes has had its effect on the Infirmary as it approaches a third century and something of the background has to be sketched in to explain the changes currently taking place.

Until the advent of the National Health Service, institutions such as the Infirmary had been managed by a Board of Management nominally responsible to its subscribers but in practice largely independent. During World War II an embryo national hospital organization emerged on an *ad hoc* basis with boards increasingly co–operating with a central administration. What transpired on the 'appointed day' (4 July 1948) was a regional organization which provided guidelines for the conduct of the health service but did not greatly intervene over details though it could exercize considerable control in that it dispensed the money. In Scotland five regional hospital boards were established including that for the North-East Region. Under these were boards of management for the individual hospitals. Thus the major initial change did not greatly disturb what already existed. The hospital boards continued to listen to and sometimes to take the advice of their medical and other staff, constrained as we have seen (e.g. p.201) by the economic shackles of the time. The desperate needs of the hospital services were partially met by a large though still uncompleted building programme which began in the 1960s and in which Aberdeen shared (see p.61). Not withstanding the high quality of hospital care available to the citizens of the North-East, which was to some extent due to the planning and provisions made before the introduction of the NHS, it seemed a miracle to many that nationally the service kept going at all. Its physical facilities were dilapidated and its complicated management was still largely the province, at hospital level, of unpaid volunteers on the boards and a few dedicated and usually overworked professionals. Some streamlining was achieved with the merger of a number of independent hospital boards in Aberdeen in 1973 but though this permitted more co-ordinated development it did not have dramatic effects. A national 'top-down' re-organization was undertaken in 1973.[2] Regional Hospital Boards were fused into Regional Health Authorities with below them areas and districts. Effectively the old hospital management committees ceased to exist. The impact of these changes at hospital level is difficult to assess but the most important thing was the persistence of consensus management with the medical profession still playing an important, if amateur, part.

The increasing financial strains which have dogged the National Health Service since its inception came ever more to the fore during the 1980s. A further change in hospital management followed a review by an independent committee under the chairmanship of the head of a supermarket chain.[3] For the first time in the mid-1980s we begin to see the introduction of 'managers' in the professional sense whose role – initially ill-defined – was to interact with health professionals and take decisions at unit and district level on priorities and the deployment of resources. This marked the beginning of the end of consensus. As the 1980s drew to a close and in consequence of political, social and financial pressures, the government introduced much more radical changes which were embodied in the NHS and Community Care Act of 1990[4] but whose effects were widely anticipated by prior discussions and negotiations. The implications of the Act are still to be worked out but even before it was passed the changing management style was influencing the Royal Infirmary.

It was not that the institution was in great difficulties over money. It is true, as has already been told, some innovations had to be delayed for a considerable period of time, but the ARI was 'solvent' by the criteria of the day which meant that it had not overspent its centrally allocated budget. Rather there was a need to continue to address the issue which owed its origin to Matthew Hay – how further to implement the general wish to concentrate acute services on the Foresterhill site. The problems were in fact more detailed practical ones such as the likely number of operating theatres and their optimum location, what should happen to the accommodation in the Hospital vacated by the University (see p.219) and what provision should be made for patients, often elderly and infirm, who after initial treatment no longer required access to acute services. Though informal consensus was gone, here was an opportunity for a small group of clinicians and managers to consider these difficult issues. They consulted widely and within six months produced a plan for the ARI for the 1990s and beyond, which met with surprisingly widespread approval. By the end of 1989 this exercise had been extended to create, with the co-operation of the Scottish Home and Health Department and the use of management consultants, two sets of business plans for the Foresterhill complex – one based on the idea of a NHS Trust Hospital, the other on the idea of a directly managed unit (DMU).[5] At the time of writing the former has been adopted.

The major impact at hospital level of the action which centred around the Act of 1990 was that clinicians, previously part of the consensus system which had expired, were slowly but inexorably having to accept a more prominent managerial role working in harness with the new-look NHS managers. Clinical co-ordinators were appointed for such important areas as theatres, laboratories, out-patients and resource management. Their role, and the speed of the changes that they introduced, varied from area to area but on the whole they came to be acknowledged and have pioneered the acceptance of greater managerial and budgetary responsibility within the services they administer. The system continues to develop and will be tested with difficult decisions over the years to come.

Two other matters which arose in the context of the Act were audit and resource management. The first had already been introduced by many clinicians for their own patients as accounts in other parts of this history attest but is now being greatly extended with the help of money from the SHHD. The latter – which aims to achieve similar efficiencies to those which apply in business enterprises – came to Aberdeen when the ARI was designated as a pilot site for the 'resource initiative', a national scheme to test new methods. An explosion of computer terminals and information exchange has followed, the effect of which will take some years to assess.

Finally, Aberdeen Royal Infirmary and other components of what has now come to be known as the Foresterhill complex are reviewing and attempting to resolve the many problems which arise at the interface with the University. The matters are intricate and though a number of plans have been completed it will be for future historians to describe these and their impact.

Notes and References

Chapter 1

1. Trans.: Accept their fate with dignity and without fuss.
2. Trans.: What does it represent?
3. Trans.: How much does it cost?

Chapter 2

1. Minutes relating to the Institution of the Aberdeen Infirmary and Lunatic Asylum 1739–42. Copied from the original 'Register' of the Infirmary.
2. French, R. K. Unpublished data in the Library of the Aberdeen Medico-Chirurgical Society.
3. Chrystal, William, was Deacon Convener of Aberdeen Incorporated Trades in 1730 and Master of Trades Hospital 1734–36. In the latter appointment he managed the Trades Hospital's funds, and was in charge of charitable work 'in times of dearth', buying in supplies for distribution to the poor, up to 1800 bolls of meal at a time. See Bain, E. *Merchant and Craft Guilds – A History of the Aberdeen Incorporated Trades.* Edmond and Spark, Aberdeen, 1887.
    Wright: a craftsman, woodworker.
4. At the time of the Union of Parliaments in 1707 Scots money was valued at 1/12 of the value of sterling. In the terms of the Union, Scots money was abolished but it continued to be used, hence the appearance in the records of sums of 1/12*d*, i.e. one penny Scots. Before decimalization in 1971, sterling was expressed in £.s.d. – i.e. pounds, shillings and pence. £1 = 20*s*. and 1*s*. = 12*d*. After decimalization £1 = 100 (new) pence.
5. Subscription List Aberdeen Infirmary, 1742.
6. Mitchell, G.A.G. The medical history of Aberdeen and its Universities. *Aberdeen University Review* 1958; **37**: 225–238.
7. Minute Book Aberdeen Infirmary, 26 October 1741.
8. Gordon of Pitlurg and Straloch. Pitlurg is some 15 miles north of Aberdeen (about three miles north-east of Ellon) and Straloch is about 10 miles to the north-west of Aberdeen.
    James Gordon (1705–1755) baptised in the parish of St Nicholas, son of Dr John Gordon of Colliston (a village four miles north-west of Arbroath), was professor of medicine at Marischal College 1734–55. No portrait of him survives though his family is strongly represented in a series of portraits previously part of the furnishings of Parkhill House Dyce. Known as the Parkhill Bequest this collection in 1895 was

donated to the care of the Governors of Robert Gordon's College and is on permanent display in the school's Auld Hoose. See Temple, W. *The Thanage of Fermartyn*. D. Wyllie and Son, Aberdeen, 1894. Also *Aberdeen Journal*, 28 September 1755.

9. The Mearns – a coastal area of land south of Aberdeen and approximately bounded in that direction by the Montrose basin. It is a rich and fertile area rising gradually to the hills of Angus and became famous in literature with the publication of Lewis Grassic Gibbon's trilogy *A Scots Quair* in 1946. The origin of the word is not well documented but may be from the Gaelic 'maor' – steward – in this case one who held the land in grant from the King.

10. Minute Book Aberdeen Infirmary, 2 November 1742.

11. Sneck: a latch, catch of a door.

12. The Well of the Woman-Hill A.D. 1580. A facsimile with an introduction by A. Kemlo. Aberdeen, Edmond and Spark, 1884.

13. A description of both Touns of Aberdeen. Edinburgh, printed for the Spalding Club, 1842, p.10.

14. Iryn and Brynstane are the vernacular forms of iron and brinstone. Brasse is more difficult to account for as the alloys of tin/copper or copper/zinc do not occur naturally. It may be another name for iron pyrites though this usage is said to be fairly recent.

15. Callirhoe: a fountain in Athens.

16. Newtyle – a hamlet about eight miles north of Aberdeen on the east side of the Ellon road in the parish of Foveran.

17. Minute Book Aberdeen Infirmary, 20 March 1744.

18. *Aberdeen Journal*, 2 April 1770.

19. Munro, A. M. *Memorials of the Provosts and Aldermen of Aberdeen*. Aberdeen, 1897.

20. *An Account of the Rise & Progress of the Infirmary at Aberdeen*. Printed by James Chalmers, Aberdeen, 1758.

21. History of Aberdeen Royal Infirmary. Reprinted from the *People's Journal*, Dundee, 1904. Though as Keith remarks 'Aberdeen never heard the sound of gunfire' the skirmish on 23 December between Lord Lewis Gordon's Jacobite inclined tenants and a force of McLeods and Munros who had been dispatched from Inverness by the Hanoverian command resulted in more dead amongst the Gordon victors than the Hanoverians. Though Aberdeen had been under nominal Jacobite control, the 'take over' of the Infirmary and Gordon's Hospital seems to have been their only aggressive act in the City. See Keith, A. *A Thousand Years of Aberdeen*. Aberdeen University Press, 1912, p.276.

22. Burnet, Andrew (1698–1769). A 'baillie and chirurgeon in Old Aberdeen and procurator for Alexander Burnet, Senior Regent in King's College'. Retired from Aberdeen Infirmary in 1751 because of ill-health and became MD King's College 1755. See *Aberdeen Journal*, 26 May 1769.

23. Livingstone, Thomas. Died 'an aged man' in 1785. 'Performed wonderful cures in the Infirmary' and with his son, William (see 1755–1800), they are regarded as 'the makers of the Infirmary'. See Rodger, Ella H.B. *Aberdeen Doctors*. William Blackwood and Sons, Edinburgh, 1893, pp.30–4.

24. Minute Book Aberdeen Infirmary, 27 August 1751.

25. Girnel – a chest for storing oatmeal.

26. Minute Book Aberdeen Infirmary, 20 November 1753.

27. Minute Book Aberdeen Infirmary, 9 April 1754.

28. *Aberdeen Journal*, 23 April 1754.

29. The inscription is interpreted as follows: I.G.M! – James Gordon, Master (of Masons); 1754 – The year of the foundation; AE R AE ARCH/5754 – era, Royal Era of Archmasonry 5754 (5754 is the Masonic date for 1754); P. – Provost, or President, James Morrison; I.M. – James Morrison was Provost in 1752–53, and president of the managers of the Infirmary in 1754.

    In the 18th century it was the custom for the Masons in Aberdeen to lay, with much ceremony, the foundation stones of important buildings. Detailed descriptions of the laying of the foundation stones for Bannerman's bridge over Virginia Street, on 11 March 1768, and for the Gilcomston Chapel of Ease on 2 May 1770 are given in the Minutes of St Machar's Lodge (No 54) of Freemasons (founded 1753).

30. Synod. For those not familiar with the organization of the Presbyterian Church in Scotland each church is managed by a Kirk Session above which is a Presbytery responsible for a number of parishes within a designated area. This in turn reports to a Synod which is in administrative charge of a number of presbyteries and which in some churches then passes its business on to a General Assembly.

31. A 'bleachfield' as its name implies, is an open space where bleached yarn or cloth is spread to dry and to receive its final whitening by exposure to sun and wind. Aberdeen had already, by the beginning of the 18th century, a strong tradition of marketing both wool and linen and their products.

32. Minute Book Aberdeen Infirmary, 6 March 1753.

33. Minute Book Aberdeen Infirmary, 11 December 1753.

34. Minute Book Aberdeen Infirmary, 21 August 1753.

35. Minute Book Aberdeen Infirmary, 2 Ocotber 1744.

36. Sowens – a dish made from oat husks and fine meal steeped in water for about a week; after straining, the liquor was again left to ferment and separate, the solid matter at the bottom being the sowens.

37. Scrophula – a disease characterized by swelling of the neck glands, often with discharging sinuses, complicated sometimes by 'white swelling' of joints and 'caries of bone' – the condition now known to be tuberculous. Known also as the King's Evil, it was thought to be cured by the Royal touch. Prince Charles Edward 'touched' for the King's Evil in Edinburgh in 1745.

38. *Aberdeen Journal*, 26 June 1750.

39. Minute Book Aberdeen Infirmary, 6 September 1743.

40. Ashlar is dressed or semi-dressed stone as distinct from rubble or fieldstone work. Though much of building in Scotland from the 15th century on is in ashlar, random rubble was cheaper and its use persists almost to this day. Aberdeen's copious supply of good quality granite (the Rubislaw quarry was opened at about the same time as the Infirmary) has always made dressed stone the first choice even though much of this is now 'synthetic' having been made by moulding quarry dust.

41. Minute Book Aberdeen Infirmary, 14 November 1758.

42. Derived from the Greek, meaning plague or pestilence, and used as a euphemism for syphilis often without the tell-tale suffix venerea. Admission and Discharge Book Aberdeen Infirmary, 1762.

43. Minute Book Aberdeen Royal Infirmary, 1821.

44. Minute Book Aberdeen Infirmary, 15 August 1769.

45. A feu is a piece of land held by feudal tenure in which the 'vassal . . . makes a return of money to a superior who owns the land'. Unlike a tenancy, a feu constituted a perpetual lease for a fixed rent. Feu's were not phased out until the middle of the 20th century.

46. Account Book Aberdeen Infirmary, 1764.

47. Boll – a dry measure of weight as capacity varying according to commodity or locality. For meal this was approximately 140 pounds (63.5 kg) so it would be reasonable to assume that this amount was about 60 hundredweight or three tons avoirdupois.

48. Minute Book Aberdeen Royal Infirmary, 21 September 1789.

49. Minute Book Aberdeen Royal Infirmary, 7 November 1769.

50. Rodger, Ella H.B. *Aberdeen Doctors*. William Blackwood and Sons, Edinburgh, 1893.

51. Account Book Aberdeen Royal Infirmary, 1787.

52. Minute Book Aberdeen Royal Infirmary, 17 December 1783.

53. The original of the Charter is preserved in the archives of the Grampian Health Board.

54. John Memis was a disputatious manager of the Infirmary from 21 January 1766 (by virtue of payment of £25) until 1791. He was involved in a long, contentious and legally highly technical action against the Board of Managers over the difference

between being styled a Physician and a Doctor of Medicine in the application for a Royal Charter for the Infirmary. The ripples of this case spread to involve James Boswell as advocate for the defence, Dr Samuel Johnson as Boswell's adviser and the President of the Royal College of Physicians in London. The action was settled against Dr Memis in the High Court at Edinburgh on 30 November 1776 with £40 costs. The Board of Management acted quickly to recover these costs and on 17 March 1777 at a Special Meeting, a threat to put Dr Memis 'to the horn' (i.e. denounced as a rebel – a process which in Scotland used to require the messenger-at-arms to proceed to the Mercat Cross at Edinburgh and blow three blasts) was recorded unless Dr Memis 'gave immediate satisfaction'. Presumably this threat was not carried out as Dr Memis remained a manager until 1791. On giving his judgement, Lord Alva concluded his remarks with compassion: 'If there was something wrong in his head, there was something wrong in their hearts'. See Lyall, A. *Medical History* 1960, **4**: 32–48.

55. History of Aberdeen Royal Infirmary. Reprinted from the *People's Journal*, Dundee, 1904. The 'free yearly produce' mentioned in the Incorporation suggests exemption from duty and taxation.
56. Minute Book Aberdeen Royal Infirmary, 21 January 1774.
57. Scrophula and consumption both referred to forms of tuberculosis.
    Sivan – the wild raspberry – but in this context and in the plural (sivans), a venereal disease characterized by raspberry-like eruptions on the genitalia. Whether this was an 18th century manifestation of syphilis is not clear.
58. Minute Book Aberdeen Royal Infirmary, 19 September 1785.
59. Porter, I.A. *Alexander Gordon MD of Aberdeen*. Aberdeen University Press, 1958.
60. Minute Book Aberdeen Royal Infirmary, 18 December 1779.
61. Minute Book Aberdeen Infirmary, 30 August 1763.
62. Admission and Discharge Books Aberdeen Royal Infirmary, 1767.
63. Minute Book Aberdeen Royal Infirmary, 16 June 1800.
64. Anderson, P.J. (ed.) *Records of Marischal College and University*. New Spalding Club, Aberdeen, 1889.
65. Gordon's Hospital was named after Robert Gordon (a great uncle of James Gordon, MD of Pitlurg and Straloch see note 8 above). Robert Gordon had no dependents and left a fortune accumulated by merchant trade with the Baltic. Much of his will was directed to build a 'hospital' on Schoolhill in 1732 now titled Robert Gordon's College. Internally it remained unfinished for several years and like the adjacent Infirmary was commandeered by the Duke of Cumberland in February 1746 when 200 men were garrisoned there. On 10 July 1750 Robert Gordon's Hospital was opened and admitted 14 boys for board and education. (The Statutes and Bye-laws were similar for Heriot's Hospital and Watson's Hospital in Edinburgh.) Alexander Simpson of Colyhill provided additional funds in 1881 and a Provisional Order gave the Governors wider powers of administration. This resulted in the formation of Robert Gordon's College with a wider range of subjects taught and the admission of day boys. The school still stands on its original site to which was added at a later date Robert Gordon's Technical College now styled the Robert Gordon Institute of Technology. See Marshall, J. The Robert Gordon Story (Parts 1–4). *Aberdeen Leopard* 1980; nos 62–5: Sept.–Dec., George Outram, East Kilbride. Also Wyness, F. *Robert Gordon's College*. Mearns Publications, Aberdeen, 1952.
66. Minute Book Aberdeen Royal Infirmary, 17 September 1787.
67. Admission and Discharge Books Aberdeen Royal Infirmary, 1777.
68. Minute Book Aberdeen Royal Infirmary, 19 March 1781.
69. 'Couching' for cataract goes back at least to Celsus (circa AD 30) and consists of needling the lens and applying pressure to displace the opacity. See Milne, J.S. *Surgical Instruments in Greek and Roman Times*. Aberdeen, 1907.
70. French, G. MS Notes on Dr Cullen's Lectures, 1776.
71. Sowens. See note 36 above.
72. Minute Book Aberdeen Royal Infirmary, 25 July 1800.

Chapter 3

1. Moir, James (1770–1861), AM Marischal College 1789, MD Edinburgh 1793 (AM was the early equivalent of MA at Marischal). Moir was a senior physician at the ARI from 1808–14 but had been a founder member of the Medical Society. He was addicted to snuff and was known as 'Snuffy' Moir. His portrait by James Giles, RSA is in the Aberdeen Medico-Chirurgical Society Hall. See Rodger, Ella H.B. *Aberdeen Doctors.* Blackwood and Sons, Edinburgh, 1893.
2. Ogilvie, John C. (1784–1839). Late 18th century physician in Aberdeen and a life manager of the ARI. His portrait was painted by James Giles, RSA. See Rodger, Ella H.B. *Aberdeen Doctors.* Blackwood and Sons, Edinburgh, 1893.
3. Blaikie, James (1786–1836). Lord Provost of Aberdeen from 1833–35. He was an advocate in Aberdeen, the son of the founder of James Blaikie and Sons. Clearly one of diplomatic talent he was described as '. . .a man of thorough integrity, kindliness of heart and unruffled evenness of temper.' He was prominent in the re-building of Marischal College. His statue is in the Town Hall. See Munro, A.M. *Memorials of the Aldermen, Provosts and Lord Provosts of Aberdeen 1272–1895.* Aberdeen,1897, pp.274–5.
4. Simpson, Archibald (1790–1847). The creator of a considerable proportion of modern Aberdeen. Architect to the Infirmary managers from 1830 to the time of his death. A full account of his work and involvement with the Royal Infirmary will be found in a series of articles by G.M. Fraser 'Archibald Simpson, Architect, & His Times' in the *Aberdeen Journal* for 5 April 1918 *et seq.*
5. *Aberdeen Herald,* 24 February 1849.
6. Councillor Andrew Sutherland, a Master of the Guild Brethren's Hospital and residing at 1 Black's Buildings adjacent to Woolmanhill, was presumably on the scene early.
7. Tryon, Robert (1808–1892). There is no explanation of why this naval officer, who was on half pay at the time, should have been in Aberdeen. He never commanded a ship though he rose to Admiral on the reserve list in 1877.
8. Anon. Letter to the managers of the Aberdeen Infirmary. By a country practitioner. Printed by John Davidson and Co., Aberdeen, 1830.
9. Anon. A Pair of Spectacles for the Magistrates and Public wherewith to view the State of Our Infirmary with some account of the State of the Medical School (so called) of this City. Printed by John Davidson and Co., Aberdeen, 1830.
10. *Regulations of the Royal Infirmary.* D. Chalmers and Co., Aberdeen, 1838.
11. An unusual example of the referral pattern of the time is seen in a letter dated 30 July 1860 sent by Dr Alexander Kilgour to the Rev. J. Watt, The Manse, Strathdon. This letter was presented to the Medico-Chirurgical Society in 1990 by Dr W.G. Todd who is grandson of the Rev. Watt.

   . . . .don't for any sake send any more of your parishoners to me with notes of introduction. . . . country people make it serve in a genteel sort of a way the purpose of an Infirmary recommendation. . . . they call at our own houses and think they are entitled to our advice there on the same terms as at the Infirmary. . . .Give them Infirmary recommendations or nothing and if they are too fine for going there, they then know that they have no right to trouble us at our own houses.

12. Report of a sub-committee on the admission of pauper patients in the Aberdeen Infirmary. George Cornwall printers, Aberdeen, 4 May 1848.
13. Smout, T.C. *People and Society in Scotland. A Century of the Scottish People 1830–1950.* Collins, London, 1986.
14. Keith, A. *A Thousand Years of Aberdeen.* Aberdeen University Press, 1950.
15. New Royal Charter. Incorporation of the President and Managers of the Infirmary of Aberdeen. Printed at the Herald Office, Aberdeen, 26 August 1852.
16. Edmond, Alexander (1836–1891). Advocate. Played a considerable part in re-structuring the management of the ARI and convened the committee for that purpose.

Created the firm of Edmonds and Ledingham which in 1991 became Ledingham-Chalmers. See *Aberdeen Journal*, 18 June 1891. *In Memoriam – biographical notes and portraits*. William Cay and Sons, Aberdeen, 1892, pp.112–6.

17. Local Acts 1887. An Act to incorporate the president and managers of the Royal Infirmary and Lunatic Asylum of Aberdeen and for other purposes. 50 and 51st Victoria; chapter LV:1–18.

18. Minute Book Aberdeen Royal Infirmary, 9 August 1883. See also Prefatory Notes anent subscriptions to the Jubilee Extension Scheme. The Treasurer's Office, 3 October 1892.

19. Anon. History of Aberdeen Royal Infirmary – its rise and progress. Reprinted from the *People's Journal*, Dundee, 1904.

20. Henderson, William (1826–1904). Trained as a banker and became a partner in a shipowning firm in 1859. Active in the public good and Lord Provost from 1886–88. Seemingly concerned with pomp and circumstance, he re-introduced the riding of the marches, created an official robe for the lord provost and was active in the extension of the ARI which marked Queen Victoria's Jubilee. A surgical ward was named after him. Knighted in 1893, he still found time to father six sons and eight daughters. Resided at Devanha House which later became a nursing home. See Munro, A.M. *Memorials of the Aldermen, Provosts and Lord Provosts of Aberdeen 1272–1895*. Aberdeen, 1897, pp.297–9.

21. Saxon Snell, Henry (1831–1904). Initially a draughtsman in the Science and Art Department, South Kensington; thereafter (1866) architect to the St Marylebone Board of Guardians; FRIBA 1871. He had a keen interest in all matters relating to planning and ventilation of hospitals, designed many hospital projects and was co-author with Dr F.J. Mouatt of the book *Hospital Construction and Management*. The firm Smith and Kelly, Architects, later became Kelly and Nicol of whom the latter was architect for the Foresterhill project. See note 16 of Chapter 4. See also Archives of Royal Institute of British Architects.

22. Black, Alexander (1801–1883). The son of an Aberdeen druggist he went into the wine and spirit trade. He latterly lived in London at 31 Hyde Park Gardens. He and his wife were prominent and continued benefactors of the ARI. See *Press and Journal*, 14 May 1891.

23. Stephen, George (1829–1921). A native of Dufftown in Banffshire who settled in Canada. George Stephen began life as a herd boy on the glebe (pasture associated with the local minister of the church) of Mortlach, later becoming an apprentice draper in a shop in Union Street, Aberdeen. Emigrating to Canada he rose to become one of that country's greatest developers, industrialists and bankers and Chairman of the Canadian Pacific Railway Company. He became the first Baron Mount-Stephen in 1891. See Gilbert, H. *The End of the Road – The Life of Lord Mount Stephen*. Vols 1 and 2. Aberdeen University Press, 1965 and 1977. Also Cunningham, Ian. *Aberdeen Postgraduate Medical Bulletin* 1991; January, 23–6.

24. Fleming, John (1847–1925). A native of Glentilt he spent his early life in Dundee and in 1884 moved to Aberdeen to oversee what had become the larger depot of his timber business. He became successively Harbour Commissioner, Convener of Lands and Fishings and Lord Provost 1898–1904. He was knighted in 1908, and was Rector's assessor to the university 1908–24 in succession to James E. Crombie (see note 27 of Chapter 19). He died of malaria contracted while on safari in Rhodesia. The timber business bearing his name still thrives having moved from the harbour to the Bridge of Don Estate. See *Aberdeen Press and Journal*, 26 February 1925.

25. Lumsden, Rachel (1835–1908). Daughter of a landed family at Glenbogie she trained at the Hospital for Sick Children, Great Ormond Street, London where she became a ward sister subsequently going to King's College as a senior nurse. Was Lady Superintendent Aberdeen Hospital for Sick Children and subsequently of the ARI from 1885 to 1897 when the nursing and the medicine there had fallen on evil times. Her contribution to the rectifying of this is recounted on p.108. See Webster, K. Rachel

Frances Lumsden of Glenbogie. *Aberdeen Postgraduate Medical Bulletin* 1988; January, 18–20.

26. Carnie, William (1825–1908). Largely self-educated, he was first apprenticed to an engraver but subsequently pursued a career in journalism. Appointed Clerk and Treasurer to the Royal Infirmary and the Royal Lunatic Asylum in 1861, a post he held until 1898. He was an authority on psalmody and 'wielded a deft pen and was a master of light and graceful verse'. See *In Memoriam – biographical notes and portraits*. William Cay and Sons, Aberdeen, 1909, pp.26–34.

27. The following recollection of 1918 and a medical ward at Woolmanhill is that of Mrs Isobel Towers of Fraserburgh, at the time six years old, on a family visit to her farmer uncle ill with pneumonia.

> Two headed Cerberus at the entrance to Hades could never have been so fearsome as the gatekeeper at Woolmanhill. Smallish but squat he almost filled the portals. "Ye canna get in" was his usual utterance – and often one didn't for those were days of blind obedience. Uncle Jamie, a widower left on his own on the Deeside farm by his soldier son gone to the war, must have had many a soaking with clothes not dried. So here he was; he who had never been ill in his life. The corridors reeked of carbolic and pungent floor polish – glistening and so slippery that one was afraid to tread. I went on tiptoe from fear of falling and dreading to make any noise. It was awe inspiring; the long ward with two lines of beds regimentally tucked in. One could see at once anything that went wrong. The ward sister had a high cap, skirt to the ground and voluminous apron. Food was meagre; there was bread, margarine and tea at teatime. An egg, brought in by the relatives, would be boiled but they were hard to get. Uncle Jamie lay there in bed with a strange, gentle reeshling (rustling) cough. He had a big chipped enamel mug as a spitoon. A lifetime teetotaller all he was having was the occasional sip of whisky. The strange hospital atmosphere of illness, carbolic, Cerberus and fear engulfed me. Uncle Jamie recovered but it took time.

This glimpse is of an era and a hospital that some may still recognize but that most will never have known.

Chapter 4

1. Hay, Matthew (1855–1932), MB CM(Hons) 1878, MD Edinburgh. Demonstrator in materia medica Royal Infirmary of Edinburgh 1878–83. Appointed professor of pharmacology and therapeutics at Johns Hopkins University School of Medicine 1884, from which he resigned before taking up duty. Professor of jurisprudence (forensic medicine) Aberdeen 1883–1926 including public health (as medical officer of health) until 1923. Founder of Aberdeen Joint Hospitals scheme. LLD Aberdeen and Edinburgh. His portrait by Charles Sim RA is in the picture gallery at Marischal College – '..the picture of the man of dreams. . .of vision'. Also a granite memorial plaque is to be found in the entrance concourse to Phase I ARI. See Simpson, W.D. *The Fusion of 1860*. Oliver and Boyd, Edinburgh, 1963, pp.273–5. Also Wilson, L.A. Matthew Hay. In *Aberdeen Medico-Chirurgical Society: A Bicentennial History 1789–1989*, ed. Milne, G.P. Aberdeen University Press, 1989; pp.190–8.

2. Logie, Norman J. See note 54 of Chapter 7.

3. Logie, N.J. The History of the Aberdeen Joint Hospitals scheme and site. In: *Aberdeen Medico-Chirurgical Society: A Bicentennial History 1789–1989*, ed. Milne, G.P. Aberdeen University Press, 1989, pp.155–178.

4. Mackintosh, Ashley. See note 10 of Chapter 6.

5. Oddly a maternity hospital was not included in the original plan but was added at a later date.

6. Meff, William (1861–1935). Lord Provost of Aberdeen 1919–25. Son of William Meff, one of the original trawler owners of the Aberdeen port. He became a leading local business man, represented Torry on the Town Council for 17 years and became Dean of Guild 1911. Knighted 1926. His portrait by Sir William Orpen is in the Aberdeen Art Gallery.

7. *Aberdeen Press and Journal*, 31 March 1927.

8. Kinloch, J. Parlane (1886–1932), MB ChB 1909, MD Glasgow. Public health officer in Aberdeen 1914. Commanded Aberdeen University Officers' Training Corps 1914–17. Served in France 1918. On return to Aberdeen he continued in public health and in 1923 was appointed reader in the university and succeeded Matthew Hay as medical officer of health. Physician-superintendent of City Fever Hospital and Woodend Municipal Hospital. Appointed Chief Medical Officer, Department of Health for Scotland in 1928. See *British Medical Journal* 1932; **1**: 311–2.

9. *Bon Accord* and *Northern Pictorial*, 2 October and 20 November 1926.

10. See Hamilton, D. *The Healers. A History of Medicine in Scotland*. Canongate, Edinburgh, 1981.

11. Lewis, Andrew J.W. (1875–1952). Lord Provost of Aberdeen 1925–9. Senior partner of John Lewis and Sons Ltd., shipbuilders and engineers Aberdeen. Trawler owner. Entered Town Council 1919. Baillie 1920. LLD 1928 Aberdeen. Knighted 1929. His portrait by Sir William Orpen is in the Aberdeen Art Gallery collection.

12. *A Short History of the ARI – from Woolmanhill 1739 to Foresterhill 1936*. Published by the ARI, 1936.
    Andrew Lewis initiated an appeal to raise funds for the new Infirmary (see note 9 above). On going to the public he was able to announce that he had already been promised about £200,000, the first half of which had come from four friends of the Joint scheme: Viscount and Viscountess Cowdray of Dunecht, Sir Thomas Jaffrey of Milltimber and Sir Robert Williams of Park*, each of whom had promised £25,000. Other major contributors were J.E. Crombie (note 27 of Chapter 19), J.A. Ross (note 68 of Chapter 10) and the Crombie-Ross Benevolent Fund who each gave £10,000. Ashley Mackintosh gave £2,500, Matthew Hay £2,000 and Andrew Lewis himself £2,000.

13. Quotation from Andrew Lewis's appeal.

14. For those not familiar with the geography of the North-East of Scotland an account of how this residence – which is 40 or so miles west of Aberdeen in the Dee valley – was chosen and developed will be found in Clark, R.W. *Balmoral – Queen Victoria's Highland Home*. Thames and Hudson, 1981. Much of the choice lay with the vagaries of the weather between east and west and the conviction – with which some might agree – of the son of her majesty's doctor that there were blue skies and unbroken sunshine to the east of the back bone of the Scottish mountains.

15. *Aberdeen Press and Journal*, 29 August 1928.

16. The architect was J.B. Nicol, FRIBA (1867–1953). Partner in the Aberdeen firm of Kelly and Nicol. For the ARI project he worked in consort with the consulting architects Pite, Son and Fairweather of London. At the opening ceremony he presented to the Duke of York a gold key to unlock the front door of the new Royal Infirmary. He was killed as a pedestrian in a road accident on the Aberdeen-Ellon road near the Belhelvie junction. See *Aberdeen Press and Journal*, 27 January 1953.

17. To contain offices, board room, kitchens, stores and dining rooms catering for a thousand people. Also living quarters for 12 resident doctors, the matron and assistant matron and bedrooms for 92 domestic staff.

18. For the way in which this was developing see Chapters 12 and 14.

19. See Aberdeen Royal Infirmary Annual Report 1931.

20. John McConachie (personal communication 1990) recalls visiting the site as a 12 year old, in the company of his father, John A. McConachie, clerk, treasurer and factor to the Infirmary (1931–1954), and A.G. Anderson (see note 59 of Chapter 10). Terrazzo flooring and piped wireless – both innovations in hospitals of that time – were being installed.

* See Hutchinson, R., Martelli, G. *Robert's People*. Chatto and Windus, London, 1971.

21. Which was to become the Aberdeen Joint Hospitals' Steam Heating and Laundry Company Ltd in 1934. See Aberdeen Royal Infirmary Annual Report, 1934.
22. Watt, Edward W. (1879–1955), MA(Hons) 1898 Aberdeen. Lord Provost of Aberdeen 1935–8. Was councillor, baillie and treasurer 1929–34. He initially joined Aberdeen Free Press of which his late father had been a proprietor. In 1902 he went to the press gallery of the House of Commons and returned to Aberdeen in 1906. He became editor of *Aberdeen Evening Gazette* and later joint manager of Aberdeen Newspapers Ltd (now Aberdeen Journals) until he retired in 1925. Lt Col in 4th Battalion Gordon Highlanders – active service on the front line 1914–18. LLD 1939 Aberdeen.
23. He was subsequently to tell a reunion of the Gordon Highlanders that he had tapped every possible source from football pools promoters to Lord Nuffield (a noted United Kingdom philanthropist heavily involved in the promotion of medicine and medical research). A notable benefactor of this fund was Peter Scatterty of Johannesburg who bequeathed £46,964 – the largest donation from one person – and whose name was given to the block for special diseases. The rest of Scatterty's fortune was disbursed to Robert Gordon's College to build a new library and to the cottage hospital at Insch from whose precincts he originated.
24. A detailed account is given in Ziegler, P. *King Edward VIII – The Official Biography*. William Collins and Co., London 1990, from which the following quotation is taken: 'The King's defence was that he had long ago told the Lord Provost that the court was still in mourning. It seemed curious to his subjects that he should be able to disport himself in the Mediterranean while in mourning, yet not visit a hospital, and that his brother should somehow be exempt from rules which applied so strictly to the monarch. . . The Aberdeen newspaper featured two photographs side by side: one of the Yorks opening the hospital, the other with the caption "His Majesty in Aberdeen. Surprise visit in car to meet guests"'.

Chapter 5

1. James, William (1842–1910). See *The Meaning of Truth*, 1909.
2. Florence Kaye. See also Chapter 8.
3. Fairweather, Geoffrey H. (1915–55), ARIBA 1939. Succeeded his father in the firm Pite, Son and Fairweather in 1946. His principal works in Aberdeen were: the university chemistry building; the extension to the medical school; the mothers' and babies' ward at the Children's Hospital; the blood transfusion service in Foresterhill east wing; and the operating theatre at the Aberdeen Maternity Hospital. He died after a long illness 'gallantly borne'.
4. Duffus, James C. (1891–1962), MA 1912, LLB 1914 Aberdeen, OBE, MC, TD. A highly successful Aberdeen advocate with a great love of the city. Served as a combatant in World War I and was severely wounded. Chairman of the General Hospitals Board 1948–62. He was described in the *Aberdeen University Review* as 'not obstinate but perhaps somewhat dogmatic' which sums up his strong personality and drive for efficient management. The south side of the ward on the third floor of Phase I (originally intended for private patients in the tradition of the Watson Fraser nursing home) is named after him and a plaque is to be found there; in 1991 this ward is for vascular surgery and the private beds have been diminished and relocated as a result of government directives. See *Aberdeen University Review* 1963; **40**: 80–1; *Aberdeen Press and Journal*, 22 November 1962.
5. Knox, J. Crawford (1891–1964), BSc 1913, MB ChB 1915 Glasgow. Medical superintendent ARI 1935–48. Senior administrative medical officer to NE Regional Health Board 1948–56. CBE 1941.
6. Beddard, F. Denys (1914–85), MB BS 1941 London (St. Mary's). Service with RAMC field units until 1945 when he was seconded to the medical directorate of 21st Army group.

Entered medical administration in 1950. Posts in the South Eastern Metropolitan Hospital Board. Came to Scotland first to the South Eastern Region and then in 1957 to Aberdeen as senior administrative medical officer. His achievements and the quality of his personality are recorded in the text of this chapter. In 1969 became chief medical officer in Northern Ireland and in 1972 deputy chief medical officer at the (then) DHSS. Retired 1978. CB 1977. HAFD notes that though he may have appeared at first encounter to be somewhat austere, on closer acquaintance his equanimity and wit, perspicacity and clear direction plus, most importantly, his ability to handle powerful and disparate personalities were invaluable and his contribution to the eventual success of the project was immense. See *British Medical Journal* 1986; **292**: 565.

7. Michie, A.M. Personal communication, 1990.
8. Mackay, W.D., Dudley, H.A.F. An artifical kidney in a general hospital group. *Scottish Medical Journal* 1963; **8**: 109–12.
9. Stephens, F.O., Dudley, H.A.F. An organisation for outpatient surgery. *Lancet* 1961; **1**: 1042–4.
10. See *British Medical Journal* 1959; **2**: 1108.
11. Report of the Professional Planning Committee 1961 (unpublished) which also contains a list of the staff involved.
12. HAFD.
13. Gordon Smylie.
14. Buff Hardie. Personal communication, 1990.
15. Baird, Matilda (May) D. (née Tennant) (1901–83), BSc MB ChB 1925 Glasgow. First chairman NE Regional Hospital Board 1947–60. National governor of the BBC in Scotland. LLD Aberdeen 1960. CBE. Freewoman of the City of Aberdeen 1966 (a double ceremony along with her Freeman husband Sir Dugald). See *Times*, 18 August 1983; *Aberdeen Postgraduate Medical Bulletin* 1984, January, 39; note 54 of Chapter 9.
16. Tousy – rough, brutal or violent.
17. HAFD recalls that many years afterwards he participated in another major hospital/medical school development within the NHS, by which time the centralization of decision making and the restrictions imposed by having to refer preliminary decisions up an administrative ladder to anonymous central planners were both frustrating and counter-productive for professional people including the architect. The bureaucracy did not produce any great improvement in the planning process or for that matter save money.
18. Smylie, Gordon. Personal communication, 1990.
19. This impression is based on the memories of a number of individuals involved in the planning process.
20 It is noteworthy that at this time the Department of Health in England and Wales was disengaging itself from the Ministry of Housing and setting up its own architectural department whose role was to be the provision of a central resource and advice. Here some would see the beginning of centralization referred to in note 17 above.
21. Shooter, R.A., Smith, M.A., Griffiths, J.D., Brown, M.E.A., Williams, R.E.O., Rippon, J., Jevons, M.P. Spread of staphylococcus in a surgical ward. *British Medical Journal* 1958; **1**: 607. See also: The staphylococcal menace. Leading article. *British Medical Journal* 1959; **2**: 684–5.
22. Smylie could do this with impunity because he was larger than Dudley.
23. Blowers, R. See Williams, R.E.O., Blowers, R., Gorrod, L.P., Shooter, R.A. Operating suite design and practice. In: *Hospital Infection: Causes and Prevention*. Lloyd Luke, London, 1966, pp.197–230.
24. Gillanders, Lewis. Personal communication, 1991.
25. Davidson, A.I.G., Smylie, H.G., Macdonald, A., Smith, G. Ward design in relation to postoperative wound infection. *British Medical Journal* 1971; **1**: 72–5.
26. P.F. Jones points out that the final allocation of accommodation to specialities followed closely the recommendations of the development sub-committee of the medical staff which had been adopted in May 1962.

Chapter 6

1. Gordon, James. See note 8 of Chapter 2.
2. Prominent amongst these was Dr Alexander Webster who used the Scottish clergy to make what would be known now as a cross-sectional study for 1755. The statistics are considered in detail in Smout, T.C. *A History of the Scottish People.* Collins, London, 1969, Chapter 11.
3. See for example, Graham, H.G. *Social Life in Scotland in the Eighteenth Century.* Adam and Charles Black, London, 1950, for a graphic account of life in 18th century Edinburgh. There is no reason to suppose that Aberdeen was any more sanitary.
4. The proximate causes of the epidemic infections in terms of bacterial organisms were still unknown. Nevertheless the evidence was beginning to accumulate though the work of pioneers was largely ignored or even scoffed at. In Aberdeen, Alexander Gordon had in 1795 published 'A treatise on child bed fever' which prevailed as an epidemic in Aberdeen from 1789 to 1792 the findings in which antedated the work of Semmelweis 50 years later. In 1854 John Snow arrested an epidemic of cholera in the Broad Street area of London by removing the handle from the pump of the common water supply. However, these were isolated instances and the recognition of specific cause had to await the establishment of the science of microbiology in the latter half of the 19th century. See Porter, I.A. *Alexander Gordon MD of Aberdeen.* Oliver and Boyd, Edinburgh, 1958; Correspondence. *British Medical Journal* 1957; **2**: 712.
5. Kilgour, A. Report of a committee to the Aberdeen Town Council. An Inquiry into the Sanitary Conditions of the Sick Poor in Aberdeen, 1840 .
6. Kilgour, Alexander (1803–1874), MD 1833 Marischal College. The son of an Aberdeen merchant. Apprenticed to a naval surgeon at the age of 13 and received his 'ticket' to attend the ARI two years later. Elected to the staff at ARI 1838. John Brown, author of *Rab and his Friends* described Kilgour as the 'Sydenham of the north' and he was clearly of great influence in medical (and other) affairs of the North-East. See *Lancet* 1874; **1**: 390. Also unpublished notes by A. Adam in the archives of Aberdeen Medico-Chirurgical Society.
7. Third Public Health Act, 1875; 38 and 39 Vict.c.55.
8. Hay, Matthew. See note 1 of Chapter 4.
9. Finlay, David W. (1840–1923), BA 1860, MD 1864 Glasgow. Physician and lecturer at Middlesex Hospital also appointed to Royal Hospital for Diseases of the Chest London. Regius professor of medicine Aberdeen 1891–1912. Known to the students of the time as 'Dauvit'. His portrait can be seen at the entrance to the Board Room at ARI. FRSE and LLD Aberdeen. See *British Medical Journal* 1923; **2**: 949–50.
10. Mackintosh, Ashley W. (1868–1937), MA 1888, MB CM 1893, MD (all hons) Aberdeen. A native of Deskford, Banffshire son of Rev. J. Mackintosh, minister at Deskford. Regius professor of medicine Aberdeen 1912–29. His memory is perpetuated by an eponymous trophy presented to the Medico-Chirurgical Society for annual golf competition and also his portrait by John B. Souter in the Society's committee room. Honorary physician in HM Household in Scotland 1928. LLD Aberdeen, KCVO 1931. See *British Medical Journal* 1937; **2**: 833–4.
11. Lyall, Sandy. See note 37 of Chapter 10.
12. Davidson, Stanley. See note 30 of Chapter 19.
13. Davidson, L.S.P. Inaugural address – summary. *Aberdeen University Review* 1930; **28**: 47.
14. For example, Ian Gordon (physician 1937–74); W.R. (Bill) Gauld (physician 1947–77 – current editor of the *Aberdeen Postgraduate Medical Bulletin*); C.D. Needham (physician 1948–75); Malcolm Macleod (senior lecturer and latterly personal professor in renal medicine 1958–84); and A. Stuart Douglas (Regius professor of medicine 1970–85).
   Gordon, Ian (1909–92), BSc (physiology), MB ChB 1932 Aberdeen. Born Buckie. Held registrar posts at the Royal Chest Hospital and Great Ormond Street, London. Served in the RAMC 1939–45 with the 15th Scottish General Hospital in the Middle East and Africa. OBE (mil) 1942. Physician in charge Ward 2 ARI 1948–74. Played an important role locally counselling and teaching medical officers returning from World War II. See *Aberdeen Postgraduate Medical Bulletin* 1974; September, 63–4.
15. Walker, William (1920–84), MA, MB ChB 1946 St Andrews. Studied arts before the war

and was commissioned in the Royal Scots in 1939. Wounded in the head in 1940 and invalided out in 1941. Senior lecturer in therapeutics at Dundee 1955–64 and thereafter consultant physician at Aberdeen City Hospital. Regius professor of therapeutics and materia medica 1973–83. An outstanding orator and humanist. See *Aberdeen Postgraduate Medical Bulletin* 1983, January, 27–9 and 1985, May 38–9.

16. This discipline developed at Woodend General Hospital following the appointment in 1970 of Dr P.W. Brunt and subsequently Drs N.A.G. Mowat and T.S. Sinclair who collaborated with the adjacent surgical unit – Messrs P.F. Jones (later Professor); J. Kyle and R.A. Keenan – until its removal to Foresterhill. A proposal during planning of Phase II to create a gastrointestinal (GI) ward with combined medical and surgical beds on the top floor never materialized (Brunt, P.W. Personal communication, 1991).

In 1990 the GI unit at Woodend moved to the second floor of the old surgical block (King George VI) at Foresterhill where the operating theatres had been refurbished into an endoscopy suite and the adjacent Nightingale wards redesignated general medical and renumbered 13/14 (previously ward 9 surgical). As we write part of this ward has become a referral unit for patients with GI bleeding and although it is increasingly interventionist it has maintained particularly close links with the resited Woodend surgical unit.

Chapter 7

1. Lister, J. On a new method of treatment of compound fracture, abscesses, etc with observations on the condition of suppuration. *Lancet* 1867; **1**: 326–9.
2. Mitchell, G.A.G. The founder of the Aberdeen School of Anatomy. In: Milne, G.P. (ed.) *Aberdeen Medico-Chirurgical Society: A Bicentennial History 1789–1989*. Aberdeen University Press, 1989, pp.71–82.
3. Ogston, Alexander (1844–1929), MB, CM 1865 Aberdeen. Initial appointment in the ARI as Ophthalmic Surgeon in 1868 (see Chapter 9). Became an assistant surgeon in 1870 on the retirement of Keith (see note 10 below). Ogston's distinguished career is considered in detail by Porter, I.A. In: Milne, G.P. (ed.) *Aberdeen Medico-Chirurgical Society: A Bicentennial History*. Aberdeen University Press, 1989, pp.179–89. Further details can be found in the text quoted in note 6. Ogston was Regius professor of surgery 1882–1909. Surgeon in Ordinary to Queen Victoria, Edward VII and George V. KCVO 1912.
4. Ogston, A. Medical training in Aberdeen and the Scottish universities. Aberdeen Medical Students' Society, 16 November 1877.
5. Lister, J. On the effects of the antiseptic treatment upon the salubrity of a surgical hospital. *Lancet* 1870; **1**: 4–6, 40–42.
6. Ogston, A. How antiseptic surgery came to Aberdeen. In: Ogston, W.H. (ed.) *Alexander Ogston KCVO*. Aberdeen University Press, 1943, pp.93–7.
7. Aberdeen Royal Infirmary Annual Report, 1863.
8. Aberdeen Royal Infirmary Annual Report, 1843.
9. The operating room, which in the meantime has been much modified structurally, persists in 1991 but its walls are peeling, the floor covered with dust and there is no trace of its former function. The building as a whole is devoted to the training of physiotherapists and to rehabilitation services.
10. Keith, William (1803–1871), MRCS England 1822, MD 1840 King's College, Aberdeen. Surgeon ARI 1838–1870. Became a well-recognized lithotomist. His memory is perpetuated by the Keith gold medal awarded to the best undergraduate in surgery at Aberdeen University. See *Lancet* 1871; **1**: 289.
11. The old form of spelling of Glenbuchat, a glen off the strath of the River Don in West Aberdeenshire.
12. Keith, W. *On the Safety and Suitableness of Chloroform*. Sutherland and Knox, Edinburgh, 1849.

13. Morgan, C.N. Surgery and surgeons in eighteenth century London. *Annals of the Royal College of Surgeons of England* 1968; **42**: 1–37.
14. Keith, W. Hospital statistics of stone in the bladder. *Edinburgh Medical Surgical Journal* 1844; **61**: 123–9 – read before Aberdeen Medico-Chirurgical Society, 4 May 1843.
15. Keith, W. Practical observations on the lateral operation of lithotomy. *Edinburgh Medical Surgical Journal* 1844; **61**: 396–417.
16. Aberdeen Royal Infirmary Annual Report, 1861.
17. Harris, S. *Woman's Surgeon*. The MacMillan Company, New York, 1950.
18. Pirrie, W. On acupressure. *Lancet* 1871; **2**: 7–9 and 42–44.
    Pirrie, William (1807–1882). A native of Fyvie in Aberdeenshire. Foundation professor of surgery at Marischal College from 1839–82. Ogston wrote of Pirrie's teaching 'I never heard a course of Surgery that approached in impressiveness and soundness the course we had from him'. See *Lancet* 1882; **2**: 965–6.
19. Ogston, A. On the comparative strength of arteries secured by the methods of ligature, acupressure and torsion. *Lancet* 1869; **1**: 524–6.
20. Dudley, H.A.F., Simpson, D.C. A surgical contretemps of 1869 and its effects. *Journal of the Royal College of Surgeons of Edinburgh* 1964; **10**: 72–7.
21. Will, J.C.O. Illustrations of antiseptic treatment in surgery. *Lancet* 1878; **2**: 78–9.
    Will, John C.O. (1845–1922), MB CM 1866, MD Aberdeen. Surgeon ARI 1874–89. Son of the late Dr James Will of Woodside. After graduating he went to Edinburgh and became assistant to Sir James Y. Simpson. FRSE. See *Aberdeen University Review* 1922; **10**: 95–6.
22. Bulloch, W. Sir Alexander Ogston. *Lancet* 1929; 1: 309-10.
23. Ogston, A. Ueber Abscesse. *Archiv fur klinische Chirurgie* 1880; **25**: 588. This paper was followed by two further ones on sepsis: Ogston, A. Micrococcus poisoning. *Journal of Anatomy and Physiology* 1882; **16**: 526–67; and Ogston, A. Report on micro-organisms in surgical diseases. *British Medical Journal* 1881; **1**: 369–75.
24. Fisher, R.B. *Joseph Lister 1827–1912*. MacDonald and Jane's, London, 1977.
25. The existence of two versions of this photograph (which is from the George Washington Wilson collection in the University of Aberdeen) in which the 'assistant' and the 'patient' change places, implies that it was taken in a studio though it undoubtedly (apart from the lack of anaesthesia) reflects the practice of the times.
26. Like the theatre in the Simpson dome, these are now shadowy disused areas under the much modified block.
27. Aberdeen Royal Infirmary Annual Report, 1893.
28. Aberdeen Royal Infirmary Annual Report, 1900.
29. Spencer Wells pioneered the operation in Britain and between 1870 and 1890 Lawson Tait in Birmingham performed some 5,000 laparotomies including 1,250 ovariotomies and was the surgeon who most clearly demonstrated that the time had come when abdominal surgery could be safely developed. See Shepherd, J.A. *Lawson Tait: the Rebellious Surgeon (1845–1899)*. Coronado Press, Lawrence, Kansas, 1980.
30. Fitz, R.H. Perforating inflammation of the vermiform appendix. *American Journal of Medical Sciences* 1886; **92**: 321–3.
31. McBurney, C. Experience with early operative interference in cases of disease of the vermiform appendix. *New York Medical Journal* 1889; **50**: 676–8.
32. Riddell, J.S. Appendicitis. *Scottish Medical and Surgical Journal* 1900; **6**: 214–22.
    Riddell, J. Scott (1864–1929), MA, MB CM 1888 Aberdeen. Surgeon ARI 1898–1919; commanding officer RAMC(V) Aberdeen Company 1904, MVO 1905, CBE 1918, LLD 1919. See *Aberdeen University Review* 1930; **17**: 111.
33. Marnoch, John (1867–1936), MA, MB CM (Hons) 1891 Aberdeen. Assistant surgeon 1893. Surgeon 1900. Regius Professor 1909–1932. Surgeon to the military hospitals of north-east Scotland 1914–18. KCVO 1928 on appointment to the King's Household in Scotland. LLD 1933 Aberdeen. See *Aberdeen University Review* 1936; **23**: 97–147.
34. Marnoch, J. On the surgical treatment of gastric ulcer, its complications and sequelae. *British Medical Journal* 1909; **1**: 834–9.

35. Anon. History of the Aberdeen Royal Infirmary. *People's Journal*, Dundee, 1904.
36. Gray, Henry M.W. (1870–1938), MB CM 1895 Aberdeen. Surgeon to ARI 1904–1923. Later Chief of Surgery, Royal Victoria Hospital, Montreal. LLD 1924 Aberdeen. See *Aberdeen University Review* 1939; **26**: 93.
37. Aberdeen Royal Infirmary Annual Report, 1908.
38. Lord Mount-Stephen. See note 23 of Chapter 3.
39. Smith, Frederick K. (1880–1947), MA, MB ChB 1903 Aberdeen. Surgeon ARI 1919–45. See *Aberdeen Postgraduate Medical Bulletin*, 1979: May, 26–8.
40. Colt, George H. (1878–1957), MB BChir 1904 (Cantab). Junior and senior resident anaesthetist St Bartholomew's; senior house surgeon Derbyshire Royal Infirmary; assistant surgeon ARI 1910; o/c surgery 43rd General Hospital RAMC Salonika 1914; surgeon ARI 1923–34. Surgeon Gravesend and North Kent Hospital and in Harley Street 1935–43. See *British Medical Journal* 1957; **2**: 1118, 1246, 1496.
41. Colt, G.H. The treatment of aortic aneurysm. *Medical Press and Circular* 1937; **194**: 499–504.
42. Aberdeen Royal Infirmary Annual Report, 1934.
43. Clark, D.N., Jones, P.F., Needham, C.D. Outcome in colorectal carcinoma: seven year study of a population. *British Medical Journal* 1980; **280**: 431–5.
44. Riddell, J.S. Listerism and the Aberdeen Royal Infirmary. *Press and Journal*, 6 April 1927.
45. Learmonth, James (1895–1967), MB ChB 1921 (Hons) Glasgow. Like W.C. Wilson (note 47 below) and Stanley Davidson (see note 30 of Chapter 19) was a combatant in World War I but recalled to complete his medical studies. Staff neurosurgeon Mayo Clinic 1924. Regius professor of surgery Aberdeen, 1932–39. Professor of systematic surgery and from 1946 also of clinical surgery University of Edinburgh 1939–56. Sucessively surgeon to George VI (on whom he operated) and to Elizabeth II. KCVO 1949. A man of formidable intellect and often forbidding mien he was essentially kind hearted and good to his colleagues and junior staff. He used frequently to recall in informal conversation that his years in Aberdeen were the happiest of his life. See *British Medical Journal* 1967; **A 58**, 117, 427.
46. Anderson, William (1886–1949), MB ChB (Keith Gold Medallist) 1901. Aberdeen RAMC 1914-18, first as battalion medical officer, later as surgeon. Mentioned in dispatches. Miltary OBE. Assistant surgeon ARI 1919. Surgeon 1935–49. Pioneer in neurosurgery and thoracic surgery. Brigadier (consultant to army in Scotland and Northern Ireland) World War II. '..he was tall, erect as befitted a soldier. . .handsome in features as a Clydesdale horse. He had a presence. . .' 'He could be "richt damn cross" about anything he regarded as a professional failure.' See *Aberdeen University Review* 1950; *British Medical Journal* 1949; **2**: 1418, 1534 and *Lancet* 1949; **2**: 1112, 1160. Also Howie, J. Portraits from memory No. 26. *British Medical Journal* 1988; **296**: 1051–2.
47. Wilson, William C. (1897–1974), MB ChB 1924 Edinburgh. A private in the Argyll and Sutherland Highlanders and later commissioned in the Black Watch, he served throughout the war of 1914–18. Thereafter pursued a career in clinical research and directed the Wilkie Research Laboratories in Edinburgh in the 1930s. Regius professor of surgery Aberdeen 1939–62. In charge No. 1 Research Station Middle East 1942–3. 'He was a physiologist practising surgery. He had a warm personality, an absence of rancour, a sense of fun and a keen eye for the ridiculous and pretentious. . .' See *Aberdeen Postgraduate Medical Bulletin* 1974; September, 46–7.
48. White, H. Surgery in the eighteenth and nineteenth centuries. In: Medvei, V.C., Thornton, J.L. (eds) *The Royal Hospital of St. Bartholomew, 1123–1973*. London, 1974, p.206.
49. One of the seniors was Sydney G. Davidson (1900–1980), MA, MB ChB 1924 Aberdeen. Surgeon ARI 1934–65. He was a conscientious objector but strove mightily in Aberdeen during the war. The editors have it on good authority that he returned to his colleagues who went to the war all the fees he obtained by looking after their patients. After retirement he became editor of the *Aberdeen Postgraduate Medical Bulletin*

1967–80. LLD 1975 Aberdeen. See *Aberdeen Postgraduate Medical Bulletin* 1980: September, 30.

Another was Andrew Fowler (1894–1971), MB ChB 1916 Aberdeen. Served in Salonika in World War I. On return he was posted to Bangour Hospital under Harold Stiles (professor of clinical surgery, Edinburgh) and struck up a lifelong friendship with Walter Mercer (later to become professor of orthopaedic surgery, Edinburgh). Officer commanding medical unit Aberdeen University Officers' Training Corps 1925–38. Commanding officer 8th(H) Fd Amb RAMC(V) 1939–40. Invalided back to Aberdeen. Assistant surgeon ARI 1922–44. Senior surgeon 1945-59. Locally renowned as a good craftsman. See *British Medical Journal* 1971; **4**: 752–3; *Aberdeen Postgraduate Medical Bulletin* 1972: January, 36–7.

Peter Konstam, OBE (personal communication) recalls coming to Aberdeen in 1941 as resident surgical officer (senior registrar equivalent) to Gordon Bruce and Professor Wilson. The only operating theatre in action at the time was on the first floor (theatre 8) – it was 'blacked out' and all operating was done in artificial light. In the 1970s he returned as a patient and noted some of the window panes in the anaesthetic room were still painted black though no one then knew why. Mr Konstam left Aberdeen in 1945 and after 11 years in Nigeria became consultant surgeon to the Orkney Isles at Balfour Hospital. He retired in 1975 and cheerfully provided locum cover for a further five years.

50. Bruce, G. Gordon (1891–1976), MB ChB (Keith Gold Medallist) 1915 Aberdeen. Surgeon ARI 1927–57. Surgeon to the Royal Household in Scotland 1939–57. See *Aberdeen Postgraduate Medical Bulletin* 1976: September, 49–50.
51. Murray, J.Greig (1919–88), MB ChB 1942, ChM Aberdeen. Senior Lecturer in Surgery, Aberdeen 1958–61. Professor of Surgery, King's College Hospital Medical School, London 1964–80. See *British Medical Journal* 1988; **296**: 508.
52. Burnett, William (1921–81), MB ChB (Hons) 1943, ChM Aberdeen. RAMC 1944–8. Trained in Aberdeen and became senior lecturer at Western Infirmary Glasgow. Professor of Surgery, University of Queensland 1963–1981. See *Aberdeen Postgraduate Medical Bulletin* 1982: January, 42.
53. Clark, Charles G. (1926–88), MB ChB 1953, MD ChM Aberdeen. Served in the RAMC in India before qualifying in medicine. Senior Lecturer in Surgery 1961–64 Aberdeen. Professor of Surgery University College Hospital London 1967–88. See *British Medical Journal* 1989; **298**: 110, 317. Also *Aberdeen Postgraduate Medical Bulletin* 1989; May, 35–6.
54. Logie, Norman J. (1904–72), MB ChB (Keith gold medallist) 1927 Aberdeen. Assistant to Professor Learmonth ARI 1931. Served in World War II with 15th (Scottish) General Hospital in Cairo. After two years he was posted to the UK to train surgical staff during the build up for the invasion of Europe. Officer in charge of surgery No. 77 General Hospital RAMC. Returned to ARI in 1945 as a general surgeon and was largely responsible for creating a urology department to which he was appointed surgeon in charge in 1967. Council member of the Association of Surgeons of Great Britain and Ireland. See *Aberdeen Postgraduate Medical Bulletin* 1972; June, 46–51.
55. Senior lecturers in surgery who became NHS consultants locally were: James Kyle, Norman Matheson, David Blair, Andrew Foote, Jack Miller, Jetmund Engeset and Zygmunt Krukowski.
56. Smith, G. Personal communication, 1990.
57. Michie, William (1912–78), MA, MB ChB 1935 Aberdeen. MBE (mil). Consultant surgeon ARI 1947–77. President Association of Surgeons of Great Britain and Ireland 1972. His brother is A.M. (Sandy) Michie, Medical Superintendent Aberdeen General Hospitals 1948–71. See *Aberdeen Postgraduate Medical Bulletin* 1978; September, 46–7.
58. Mavor, George E.M. (1919–73), MA, MB ChB (Hons) 1944, ChM Aberdeen. Rockefeller research fellow at Rochester University Medical School, New York. Consultant surgeon ARI 1959. Trained as a general surgeon he made outstanding contributions to vascular surgery. Council member of the RCSE. He died after a gastrointestinal operation. See *Aberdeen Postgraduate Medical Bulletin* 1974; May, 44–6.

59. Krukowski, Z.H., Matheson, N.A. The management of peritoneal and parietal contamination in abdominal surgery. *British Journal of Surgery* 1983; **70**: 440–1.
60. Krukowski, Z.H., Matheson, N.A. Ten-year computerised audit of infection after abdominal surgery. *British Journal of Surgery* 1988; **75**: 857–61.
61. Krukowski, Z.H. Personal communication, 1991.
62. Smith, G. Hyperbaric oxygen therapy. *Zodiac (Journal of the Aberdeen University Medical Faculty)* 1965; **12**: 30–2.
63. For an example of the multi-disciplinary approach required for complex decompression illness, see Norman, J.N., Childs, C.M., Jones, C., Smith, J.A., Ross, J., Riddle, G., MacKintosh, A., McKie, N.I., Macaulay, I.I., Fructus, X. Management of a complex diving accident. *Undersea Biomedical Research* 1979; **6**: 209–16.

Chapter 8

1. Minute Book Aberdeen Infirmary, 1 May 1744.
2. Minute Book Aberdeen Infirmary, 2 October 1744.
3. Baird, Jean. The first hospital midwife 1763–6. She was not replaced as the admission of women in labour ceased.
4. The town sergeant was one of five under the charge of the Provost's officer. Robert Robertson was engaged in 1750 at the rate of five shillings (25p) per quarter 'for his attendance in Bedlam', this sum being raised to £2 per annum in 1761-2 until May 1768 when the arrangement was discontinued.
5. Minute Book Aberdeen Infirmary, 21 June 1768.
6. Milne, G.P. *The History of Midwifery in Aberdeen*. In: Milne, G.P. (ed.) *Aberdeen Medico-Chirurgical Society. A Bicentennial History*. Aberdeen University Press, 1989, pp.239–40.
7. Minute Book Aberdeen Royal Infirmary, 28 October 1801.
8. Minute Book Aberdeen Royal Infirmary, 17 November 1801.
9. In: Ogston, W.H. (ed.) *Alexander Ogston KCVO*. Aberdeen University Press, 1943, p.93. Ogston's description is not borne out by a census in 1851 which records 18 resident nurses with only two aged 52 and 57 qualifying for a possible description of 'old crone.' All the women were from country districts and not Aberdeen itself.
10. Presumably but not certainly the Simpson Building.
11. Mutch – a close fitting cap worn by married women.
12. Kilgour, Alexander. See note 6 of Chapter 6.
13. Minute Book Aberdeen Royal Infirmary, 7 October 1823.
14. Minute Book Aberdeen Royal Infirmary, 16 September 1816.
15. Minute Book Aberdeen Royal Infirmary, 25 September 1837.
16. Minute Book Aberdeen Royal Infirmary, 3 January 1870.
17. Woodham-Smith, Cecil. *Florence Nightingale*. Constable, London, 1950.
18. Aberdeen Royal Infirmary. Report anent nursing arrangements. G. Cornwall and Sons, Printers, Aberdeen, 3 June 1873.
19. Ogston, A. Aberdeen Royal Infirmary. Report anent nursing arrangements. G. Cornwall and Sons, Printers, Aberdeen, 3 June 1873, p.6.
20. Protestant deaconesses. In: Aberdeen Royal Infirmary. Report anent nursing arrangements. G. Cornwall and Sons Ltd, Printers, Aberdeen, 3 June 1873, pp.10–11.
21. Aberdeen Royal Infirmary. Report anent nursing arrangements. G. Cornwall and Sons Ltd, Printers, Aberdeen, 3 June 1873, p.2.
22. Dobbie, Marion. Head nurse ARI 1874–5. Trained at Liverpool. Came to Aberdeen from a post in Brighton. On leaving she became matron at Broomhill Home for Incurables near Glasgow. Although only in post at ARI for a year she received a letter of commendation from the managers after she demitted office.
23. Bothwell, Margaret (1844–99). Head nurse ARI 1875–85. Born at Stoneywood, spent

childhood at Keithhall near Inverurie. Trained at the Nightingale school for nurses at St Thomas' Hospital London 1871–2. Royal Infirmary of Edinburgh 1872–5 under the leadership of Elizabeth Ann Barclay. On leaving ARI she became matron at Aberdeen City Hospital 1887–96.

24. Minute Book Aberdeen Royal Infirmary, 15 November 1876, in which a badge is recommended instead.

25. Donaldson, Robert (1749–1829), philanthropist. Supported Robert Donaldson's school in Back Wynd Aberdeen. Founder of Donaldson's fund initially intended for religious and educational purposes. A trustee of this fund who was also a manager of the ARI made money available to support and encourage women to train as 'sick nurses' in 1875 and led to the term Donaldson probationers. See *Aberdeen Journal* 13 May 1829.

26. Minute Book Aberdeen Royal Infirmary, 19 January 1875.

27. Minute Book Aberdeen Royal Infirmary, 15 October 1884.

28. Probationer – this term had now come into use for those on the lowest rung of the training ladder and presumably still subject to rejection by the authorities. It persisted into the 1940s.

29. Fraser, Angus (1838–1912), AM 1856 (Marischal), MD CM 1862, LLD 1901 Aberdeen. Senior physician and lecturer in clinical medicine at ARI until 1909. Assessor in the University Court 1889 See *Aberdeen Daily Journal*, 3 April 1912.

    Garden, R.J. See note 28 of Chapter 9.

30. Lumsden, Rachel. See note 25 of Chapter 3.

31. Board Minutes, 26 October 1885.

32. This remained in existence until 1935 when it was succeeded by a national scheme.

33. Tatham, Margaret F. Trained at the London Hospital 1886.

34. McNaughton,Grace. Matron ARI 1898–1912 died in post after a long illness.

35. Edmondson, Elizabeth (1863–1949). Matron Barnsley Infirmary before appointed matron Aberdeen Royal Infirmary 1912–1935. Principal matron, Military Hospital Aberdeen 1914–18. Adviser to the board on the new hospital at Foresterhill (but retired before re-location of ARI). Founder member of the Royal College of Nursing and of its Council. Member of the General Nursing Council. Although a lady of independent means, the popular rumour that she was not paid is untrue.

    In 1920 she supported, with the co-operation of a number of wives of the medical staff, the establishment of a Linen Guild for the Infirmary. This charitable organization gave sterling service in the supply of woollen garments and accessories for the comfort of in-patients until it was disbanded in 1990. The first president was Lady Gray (see note 36 of Chapter 7) and latterly the headquarters was in a property in Union Grove where these public-spirited ladies met on Wednesdays to pool their creations and acquisitions which were subsequently distributed within the hospital.

36. Minute Book Aberdeen Royal Infirmary, 8 July 1912.

37. Riddell, Scott. See note 32 of Chapter 7.

38. Minute Book Aberdeen Royal Infirmary, 26 November 1915.

39. Annual Report Aberdeen Royal Infirmary, 1913.

40. Preliminary training school – a 'hut at Woolmanhill' – Florence Kaye personal communication 1991 (see note 44 below).

41. Minute Book Aberdeen Royal Infirmary, 23 April 1919.

42. Adam, A. Personal communication, 1991. A close relative trained as a nurse at Woolmanhill in the 1920s.

43. Knox, J. Crawford. See note 5 of Chapter 5.

44. Kaye, Florence. Miss Kaye – who was awarded the OBE at the time of her retirement – is now living in Knaresborough and has provided much useful information for this account.

45. Crombie-Ross hall. This is a one storey building connecting the two wings of the nurses' home – built with funds (£3,500) donated by the trustees of the Crombie-Ross benevolent fund. The fund was used for a number of purposes including the Crombie-Ross lectureship in psycho-pathology in 1938 and the subsequent chair of

mental health (see p.158). There is also a commemorative plaque to the fund in the original Foresterhill surgical block which it helped to build. Crombie, James E. (see note 27 of Chapter 19); Ross, John A. (see note 68 of Chapter 10).

46. Kaye, Florence. Personal communication, 1991.

47. A total of eight: M. Bremner, J. Curran, E.A. Dalgarno, M.M. Mackay, C. Nicolson, I. Spence, M. Urquhart and K. Walker.

48. Miss Kaye records that if there was a bombing raid she had no need to call out staff – they were already there on their own initiative.

49. The Aberdeen Formula. See Crompton, H.M. Occasional papers. In: *Nursing Times* 26 August and 2 September 1976.

50. The Nurses Act 1919, HMSO.

51. Home sister was the term referring to the sister in charge of the nurses' home and initially this post was combined with that of sister tutor.

52. Minute Book Aberdeen Royal Infirmary, 16 February 1927. Catherine Muirhead was appointed on the resignation of a Sister Lacon.

53. Minute Book Aberdeen Royal Infirmary, 28 September 1933. This appointment of Sister Stephen was on Miss Edmondson's recommendation.

54. Nurses Act (Scotland). HMSO 1943.

55. Minute Book Aberdeen Royal Infirmary, 9 September 1943.

56. Aberdeen Pre-nursing College was initially in the Foresterhill nurses' home and later moved to the east wing.

57. Project 2000 – in 1986 the United Kingdom central council for nursing, midwifery and health visiting produced a document entitled 'A new preparation for practice'. An important finding was that the number of 18 year-olds is declining with a projected nadir in 1995 when there will be a potential annual shortfall of around 3,000 recruits to the profession. Various proposals have been made to take account of this largely based on encouraging qualified nurses to remain in post or to return to work. See Burnard, P., Chapman, C. *Nurse Education – the Way Forward*. Scutari Press, London 1990. (The publishing house of the nursing profession is named Scutari after the location of Florence Nightingale's hospital in Crimea.)

58. First Report of Nurses' Salaries Committee, HMSO, 1943.

59. Macklin, Alexander H. (1889–1967), MB ChB 1912, MD Manchester. Medical officer to the Imperial Trans-Antarctic Expedition in 1914 under Sir Ernest Shackleton sailing in the ill-fated *Endurance*. The story of this 'great adventure' is well known. Returned from the Antarctic in 1916 and joined the RAMC in France, Italy and later in Russia and Lapland where he commanded a sledge field ambulance. In World War II he was ADMS in Abyssinia and East Africa; awarded OBE, MC and TD. Previously a chloroformist and later assistant physician at Dundee Royal Infirmary. Appointed assistant physician to ARI 1946. He 'retired' aged 71 and unwilling to leave work continued in a succession of locum house officer posts at ARI until his death. FRGS. His favourite quote was '. . . we do not regret the things we have done half so much as the things we have not done. . .' See *Aberdeen University Review* 1967; **42**: 140–2.

60. Gauld, W.R. Personal communication, 1991. He himself carried this responsibility as a medical registrar and senior registrar when the medical and surgical chiefs were A.G. Anderson and Willie Anderson, respectively.

61. See Chapter 5.

62. Part time nurses in Foresterhill. Annual Report Aberdeen Royal Infirmary, 1947.

63. Whitley, John H. (1866–1935). Liberal MP for Halifax 1900–28. The eponymous term Whitley Council is in his memory and describes a negotiating body. It stems from the committee on the relations between employers and employed set up in October 1916 under his chairmanship. He was latterly speaker of the House of Commons. See Abel-Smith, B. *A History of the Nursing Profession*. Heinemann, London, 1960.

64. Salmon Report. This was produced by a committee of the Ministry of Health and Scottish Home and Health Department entitled Senior Nursing Staff Structure. It was named after its chairman Brian Salmon who at the time was vice-chairman of the

board of governors of the Westminster Hospital Group and also chairman of J. Lyons and Co.

65. Nurses badge – the design of the current badge is based on the crest of the Grampian Health Board with an outer circular blue border with the words Grampian Foresterhill College.

In heraldic terms the crest is divided vertically in two halves: the left half depicts the Angel of Mercy clasping the Book of Knowledge, the Dove of Peace and the Owl representing wisdom, holding a gavel with a serpent entwined around it. Taken from the Arms of the Royal College of General Practitioners this registers the Board's interest in both community and hospital care. The serpent on a staff is the sign of the medical profession originating from the Greek God of Medicine, Aesculapius. This God whose rights and ceremonies appear to have been influenced by serpent worship, was trained in healing and reputed to have been able to restore the dead to life. On the right of the crest the St Andrews Cross of Scotland is depicted covered by the shield and the crosslet of the Earls of Mar which constitutes the Grampian Regional Arms.

Chapter 9

1. Ogston, W.H. (ed.) *Alexander Ogston KCVO: an Autobiography*. Aberdeen University Press, 1943.
   Ogston, A. Unrecognised lesions of the labryinth. *Lancet* 1894; **2**: 114–7.
2. Peterkin, Henry (1877–1954), MA, MB CM 1900 Aberdeen. Travelled as ship's surgeon and then studied ENT for a year in Vienna. Started in practice in Aberdeen and was appointed as an assistant surgeon in the speciality with beds in the wards of Sir John Marnoch. Eventually he was appointed as the first specialist in the field. Served 1st Scottish General Hospital 1914–19. '. . .a kenspeckle figure – tall, erect and always sartorially and professionally correct. . .' See *British Medical Journal* 1954; **2**: 305; *Aberdeen University Review* 1954; **36**: 98.
3. Booth, J. MacKenzie (1856–1919), MB CM 1877 Aberdeen. After a varied experience in general practice and as a ship's surgeon was on the staff of the Dispensary 1880–91. Anaesthetist to ARI from 1886–90. Appointed assistant surgeon in 1892 and remained in this post until 1904. Primarily remembered for his work in ENT surgery but earlier in his career he was associated with gynaecology (see note 49 below). See *Aberdeen University Review* 1919; **6**: 292.
4. Souper, H. Ross (1887–1936), MA, MB ChB (Hons) 1912 Aberdeen. He was a talented organist. Served with RAMC in France and Mediterranean 1914–18. Became orthopaedic surgeon to Ministry of Pensions Hospital in Newcastle but thereafter embarked on a career in ENT surgery. See *Aberdeen University Review* 1936; **24**: 95.
5. Otty, Jack H. (1904–74), MB ChB 1927 Aberdeen. ENT surgeon, Aberdeen Royal Infirmary 1930–6. Subsequently consultant ENT surgeon in Bradford but maintained a life-long interest in Scottish affairs in his field. See *British Medical Journal* 1974; **2**: 617.
6. Gerrie, John (1908–49), MB ChB (Hons) Aberdeen 1930. Assistant surgeon ENT department at ARI 1934. Surgeon in charge 1946. Died while attending BMA conference in Harrogate. See *Aberdeen University Review* 1949; **33**: 207.
7. Collins, E. Godfrey ('Wilkie') (1902–76), MB ChB 1925 Edinburgh. Trained in Edinburgh and became ENT surgeon to the Royal Northern Infirmary, Inverness in 1929. Served 1939–45 in RAMC and captured at Tobruk in 1942. 'Unlike many facets of the NHS, the Regional ENT Service devised by Mr Collins has required little modification in three decades. . .' See *Aberdeen Postgraduate Medical Bulletin* 1977; January, 52–3.
8. Weir, Charles D. (1916–92), MB ChB 1938 Edinburgh. World War II RAMC service in

the Middle East and Western Desert; Military Cross decoration. Consultant otolaryngologist to the NE Regional Hospital Board 1950–77. A retiral valedictory described him '. . . of vigorous personality, depth of experience, helpfulness and sense of humour'. See *Aberdeen Postgraduate Medical Bulletin* 1978; May, 48–9. Charles Weir contributed to this chapter but died before publication.

9. Miss Pickford. Personal communication, 1990.
10. Todd, W.G. Personal communication, 1990.
11. Ridley, Ernest. See note 90 of Chapter 10.
12. Report of the Committee on Senior Nursing Staff Structure. Ministry of Health and Scottish Home and Health Department, 1966.
13. Watson, Fiona. A history of ophthalmology in Aberdeen. *Aberdeen Postgraduate Medical Bulletin* 1984; September, 27–31.
14. Cadenhead, John (1799–1862). Little is known to the editors about this physician and oculist. He became a junior member of the Medical Society in 1814. Educated at Marischal College and apprenticed at Charing Cross in London under a Dr Guthrie. See Rodger, Ella H.B. A group of Aberdeen doctors. In: *Aberdeen Doctors at Home and Abroad*. Blackwood and Sons, Edinburgh, 1893, p.290.
15. Minute Book Aberdeen Royal Infirmary, July 1837.
16. Minute Book Aberdeen Royal Infirmary, 7 May 1838.
17. McGrigor, James (1771–1858), AM 1788 Marischal College. Founder member of the Aberdeen Medical Society which later became the Medico-Chirurgical Society. Apprenticed to George French in the Aberdeen Royal Infirmary 1788–93. Attended classes in Edinburgh 1789–91. Achieved fame as the founder of the Royal Army Medical Corps. Knighted in 1814. Commemorated by a portrait by William Dyce, R.A. in the Medico-Chirurgical Hall and a red granite obelisk erected initially in the quadrangle at Marischal and removed in 1906 to its present site in the Duthie Park. In London his statue is in the garden of the RAMC headquarters at Millbank. See Blanco, R.L. *Wellington's Surgeon General*. Duke University Press, Durham, NC, 1974. Also Whyte, A.G.D. The McGrigor manuscripts. In: Milne, G.P. (ed.) *Aberdeen Medico-Chirurgical Society. A Bicentennial History 1789–1989*. Aberdeen University Press, 1989. Also Gauld, W.R. Sir James McGrigor 1771–1858. In: Milne, G.P. (ed.) *Aberdeen Medico–Chirurgical Society. A Bicentennial History 1789–1989*. Aberdeen University Press, 1989.
18. Minutes of the Board of Managers of Aberdeen Royal Infirmary, February 1863.
19. Wolfe, John R. (1824–1904), MD 1856 Glasgow. Born in Breslau (now Wroclaw in South Central Poland). Senior surgeon to Garibaldi and inspector of his troops. He came to Aberdeen in 1863 and returned to Glasgow in 1868 where he founded the Ophthalmic Institute and became professor of ophthalmology at St Mungo's College. First described the use of a full thickness skin graft (taken from behind the ear) to correct ectropion and other eyelid deformities caused by loss of skin. Resigned circa 1892 and practised as an ophthalmologist in Melbourne, Victoria where he became surgeon oculist to the Governor of Victoria. Returned to Glasgow circa 1900. He is described by one historian as '. . .without doubt a very flamboyant character and in the eyes of many people a charlatan.' He is also credited, though without satisfactory documentary evidence, with the first human corneal transplant. See Riddell, W.J.B. *The Glasgow Ophthalmic Institute 1868–1968*. Board of Management for Glasgow Royal Infirmary and Associated Hospitals, 1968.
20. Davidson, A. Dyce (1846–86), MA, MB CM (Hons) 1866 Aberdeen. Studied in Paris and was appointed surgeon to the Eye Institute. He was then first chloroformist at Aberdeen Royal Infirmary 1871–5. Held the joint posts of professor of materia medica and of lecturer in opthalmic surgery from 1878 until his death and continued in general practice as well as his speciality. His exit was a dramatic one with the onset of cerebral symptoms during a lecture, collapse and death within three hours See *Aberdeen Journal*, 23 October 1886.
21. Davidson, J. McKenzie. See note 4 of Chapter 12.

22. Usher, Charles H. (1865–1942). A nephew of Andrew Usher the brewing benefactor of Edinburgh University. Graduated from Cambridge and St Thomas' 1890. Studied under Nettleship. Appointed ophthalmologist to the ARI in 1895. Nettleship prize winner and president of the Ophthalmological Society of the United Kingdom. Bowman lecturer. 'A tall dignified man. . . he commanded immediate respect – and got it'. See Cockburn, C. *Aberdeen Postgraduate Medical Bulletin* 1975; September, 40–2.

23. Souter, W. Clark (1880–1959), MB ChB 1903 Aberdeen. Was ship's surgeon on the *Terra Nova* which went to relieve the Scott expedition in 1903–4. Trained at Moorfields Eye Hospital in London. See *Aberdeen University Review* 1959; **38**: 208–9; Souter, W.C. The story of our Kayak. In: Milne, G.P. (ed.) *Aberdeen Medico-Chirurgical Society: A Bicentennial History 1789–1989*. Aberdeen University Press, 1989.

24. Smith, H. Edgar (1880–1956), MA, MB ChB 1910 Aberdeen. Initially interested in the diplomatic corps he changed to medicine and formed a longstanding professional relationship with Usher (see note 22 above). Attached 1st Scottish General Hospital 1914–16 and served with Usher in Salonika 1916–18. Created the Newburgh bird sanctuary. See *Aberdeen University Review* 1956; **46**: 428–9, which also summarizes obituaries in the *British Journal of Ophthalmology* and the *British Medical Journal*.

25. Law, Beatrix B. (1899–1987), MA, MB ChB 1923, MD Aberdeen, DO Oxon 1930. Ophthalmic surgeon ARI 1930. Surgeon in Charge 1946–61.

26. Mutch, Joseph R. (1895–1953), MB ChB 1934, MD Aberdeen, DO England 1935. Assistant ophthalmic surgeon ARI 1939. Consultant ophthalmic surgeon to North East Regional Hospital Board. See *Aberdeen University Review* 1953; **35**: 211.

27. In 1976 Mr Charles Cockburn donated a sum of money towards the establishment of a university chair of ophthalmology. This was put towards a university development trust and in 1983 a large donation through Sir Hugh Fraser allowed the establishment of a university department of ophthalmology. Sir Hugh asked that the department be named after his grandparents, Sir Andrew and Lady Lewis (see note 11 of Chapter 4). It was decided that the chair should be named the Cockburn chair. In addition a substantial grant was obtained from the Frost foundation, through Sir Stephen Miller, an Aberdeen graduate (1937), who was surgeon oculist to HM the Queen 1974–80.
    Cockburn, Charles (1909–1992), MA, MB ChB 1933 Aberdeen. Son of a farmer at Rhynie, Aberdeenshire. Served in the RAMC 1939–45 and was consultant adviser in ophthalmology in Malta. Territorial Decoration. Consultant eye surgeon to Royal Aberdeen Children's Hospital and Aberdeen Royal Infirmary 1946–73. Performed the first corneal transplant graft at Aberdeen Royal Infirmary 4 April 1950. LLD Aberdeen. Mr Cockburn contributed to this chapter but died before publication.

28. Garden, Robert J. (1849–1903), MB CM (Hons) 1872, MD Aberdeen. Assistant surgeon ARI 1874, and later senior surgeon and lecturer in clinical surgery. Also held appointment as lecturer on diseases of the skin. See *British Medical Journal* 1903; **2**: 1184.

29. Garden, R.J. *Skin Diseases. Synopsis of Lectures on Diseases of the Skin*. Bon Accord Press, 1889.

30. Ogston, A. Ueber Abscesse. *Archiv fur klinische Chirurgie* 1880; **25**: 588.

31. Ogston, A. Report upon micro-organisms in surgical diseases. *British Medical Journal* 1881; **1**: 369–75. For an account that puts the work of Ogston into a dermatological context, see Lyell, A. Alexander Ogston (1844–1929) – Staphylococci. *Scottish Medical Journal* 1977; **22**: 277–8.

32. Christie, John F. (1870–1931), MA, MB CM 1895 Aberdeen. House physician at ARI to Robert Garden and Blaikie Smith. Went to Germany with Henry M.W. Gray for further study. On return to Aberdeen appointed assistant physician at ARI and became chief of the skin department on the retirement of Garden in 1901. Additional appointment as lecturer in venereal diseases to the University 1928–31. See *Aberdeen University Review* 1931; **18**: 306.

33. Minute Book Aberdeen Royal Infirmary, 15 April 1901.

34. Anderson, Thomas E. (1903–73), MB ChB (Hons) 1926, MD Aberdeen. House

physician to Sir Ashley Mackintosh who encouraged his interest in dermatology. Subsequently worked for two years as holder of an Anderson Travelling Fellowship in medicine at the Pasteur Institute in Paris. Appointed assistant physician at ARI (dermatology and venereal disease) in 1929 and became head of the Skin Department in 1931 on the death of John Christie (see note 32) and continued as assistant in Venereal Diseases to Dr Bowie. Served as an RAMC specialist in the two disciplines in World War II. Consultant dermatologist to NE Regional Health Board 1948–68. 'conservative in attitude and outlook. . .holding to the ancient ways and having no patience with the cult of youth and the accompanying long hair and their disrespect for tradition and for their elders'. See *Aberdeen Postgraduate Medical Bulletin* 1974: May, 42–5.

35. Lyell, A. Toxic epidermal necrolysis: an eruption resembling scalding of the skin. *British Journal of Dermatology* 1956; **68**: 355–61.
36. L. Stankler, Marion White and A.D. Ormerod.
37. Duncan, George M. See note 5 of Chapter 13.
38. Bowie, Frederick J.T. (1897–1973), MB ChB 1924 Aberdeen. Enlisted with the Gordon Highlanders before he had attained the age of 18 years and served in France 1914–18 as a sniper in the ranks until he was commissioned. Returning from the war he started medicine in 1919. Assistant physician to John Christie in 1926 and head of the Venereal Diseases Department 1931–59. Consultant in Venereal Diseases for all armed forces in Northern Scotland throughout World War II. See *Aberdeen Postgraduate Medical Bulletin* 1974; May, 44.
39. Rutherford, Hugh W. (1915–88), MB ChB 1942 Aberdeen. VD specialist in RAMC 1944–7. Became divisional Medical Officer of Health in Lancashire before returning to Aberdeen in 1952 as assistant chest physician (tuberculosis) at the City Hospital. In 1958 he took up an additional part-time appointment in Venereal Diseases and gradually this became a full-time commitment. Appointed consultant venereologist 1966–80. See *Aberdeen Postgraduate Medical Bulletin* 1988; September, 38–9.
40. *Oxford English Dictionary*.
41. Baird, D. In: Rorie, D. (ed.) *The Book of Aberdeen*. Compiled for the 107th Annual Meeting of the British Medical Association. W&W Lindsay, Aberdeen, 1939.
42. Dyce, Robert (1798–1869). Foundation Regius professor of midwifery, Aberdeen, 1860. See Milne, G.P. The history of midwifery in Aberdeen. In: Milne, G.P. (ed.) *Aberdeen Medico-Chirurgical Society. A Bicentennial History 1789–1989*. Aberdeen University Press, 1989, Chapter 17, p.231.
43. Inglis, Andrew (1837–1875). Regius professor of midwifery, Aberdeen, 1869–75. See Milne, G.P. (note 42).
44. Stephenson, William (1837–1919), MD Edinburgh 1864. Regius professor of midwifery 1875–1912. A pupil of James Young Simpson. He practised as a paediatrician and was 'very popular as a lecturer and his wit delighted the students.' His portrait hangs in Marischal College. See Milne, G.P. (note 42) and *British Medical Journal* 1919; **1**: 295.
45. Stephenson, W. *The Midwifery Chair in its Relations to Medical Education – an Introductory Lecture*. John Baxter and Sons, Printers, Edinburgh, 1876.
46. Aberdeen Dispensary Annual Report, 1893.
47. Lock wards were for the treatment of venereal disease. The origin of this word, first recorded in 1700 (see *Oxford English Dictionary*), is obscure. It would seem likely that it relates to the punitive attitude taken towards venereal disease, and that in the late 17th and early 18th century patients were retained under lock and key for treatment. The word died out in medical use during the early 20th century.
48. Aberdeen Royal Infirmary Minute Book, 7 December 1897.
49. Booth, James MacKenzie. See note 3 above.
50. For the general form of the Woolmanhill buildings (see Chapter 3).
51. McKerron, Robert Gordon (1863–1937), MB CM 1888 Aberdeen. Trained in general practice and physiology and succeeded William Stephenson whose assistant he had been in the chair of midwifery in 1912. He was much crippled by rheumatoid arthritis.

His 'classic' *Pregnancy, Labour and Childbed with Ovarian Tumour based on 1,290 Cases* (including 704 of his own) appeared in 1903. See *British Medical Journal* 1937; **1**: 733, 789. Also Milne, G.P. *Aberdeen Postgraduate Medical Bulletin* 1972; February, 25–6.

52. Davidson, George S. (Jeff) (1892–1960), MB ChB 1916. Served in Salonika 1917–18. Assistant obstetrician Aberdeen Maternity Hospital 1923. Gynaecologist to ARI 1930–50. Tutor in clinical surgery Aberdeen University 1923–30. Founder member of the Royal College of Obstetricians and Gynaecologists. See *British Medical Journal* 1960; **2**: 75.

53. Milne, G.P. Personal communication, 1991.

54. G.P. Milne writes: '. . .in 1936 Dugald Baird and Chassar Moir more or less tied for the appointment of professor and it was left to the then secretary of state for Scotland – Walter Elliot – to decide in favour of one or the other. Dugald Baird told me that Walter Elliot met him in a hotel in Edinburgh and in a rather informal way recommended him for the appointment to the chair.'

Baird, Dugald (1899–1986), BSc, MB ChB 1922, MD Glasgow. Trained in Glasgow in gynaecology and midwifery during which time he developed a great interest in clinical epidemiology as well as gaining a gold medal for his MD on the urinary tract in pregnancy. Appointed to the Regius chair in Aberdeen in 1937. Retired 1964. During his time in Aberdeen he became nationally and internationally famous for his work in the fields of social deprivation, nutrition and the effects of these on pregnancy and childbirth. Knighted in 1959. See also Lady May Baird (note 15 of Chapter 5). For a more detailed appreciation, see *Aberdeen Postgraduate Medical Bulletin* 1987; May, 36–7; *British Medical Journal* 1986; **293**: 1446; and *Lancet* 1986; **2**: 1289.

55. Dugald Baird (see note 54); George S. Davidson (see note 52); Archibald S. Duncan 1946–50, who went to Cardiff as professor and thereafter as dean of medical education in the University of Edinburgh; James Walker, 1947–55, who then became professor in Dundee.

56. R.M. Bernard; K.J. Dennis; W.T. Fullerton, 1962–89; A.I. Klopper, 1959–87, who was latterly a personal professor in reproductive endocrinology; I. MacGillivray, Regius professor 1964–84; G.P. Milne, 1950–76; G.H. Swapp; J.F.B. Wyper 1948–80.

Bernard, Robert McF. (1918–89), MB ChB 1940 Aberdeen. Major, RAMC with 56 (Lond) Infantry Div. 1942–6. Consultant in obstetrics and gynaecology to Aberdeen General and Special Hospitals 1953–71. Departed to take up post in the World Health Organisation based in Geneva and became widely recognized for his work in family planning in developing countries.

Dennis, K. John (1929–89), MB ChB 1952 Edinburgh. Born in Czeckoslovakia and orphaned at the age of nine he was taken out on one of the last Red Cross trains to leave the country. Subsequently brought up in Selkirk. Became one of Baird's acolytes after qualifying in medicine and was a senior lecturer in Aberdeen until 1972 when he became professor in Southampton. See *British Medical Journal* 1990; **1**: 460.

57. Turnbull, Alexander C. (1925–90), MB ChB 1947 Aberdeen, CBE 1982. Senior lecturer and honorary consultant under Dugald Baird at ARI 1961–6. Subsequently professor in Cardiff 1966–73 and thereafter Nuffield professor in Oxford. Knighted 1988. See *Aberdeen Postgraduate Medical Bulletin* 1991; January, 36. Also *British Medical Journal* 1990; **301**: 549.

Other lecturers in Professor Baird's department who became professors in the places mentioned, not including Australasia and the Far East, were: Ian D. Cooke, University of Sheffield; Denys V.I. Fairweather, University College Hospital, London; Malcolm C. MacNaughton, University of Glasgow, President of the Royal College of Obstetricians and Gynaecologists, knighted 1987; and David B. Stewart, University of the West Indies.

58. Wyper, J.F.B. Pregnancy after primary infertility investigation. *British Medical Journal* 1962; **1**: 273–6.

59. Dr (Betty) Macgregor came to Aberdeen in 1959 when her husband was appointed to the Regius chair of materia medica in the university (see note 43 of Chapter 10). In

1988 it was a stipulated condition that the Harris Birthright grant (see note 60 below) would only be awarded if Dr Macgregor, who was intending to retire, would continue as a director in company with A.A. Templeton and F. Walker, Regius professors of obstetrics and gynaecology, and pathology, respectively.

60. Birthright. A charitable trust affiliated to the Royal College of Obstetricians and Gynaecologists to support research into the health of women and babies. Sir Philip Harris, who built up the Harris Queensway carpet and furniture retail chain, is a generous supporter of Birthright.

61. Stephen, George. See note 23 of Chapter 3.

62. Primrose, Thomas (1808–86), MA 1825 Marischal College. Legal apprenticeship with Charles Chalmers in Aberdeen. Joined Society of Advocates in 1833. Entered independent practice in Aberdeen and later, commissioned by his apprenticeship firm, he went to the United States to wind up the affairs of the North American Investment Company. Successful there he stayed on for a number of years and amassed a fortune. Retired to Aberdeen in 1866. Unmarried and with only one sister, his estate was left in the hands of trustees. See Henderson, J.A. *History of the Society of Advocates*. Milne and Hutchison, Aberdeen, 1912.

63. Proctor, D. Personal communication, 1991.

64. Michie, A.M. Personal communication, 1991.

65. Baird, May. See note 15 of Chapter 5.

66. Beddard, Denys. See note 6 of Chapter 5.

67. Williamson, William (1817–93). A foundation licentiate (amongst another 120) of the Royal College of Surgeons of England in 1860. Initially in practice in Leicester he was dental surgeon to the Infirmary from 1862–81 and was one of the 13 present at the inaugural meeting of the Odonto-Chirurgical Society of Scotland in 1867.

68. See Menzies Campbell, J. Dentistry then and now. Pickering and Inglis, Glasgow, 1963. Also *British Journal of Dental Science* 1871; **14**: 305.

69. Williamson, William H. (1853–1912), MB CM Aberdeen 1874. Medical officer in charge of the Dental Department ARI 1881–98.

70. Crombie, James M. (1873–1932). MB CM Aberdeen 1895. Trained at Guy's Hospital, London. Medical officer in charge of the Dental Department ARI 1898–1932.

71. Crombie, Hugh McK. (1903–61), MB ChB Aberdeen 1925. Medical officer in charge of the Dental Department ARI 1932–48. Consultant dental surgeon to ARI and North-East Regional Hospital Board 1948–61.

72. Mitchell, Alexander (1881–1953), MA, MB ChB (Hons) 1905, ChM Aberdeen. Lecturer in surgical diseases of children 1928. Surgeon in charge of orthopaedic department ARI 1936–45. See *Aberdeen University Review* 1953; **35**: 206. Also Rennie, A.M. Alexander Mitchell. *Aberdeen Postgraduate Medical Bulletin* 1979; September, 6–7.

73. Hay, George (1917–78), MB ChB 1938 Edinburgh. Joined the Emergency Medical Service when declared unfit for the RAMC due to impaired hearing. Became registrar to Alex Mitchell at Stracathro in 1941 and consultant orthopaedic surgeon to NE Regional Board in 1948. After one year in Aberdeen returned to Stracathro where he gave loyal service for the subsequent 27 years. He had a particular interest in the Limb Fitting Service. See *Aberdeen Postgraduate Medical Bulletin* 1979; January, 44–5.

74. MacKenzie, Ian G. (1921–86), MB ChB 1946, MD Edinburgh. Consultant orthopaedic surgeon ARI 1958–83. Trained under H.J. Seddon both in Oxford and London (Royal National Orthopaedic Hospital). See *Aberdeen Postgraduate Medical Bulletin* 1986; September, 43.

75. Dunn, Naughton (1884–1939), MA, MB ChB 1909 Aberdeen. Was the son of a well-known Aberdeen boot and shoe retailer. After graduating he became house surgeon to Robert Jones in Liverpool the following year. Returned from active service with the RAMC in 1916 and was transferred to establish a military orthopaedic centre at Birmingham. Founder member of the British Orthopaedic Association and became a leading figure at the Robert Jones and Agnes Hunt Orthopaedic Hospital at Oswestry. LLD 1937 Aberdeen. See Raffan, A.W. Naughton Dunn and the Shorthouse Bequest.

In: Milne G.P. (ed.) *Aberdeen Medico-Chirurgical Society: A Bicentennial History 1789–1989.* Aberdeen University Press, 1989; pp.257–67.

Chapter 10

1. Waller, A.D. A demonstration on man of electromotive changes accompanying the heart's beat. *Journal of Physiology* 1887; **8**: 229.
2. Einthoven, W. The different forms of the human electrocardiogram and their signification. *Lancet* 1912; **1**: 853–61.
3. Croll, William F. (1875–1959), MA 1895, MD Aberdeen. Physician in charge of the cardiographic department and consultant 1920–35. He will be remembered for 'his methodical clinical teaching, his upright bearing, commanding personality and playful humour'. See *Aberdeen University Review* 1959; **37**: 207.
4. Howie, J. Personal communication, 1990.
5. Duthie, Robert J. (1901–71). Assistant physician 1935–47. Physician 1947–59 (ward 3). Succeeded Dr W.F. Croll in charge of the ECG department in 1935. He had studied under Dr Croll and at the Brompton Hospital London. 'He led a busy life; in addition to his hospital commitments he was much in demand for domiciliary consultations over a wide area of North and East Scotland. Although he could occasionally be quick tempered, it was never for long and he was unfailingly kind and supportive to his patients and junior staff. Well ahead of his time he outspokenly condemned cigarette smoking'. See *Aberdeen Postgraduate Medical Bulletin* 1971; April, 51.
6. Hendry, Alexander W. (see note 60 below).
7. Craig, John (see note 61 below).
8. Robert S. Aitken succeeded L.S.P. Davidson as Regius professor of medicine at Aberdeen 1939–48. Vice Chancellor, University of Birmingham 1953–68. Now retired and living in Birmingham. Knighted in 1960.
9. Anderson, William (see note 46 of Chapter 7).
10. Gowar, F. Sambrook. Personal communication, 1990.
11. Keers, Robert Y. (1908–83), MB ChB Edinburgh 1930. He contracted tuberculosis while a student but recovered with sanatorium treatment. Superintendent Tor-na-Dee Sanatorium 1939–57 and also of Glen-o'-Dee. He left Deeside when, in the words of the *British Medical Journal* obituary, '. . .his benevolent and effective brand of paternalistic autocracy. . . did not wholly mesh with . . .the mechanisms of the NHS'. Worked as a consultant chest physician in the Potteries until his retirement in 1973. See *British Medical Journal* 1983; **286**: 70, 314; letter from Dr Robert Fraser in *Aberdeen Medico-Chirurgical Archives*.
12. Wilson, Howard B. (1908–58), MB ChB (Hons) 1930 Aberdeen. A founder of modern anaesthesia in the north-east of Scotland. War service with the RAF. Consultant anaesthetist 1948–58. Regional Director 1954–8. Piloted his own aeroplane. Died in status asthmaticus. See *British Medical Journal* 1958; **2**: 330–1.
13. Davidson, Lawson D. (1922–89), MB ChB 1945 Aberdeen. Consultant anaesthetist 1962–89. Had a large practice in chairside dental anaesthesia. See *Aberdeen Postgraduate Medical Bulletin* 1990: January, 38.
14. Bell, Douglas (1902–75), MB ChB Edinburgh 1924. Tuberculosis officer to county of Aberdeen 1937. RAMC 1940–5 in Middle East. Deputy medical officer of health and regional tuberculosis officer Aberdeen 1945–67. Consultant chest physician. OBE 1968. 'A tireless worker who set a high standard in his clinical practice and expected the same from his subordinates. . .' See *British Medical Journal* 1975: **2**; 598.
15. Morgan, Thomas N. (1908–69), MB ChB(Hons) Aberdeen 1931, MD(Hons). Consultant physician. A man of many parts and sometimes sardonic humour, he was not only a broadly based physician and neurological enthusiast but also at one time the only physician to wield the early gastroscope. He was in addition an accomplished artist and

cognoscente of the art world. See *British Medical Journal* 1969; **1**: 581; *Aberdeen Postgraduate Medical Bulletin* 1969: October, 59.

16. de Silva, R.A. John MacWilliam, Evolutionary biology and sudden cardiac death. *Journal of the American College of Cardiology* 1989: **14**; 1843–9.

    MacWilliam, John A. (1857–1937), MB CM 1880, MD Aberdeen. Studied further in Leipzig and Berne. In 1882 became assistant to Schafer at University College London. Regius professor of physiology at Aberdeen and honorary physiologist to the Royal Infirmary 1886–1927. LLD Aberdeen 1928. He was the first to describe ventricular fibrillation, see Fibrillar contraction of the heart. *Journal of Physiology* 1887; **8**: 296–310. He also first described the possibilities of cardiac pacing, see Electrical stimulation of the heart in man. *British Medical Journal* 1889; **1**: 348–50.

17. Patterns for Health Services in Scotland. Cardiac Surgery. A report by a programme planning group of the Scottish Health Service planning council. Scottish Home and Health Department, St Andrews House, Edinburgh, September 1977.

18. Though we have only anecdotal evidence for the statement, this was the late Robert McCormack of Edinburgh, an outstanding pioneer of cardiothoracic surgery in Scotland, but renowned also for his confident dogmatism. See *British Medical Journal* 1981; **283**: 1065.

19. Howie, W. Bruce McN. (1920–85), MB ChB 1946 Edinburgh, OBE 1984. Senior administrative medical officer North Eastern Regional Hospital Board 1971–4; chief administrative medical officer 1974–84. 'Not a gregarious person by nature and with a tendency to shyness, he was nevertheless engaging and entertaining company. . .' See *Aberdeen Postgraduate Medical Bulletin* 1985: September, 35.

20. *Aberdeen Press and Journal*, 16 January 1980. It has not been possible accurately to identify the 'spokesman' but it is known that some members of the board remained hostile at this time to the development of a full range of cardiac surgery in Aberdeen.

21. Hansard (Parliamentary Debates) Fifth Series, vol. 983. Session 1979, vol. 978, l5 February 1980: Open heart surgery (Aberdeen) 2022–3. Session 1979–80, 30 April 1980, 554–5: Cardiac surgery units – funding. The accounts are worthy of reading in detail for the grasp of the subject shown by the local member, Robert Hughes, and by the rebuttal from the government based on the testimony to the Kaye Committee (see note 17) by two professional members of the Aberdeen staff.

22. Leslie Pratt – an Aberdeen citizen who had been cured surgically of a pharyngeal pouch.

23. Palmer, Kenneth N.V. (1920–82), MB BS London (Middlesex Hospital) 1944. Served RAF 1948–50. Senior lecturer and latterly reader in medicine Aberdeen University 1953–80. 'He enjoyed his work, liked a joke, but most of all he loved life.' See *Aberdeen Postgraduate Medical Bulletin* 1983: May, 39.

24. Banting, F.C. The internal secretion of the pancreas. *Journal of Laboratory and Clinical Medicine* 1922; **7**: 251–6.

25. Macleod, John J.R. (1876–1935) MB ChB (Hons) 1898 Aberdeen. Professor of physiology in University of Toronto 1918 following a staff appointment at Western Reserve University, Cleveland. Before the discovery of insulin he had contributed much to the understanding of carbohydrate metabolism: '. . .his reputation. . . as one of the world's greatest physiologists was established apart altogether from his work on insulin.' Co-sharer of the Nobel prize in physiology and medicine 1923. Regius professor of physiology Aberdeen 1928–35 and consultant physiologist to ARI, Rowett Institute and Torry Fishery Research Station. FRS, LLD 1925 Aberdeen. See *Aberdeen University Review* 1935; **22**: 200–3.

26. The modern classification is into type I disease which occurs principally in the young and seems to indicate some form of active destruction of islet cells, and type II, more common in later life, where degenerative changes and obesity have a role.

27. Fraser, Thomas (1872–1951), MA, MB ChB 1898 Aberdeen. Held assistantships in the departments of physiology, materia medica and anaesthetics before being appointed assistant physician to ARI and subsequently a senior physician. Commanding officer

89th (1st Highland) Fd Amb RAMC; ADMS 1918. Member of General Medical Council 1941–6. CBE(mil) 1919. DSO, TD, DL, LLD Aberdeen. '..he was most correct and proper, indeed even by most standards fastidious, but he clung to the etiquette and enjoyed great kudos for that'. See *Aberdeen University Review* 1951; **34**: 127; *British Medical Journal* 1951; **1**: 96–7.

28. Rennie, John (1865–1928), BSc(Hons) 1898, DSc Aberdeen. Assistant to Professor J. Arthur Thomson in the natural history (zoology) department Aberdeen University 1899–1917. Then appointed lecturer in parasitology and experimental zoology with a laboratory of his own. As well as collaborating with Dr Fraser (note 4) in diabetic research he identified a mite which was the cause of Isle of Wight bee disease – a serious scourge in apiculture. See *Aberdeen University Review* 1928; **16**: 55.

29. The two physicians, Josef von Mering (1849–1908) and Oscar Minkowski (1858–1931), were working in the laboratory of the medical clinic at the University of Strasbourg under the direction of Professor Bernard Nauyn in 1889 when they published their paper on 'Diabetes mellitus after extirpation of the pancreas in the dog'. Their initial report was barely one page in length and this highly economical but scientifically precise and incisive report was said to be how such findings should be presented. von Mering also co-discovered the barbiturate class of compounds. See Major, R.H. *Classic Descriptions of Disease*. C.C. Thomas. Springfield, Illinois, 1932.

30. Rennie, J., Fraser, T. The islets of Langerhans in relation to diabetes. *Biochemical Journal* 1906; **2**: 7–19.

31. Macleod, J.J.R. The source of insulin. *Journal of Metabolic Research* 1922; **2**: 149–72.

32. The records for 1918–22 have unfortunately been destroyed.

33. Macleod, J.J.R. Insulin and diabetes. *British Medical Journal* 1922; **2**: 833–5.

34. Anonymous. Insulin and diabetes. Leading article. *British Medical Journal* 1922; **2**: 882.

35. Data in the archives of the Physiological Society. Quoted by permission of Professor R.C. Garry.

36. Aberdeen Royal Infirmary Annual Report, 1923, p.16.

37. Lyall, Alexander (1897–1974), MA, MB ChB 1923 (Hons). Volunteered to join the Gordon Highlanders in 1915. Severely wounded at the second battle of Ypres 1917. Spent a year in anatomy doing anthropological research on the 'Beaker' people. Thereafter worked for two years at the Dunn Laboratory, St Thomas' Hospital with Professor Hugh MacLean. An Aberdonian who was active in the field of diabetes. Lecturer in clinical chemistry and clinical chemist to the Infirmary 1926–61. Founder and lifetime honorary president, Aberdeen branch of the British Diabetic Association. See *Aberdeen Postgraduate Medical Bulletin* 1974; September, 47–8.

38. Aberdeen Royal Infirmary Annual Report, 1932, p.12.

39. Davidson, Stanley (see note 30 of Chapter 19).

40. Campbell, David (see note 32 of Chapter 19).

41. This piece of furniture has been carefully preserved and travels wherever the clinic has subsequently moved. It is currently in the clinic at Woolmanhill.

42. Thomson, M.E. (Maisie) (1900–91). Trained in dietetics and domestic science as well as nursing. She retired in 1959. For a more detailed description of her work, see Chapter 18 (Dietetics).

43. Macgregor, Alastair G. (1919–72), BSc, MB ChB 1943, MD Glasgow. Trained as physician in Glasgow and Sheffield. Senior lecturer in therapeutics at University of Edinburgh 1952–9. Regius professor of materia medica and therapeutics Aberdeen and honorary physician to ARI 1959–72. See *Aberdeen Postgraduate Medical Bulletin* 1972; October, 64–5; and also note 7 of Chapter 14; note 59 of Chapter 9.

44. A specialist health visitor later supplemented by a number of part-time lady doctors who continue to be employed though inadequately rewarded.

45. In the UK: Robin Scott, Colin McIntosh and Colin Paton. In Iceland: Thor Helgasson and Ingvar Teitsson.

46. Alexander (Sandy) Logie, Leslie Borthwick, Donald Pearson and Michael Lean.

47. Dr Michael Williams, consultant physician.

48. By a quirk of fate this had earlier been the ward area in which Fraser and Rennie had tried their experiments with fish glands.
49. In a personal communication to Dr Williams, Sir James Howie does not recollect this particular incident but attests to the fact that he was much concerned to educate diabetics in the reality of their disease and in how to manage it.
50. Davidson, Stanley (see note 30 of Chapter 19).
51. Fullerton, Harold (1905–70), MA, MB ChB (Hons) 1931, MD Aberdeen. Subsequently studied at Harvard and returned to a Beit fellowship in Aberdeen under Professsor Stanley Davidson. Lecturer in medicine 1937, Regius professor of medicine 1948–70. 'Quiet, modest and imperturbable, he was readily approachable and gave unstinting help to young graduates. . .' See *Aberdeen Postgraduate Medical Bulletin* 1970; October, 28; *British Medical Journal* 1970; **2**: 229.
52. Dott, Norman McO. (1897–1973), MB ChB 1919 Edinburgh. A recognized pioneer of British neurological surgery and the first whole-time neurosurgeon in Scotland. Trained under Harvey Cushing in Boston. See Rush, C., Shaw, J.F. *With Sharp Compassion – Norman Dott*. Aberdeen University Press, 1990.
53. Nichols, W. Martin (1910–79), MB ChB(Hons) 1932 Glasgow. Son of a professional musician who played with various orchestras resulting in worldwide travel and schooling in England, Sydney and Minneapolis. Trained initially in the Western Infirmary, Glasgow and later under Wilder Penfield at McGill University, Montreal. On his return to this country he was assistant to Geoffrey Jefferson in Manchester. In 1939 he was posted to the RAMC neurosurgical unit of Hugh Cairns at Oxford and to No.1 Mobile Neurosurgical Unit which went to France. In 1940, during the Dunkirk evacuation, he was attached to a hospital ordered to remain in France to care for the sick and wounded, and thereafter spent the next four years as a prisoner of war. Founder of modern neurosurgery in Aberdeen and President of the Society of British Neurological Surgeons in 1972. He is best remembered as a polymath who could talk instructively on apparently any subject and as a finalist in 'Brain of Britain'. After retirement he enrolled in the university to read geology and was a member of the Aberdeen team in television 'University Challenge'. '. . . a kindly, friendly man bubbling over with enthusiasm'. See *Aberdeen Postgraduate Medical Bulletin* 1980; January, 38. Also Presidential address – detained personnel. *Zodiac (Journal of Aberdeen Medical Students Society)* 1951; **2**: 91–4.
54. Nichols, W.M. A new venture. *Zodiac* 1950; **1**: 222–4.
55. Fullerton, Harold (see note 51 above).
56. Morgan, Thomas N. (see note 15 above).
57. Ferrier, David (1843–1928), MA(Hons) 1863 Aberdeen, MB CM(Hons) 1868, MD Edinburgh. Professor of forensic medicine King's College London 1872. Professor of neuropathology, University of London 1889. He was the first of those who graduated MA after the fusion in 1860 of the two universities in Aberdeen to be given the degree LLD. FRS 1876. Knighted 1911. See *Aberdeen University Review* 1928; **15**: 284.
58. Mackintosh, Ashley (see note 10 of Chapter 6).
59. Anderson, A. Greig (1885–1961), MA, MB ChB(Hons) 1909, MD Aberdeen. War service in RAMC with 43rd and 52nd General Hospitals, British Salonika Force. Assistant physician ARI 1919. Lecturer in clinical medicine 1932. Honorary physician to HM Household in Scotland 1936–55. Popularly known as 'A.G.'. KCVO 1956. See *Aberdeen University Review* 1961; **39**: 118–22; Anon. AG. *Aberdeen Postgraduate Medical Bulletin* 1980; May, 4–6.
60. Hendry, Alexander W. (1888–1972), MB ChB 1914, MD Aberdeen. RAMC service in World War I. OBE (mil). A general physician with a leaning towards neurology and psychiatry, particularly the latter, and was the only physician of the time to instruct students before a department of psychological medicine was established. Affectionately known as 'Pop'. '. . .a quiet, modest man, gentle and humble. . .' See *Aberdeen Postgraduate Medical Bulletin* 1972; October, 65–6. Also *Aberdeen University Review* 1972; **45**: 124.

61. Craig, John (1898–1977), MB ChB(Hons) 1921 Aberdeen. Assistant physician ARI 1932–47. Appointed senior physician to the Children's Hospital at the age of 26 after training under Sir Robert Hutchison at Great Ormond Street and at L'Hopital des Enfants Malades. Professor of child health Aberdeen 1948–63. LLD Aberdeen. See *Aberdeen Postgraduate Medical Bulletin* 1977; September, 42–4.

62. Wolfe, John (see note 19 of Chapter 9).

63. Innes, Francis L.F. (1919–88), MB ChB 1941 Aberdeen. Royal Air Force 1942–6. Senior surgical registrar in Aberdeen before transferring to Churchill Hospital, Oxford 1954–9. Consultant at Norfolk and Norwich 1959–84.

64. Wallace, Alexander (Alister) B. (1907–75). A founder of the care of burns in Scotland and internationally renowned. Trained many plastic surgeons through his appointments at the Royal Hospital for Sick Children, Edinburgh and Bangour Hospital, West Lothian. See *British Medical Journal* 1975; **1**: 158. Also *The Bangour Story*. Aberdeen University Press, 1991.

65. Muir, I.F.K., Barclay, I.L., Settle, J.A.D. *Burns and Their Treatment*, 3rd edn. Butterworth, London, 1981.

66. Anderson, Alexander G. (see note 59 above).

67. Ross, Thomas A. (1875–1941), MB CM 1897, MD Edinburgh. Director of Cassel Hospital for functional nervous disorders at Swaylands, Penshurst. Author of *The Common Neuroses and their Treatment by Psychotherapy*. Edward Arnold and Co, London, 1937. See *British Medical Journal* 1941; **1**: 463.

68. Ross, John A. (1885–1967). Succeeded his father in 1907 as managing director of J. and J. Crombie textile manufacturers. A generous benefactor of Aberdeen medicine through the Crombie-Ross benevolent fund. His own memorial is the Ross Clinic opened in 1959 in the grounds of Royal Cornhill Hospital. LLD Aberdeen 1941. See Allan, J. *Crombies of Grandholm and Cothal 1805–1960*. Central Press, Aberdeen, 1960. See note 45 of Chapter 8.

69. MacCalman, Douglas R. (1903–57), MB ChB 1927, MD Glasgow. Trained at Harvard and Johns Hopkins. Assistant physician 1934 Victoria Infirmary Glasgow. Crombie-Ross lecturer Aberdeen 1938 and physician to ARI. Crombie-Ross professor of mental health Aberdeen 1946. Professor of psychiatry Leeds University 1948–57. See *British Medical Journal* 1957; **1**: 405–6.

70. W. Malcolm Millar, CBE, who was subsequently professor of mental health from 1949–77, was the first senior lecturer and Wallace Ironside the first registrar funded by the hospital. The latter went on to become professor of psychological medicine first in Otago, New Zealand and thereafter at Monash University, Melbourne, Australia. Marion Whyte, a social worker, was also given a university appointment.

71. Millar, W.M. Personal communication, 1991.

72. Duffus, J.C. (see note 4 of Chapter 5).

73. Davidson, Stanley (see note 30 of Chapter 19).

74. Cocky Hunter's. This second–hand saleroom (owned by Alexander Hunter) was legendary in its time in Aberdeen. It occupied premises at one time in Rosemount on ground subsequently the site of Rosemount Square. After a fire in the 1930s (started, it is thought, by monkeys kept in a cage and which had maliciously been thrown some matches), the business removed to Castlehill into premises once occupied by the Aberdeen Royal Sick Children's Hospital. The latter went to the Foresterhill site in 1929 and subsequently changed its title to the Royal Aberdeen Hospital for Sick Children. The Castlehill buildings were demolished in the 1980s.

75. Minutes of Board of Directors, 22 December 1909 – Dr Levack's request is deferred and the Clerk asked to get information on the practice of other hospitals. The matter is considered again on 12 January 1910 by which time Dr Levack thinks that more radium than he originally requested will be required. The revised cost considered by the directors on 26 January is £150. The matter is again deferred and seems to have lapsed.

76. See Editorial notes. *British Journal of Radiology* 1929; **NS2**; 414–20.

77. Cruickshank, John (see note 11 of Chapter 13).
78. MacRobert, Georgina (1851–1905), née Porter. The first wife of Sir Alexander MacRobert Bart of Douneside by Tarland. In 1906 MacRobert, a self-made businessman and one time manager of Cawnpore woollen mills in India, donated £25,000 to create a cancer research fund at Aberdeen University to be called the 'Georgina MacRobert Fellowship' in memory of his wife who suffered a painful terminal malignancy. Robert Gordon's College also benefited from MacRobert's generosity in the building of the school hall, after whom it was named. Various departments in Aberdeen University have received substantial funding from the Trust, some within the last few years. Included also is the Royal Air Force Benevolent Fund which received a neighbouring mansion on the estate, entitled Alastrean House. The name is a composite from the Latin which translated gives 'a place of honour by the hearth of the winged heroes of the stars'. By coincidence it is also a composite of the names of MacRobert's three sons by his second wife Rachel; Alasdair, Roderic and Iain, the first of whom was killed in 1938 and the latter two in World War II. See *Aberdeen Press and Journal*, 6 and 7 November 1974. Also *The Glasgow Herald*, 12 May 1990, p.21.
79. Evans, William G. (1903–90), MB BS London (St Mary's) 1926. After leaving Aberdeen he was successively radiotherapist at Lambeth and St Bartholomew's Hospitals.
80. Griffith, Harry D. (see note 3 of Chapter 14).
81. Annual Report Aberdeen Royal Infirmary, 1939.
82. A fishing village on the coast just south of Aberdeen where granite was formerly quarried.
83. Griffith, H.D., Philip, J.F., Swindell, G.E. Skin reaction to protracted irradiation. *British Journal of Radiology* 1954: **NS27**; 107–12. It should also be noted that a long–standing member of the clinical staff had cataract extractions for what may have been radiation-induced opacity in 1976.
84. Griffith, H.D. Aberdeen's radium in war-time. *Zodiac (Journal of the Aberdeen University Medical Faculty)* 1950; **1**: no.6; 190–1.
85. National Radium Commission 1942. Organisation for the treatment of cancer.
86. Recording of Cancer Cases (annotation). *Lancet* 1944; **2**: 572.
87. Stebbing, G.F. Diagnosis of cancer in a National Medical Service. *Lancet* 1945; **2**: 65–8.
88. Aberdeen Royal Infirmary Annual Report, 1946.
89. The post was originally offered to Dr Robert Morrison who declined it on learning that administrative responsibility was to be split within the malignant diseases unit. (Morrison, personal communication, 1991).
90. Ridley, Ernest F. (1915–75), MB ChB St Andrews 1940. RAMC in Middle East with armoured division; mentioned in dispatches. Consultant radiotherapist North East Scotland Regional Board 1950–75. 'Of a quiet, gentlemanly disposition. . .' he was largely responsible for the development of modern radiotherapy at the ARI. A contemporary writes: '. . .EFR never pushed himself but. . . in his own quiet way had many good suggestions'. See *Aberdeen Postgraduate Medical Bulletin* 1976; January, 59.
91. Unpublished documents of the Scottish Standing Cancer Committee.
92. Philip, J.F. *Malignant Disease. A report of the results of treatment in Aberdeen Royal Infirmary during the decade 1930–39.* Aberdeen University Press, 1949.
93. Oncology in Aberdeen owes a great debt to Miss M. Clark, administrative secretary to the Malignant Disease Unit for the arduous, concentrated effort she put into the development of cancer registration for over 40 years and to the contribution she made to cancer registration for Scotland in general.
94. Davidson, Stanley (see note 30 of Chapter 19).
95. Robert Aitken (see note 8 above).
96. Annual Report Aberdeen Royal Infirmary, 1946, pp.23–4.
97. Bain, Logie S. (1914–88), MB ChB 1937 Aberdeen. House officer Tor-na-Dee, ARI and Aberdeen Maternity Hospital until 1939. RAMC 1939–45 mainly in the Middle

East and Mediterranean. In charge Rheumatology in-patient unit Stracathro 1945–53. Consultant-in-charge Department of Physical Medicine and Rheumatology 1953–79. A noted player of rugby and later golf. 'His pawky . . . sense of humour must have helped . . . to create an optimistic outlook and bring a ray of hope to many languishing in the depths of despair'. Part of an Aberdeen medical dynasty which included two brothers – an anaesthetist and a radiologist. See *British Medical Journal* 1988: **1**; 1747; *Aberdeen Postgraduate Medical Bulletin* 1988; May, 39–40.

98. Report of the Special Commissioners. The Scandals of Massage, parts 1–3. *British Medical Journal* 1894; **2**: 1003, 1069, 1140.

99. Announcement of the Society of Trained Masseuses. Nursing Notes, February 1895.
    In 1896 the Society invited medically qualified patrons and by 1900 when the membership had exceeded 250, the Society became the Incorporated Society of Trained Masseuses. Twenty years later it merged with the Institute of Massage and Remedial Gymnastics and with a Royal Charter became the Chartered Society of Massage and Medical Gymnastics. In 1942 the current title – the Chartered Society of Physiotherapists – was adopted with headquarters in London. At the time of writing the Society has 25,000 members.

100. Minute Book Aberdeen Royal Infirmary, 9 January 1781.

101. Annual Report Aberdeen Royal Infirmary, 1934, p.22.

102. Annual Report Aberdeen Royal Infirmary, 1942, pp.13–14.

103. Annual Report Aberdeen Royal Infirmary, 1945, p.31. This was also the year that Mrs Margaret Milholm, senior masseuse, retired after 24 years of service.
    In 1946 the Margaret Ann Cran bequest of £12,500 was put towards extending the facilities for the treatment of rheumatism and fitting out a gymnasium adjacent to the Orthopaedic Out-patient Department at Foresterhill on the south side of the Infirmary buildings between the orthopaedic ward and the X-ray Department. Some of the internal structure was constructed with hollow glass bricks as a novel way of transmitting daylight and in 1991 they are still in evidence.

104. Annual Report Aberdeen Royal Infirmary, 1947, pp.28–30.

105. She left to go to the Children's Hospital in Sheffield eight years later. There was still no school in Aberdeen.

106. The principal was Rosemary E.J. Lane, MBE, who had previously been on the staff at the London Hospital. Under her guidance the school flourished and became linked with the Robert Gordon Institute of Technology in 1990. Miss Laing retired in 1986.

107. Dr Balch retired in 1979 after spending 31 years in the Department of Rheumatology.

108. J.A.N. Rennie and C.J. Eastmond were both appointed in 1979, and D.M. Reid in 1986.

Chapter 11

1. Use of ether in surgical operations. *The Aberdeen Journal*, 10 February 1847.

2. Keith, William (see note 10 of Chapter 7).

3. Aberdeen Royal Infirmary Minute Book, 17 October 1856.

4. Pirrie, W. Death of patient while under the influence of chloroform. *British Medical Journal* 1871; **2**: 124.

5. Davidson, A. Dyce (see note 20 of Chapter 9).

6. Ogston, Alexander (see note 3 of Chapter 7).

7. Dalgarno, James J.Y. (see note 7 of Chapter 12).

8. Booth, J. MacKenzie (see note 3 of Chapter 9).

9. Robertson, James (1880–1918), MB ChB 1904, MD, ChM Aberdeen. Medical practitioner and assistant anaesthetist at ARI 1910–18. Commanding officer 2/1st Highland Field Ambulance RAMC. Killed in action in France near Bapaume 1918. Father of one of the first students in the Aberdeen School of Radiography. See *Aberdeen University Review* 1966; **41**: 241.

10. Anderson, William (see note 46 of Chapter 7).
11. Richards, Robert (1887–1965), MA, MB ChB 1910, MD Aberdeen. FRCSE DPH. Pathologist to 43rd (lst Scottish) General Hospital RAMC in Salonika 1916–18. Medical practitioner in Aberdeen from 1919. Assistant anaesthetist 1919–22. Assistant to Matthew Hay (professor of public health and forensic medicine) 1920–6. Lecturer and head of department of forensic medicine 1932–56. (The chair of jurisprudence – forensic medicine – was discontinued on Hay's retiral in 1926.) See *British Medical Journal* 1966; **1**: 618.
12. Johnston, John (1878–1962), MB ChB 1909 Aberdeen. Anaesthetised Prince Albert (subsequently King George VI) in 1914 for an appendicectomy performed by John Marnoch and Alexander Ogston (see notes 33 and 3 of Chapter 7). The operation was done at the Northern Nursing Home (subsequently the Watson Fraser) next door to where Johnston lived. See *Aberdeen Daily Journal*, 10 September 1914.
13. Ogston, Alexander (1869–1940), MA, MB CM 1893 Aberdeen. No relation of his namesake the professor of surgery. Senior anaesthetist to ARI 1912–29. Honorary consulting anaesthetist 1929–40. Devised a modified mask for the administration of volatile anaesthetics which incorporated advances in the understanding of the maximum use of the gauze surface and of vaporization.
14. Mackenzie, J. Ross (1879–1963), MB ChB 1906, MD Aberdeen. A man who had suffered from trigeminal neuralgia, his facial twitch became evident under conditions of stress. He published a textbook: *Practical Anaesthetics*. London, Bailliere, Tindall and Cox, 1944. William Anderson was once know to chide Mackenzie that as a surgeon he had read the whole book while waiting for the induction of a patient (Raffan, A.W. Personal communication.) See *Aberdeen University Review* 1963; **40**: 301.
15. Aberdeen Royal Infirmary Minute Book, 8 April 1937. The first appointee was Rosalind Milne, followed by A.B. Christie (subsequently consultant anaesthetist at the Victoria Infirmary, Glasgow) and by A.W. Raffan.
16. MacWilliam, J.A. Report of an experimental investigation of the action of chloroform and ether. *British Medical Journal* 1890; **2**: 890–2.See also note 16 of Chapter 10.
17. Blaikie Smith, Patrick (1849–1909), MB CM(Hons) 1870, MD Aberdeen. Son of William Smith, City Architect for Aberdeen. Assistant to Professor Brazier (chemistry) 1872–5. Chloroformist to ARI 1875–6. Assistant physician 1887–95. Retired to San Remo due to ill health.
18. Blaikie Smith, P. A new inhaler for the administration of ether. *Lancet* 1884; **2**: 19.
19. Ogston, A. Notes on the administration of ether by the perhalation method. *British Journal of Anaesthesia* 1924; **2**: 76–83.
20. Johnston, J. Minutes, Scottish Society of Anaesthetists 1936. Raffan recalls (personal communication) that he was sent to anaesthetize a similar patient for Clark Souter (see note 23 of Chapter 9) and used intravenous techniques. Ross Mackenzie shouted to him on his return 'you had better run and see if the patient is still alive. . .'
21. Usher, C.H. Observations on the retinal blood stream at the time of death. *Ophthalmic Review* 1896; December, 1–13. See also note 22 of Chapter 9.
22. Robson, Thomas O. (1883–1954), MB ChB 1916 Aberdeen. Medical practitioner in Aberdeen 1922–54, succeeding Dr George M. Edmond. Assistant anaesthetist 1922–46. Became consultant in charge of anaesthesia for the NE Scotland Regional Hospital Board in 1948.
23. MacDonald, Thomas J.C. (1899–1966), MB ChB 1924, MD, PhD Aberdeen. Noted for his research contributions. His MD and PhD were on anaesthetic subjects and the latter, related to aliphatic halogen compounds, anticipated the introduction of a new generation of inhalationals such as halothane. He became a full–time anaesthetist in 1948.
24. Wilson, Howard (see note 12 of Chapter 10).
25. Bain, John W.L. (1903–78), MB ChB 1936 Aberdeen. RAMC service initially with 15th Scottish General Hospital and then as anaesthetist in a field surgical team. With his surgical colleague, Hanna, they became known throughout the 8th Army for their skill

and dependability. Consultant anaesthetist 1951–68 ARI. One of three brothers (including a rheumatologist and radiologist), all of whom were at one time on the ARI staff.
26. Rollason, W. Norman (1917–90), MB ChB 1940 Birmingham. RAF 1942–7. Consultant anaesthetist in Hull before appointment at ARI (1959–1981) as consultant in administrative charge of anaesthesia to the regional board in succession to Howard Wilson. See *Aberdeen Postgraduate Medical Bulletin* 1990: September, 40.
27. Nichols, Martin (see note 53 of Chapter 10).
28. The first trauma patient successfully treated by dialysis was in 1961 – a lady who had had a traumatic amputation of the mid-thigh by a hit and run driver and was left hypotensive in a ditch for several hours. She required repeated dialysis and revisions of her stump.
29. Mainly by David C. White, consultant anaesthetist at ARI 1964–71. He re-located to the Clinical Research Centre, Northwick Park Hospital, Harrow.
30. Smylie, H.G. Personal communication, 1991.
31. It is of interest to note that this concept is being revived in 1991 in relation to the early training of surgeons and physicians.

Chapter 12

1. Correspondence in Berlin. Photography through opaque screens. *Lancet* 1896; **1**: 205.
2. Annotation. The searchlight of photography. *Lancet* 1896; **1**: 112.
3. Annotation. The new photographic discovery. *Lancet* 1896; **1**: 245.
4. Davidson, James McKenzie (1868–1919), MB CM 1882 Aberdeen. Ophthalmic surgeon to the Royal Infirmary from 1886–97. He foresaw the importance of radiology both in eye work and in general and made a pilgrimage to Wurzburg to see Roentgen. Was prominent in the development of X-ray localization of foreign bodies including the use of stereoscopic radiology. Knighted in 1912. President of the Roentgen Society 1912. His original foreign body eye localizer and electrical circuit breaker are housed in the Marischal museum. See *Aberdeen University Review* 1919; **6**: 292; *Nature*, 10 April 1919.
5. MacGregor, Alexander (1854–1902), MB CM 1878 Aberdeen. First commanding officer of the Aberdeen Division Volunteer Medical Staff Corps – now the Aberdeen Companies of the RAMC(V). Physician North London Hospital for Consumption and Diseases of the Chest.
6. Aberdeen Royal Infirmary Minute Book, 5 February 1896.
7. Dalgarno, James J.Y. (1861–1910), MA 1883, MB CM 1887 Aberdeen. Assistant anaesthetist 1895–6. Anaesthetist and medical electrician 1896–7. Anaesthetist 1897–1910. Also in general practice and medical officer to Aberdeen Parish Council at Oldmill Hospital. Died while in Tain to anaesthetize a patient for Mr H.M.W. Gray.
8. Galloway, Alexander R. (1864–1939), MA 1884, MB CM 1888 Aberdeen. Assistant anaesthetist and assistant medical electrician 1896–7. Subsequently surgeon to the Opthalmic Institution and the Asylum for the Blind.
9. Levack, John R. (1870–1940), MB CM (Hons) 1891 Aberdeen. Son of David Levack, druggist in Aberdeen. He lived at 10 Golden Square and became a specialist in ophthalmology guided by his friend and mentor James McKenzie Davidson (see note 4 above). Medical electrician/radiologist at ARI 1897–1931. G.P. Milne recalls him as a senior member of staff in the 1930s and the X-ray injuries to the skin of his hands due to years of inadequate protection. He was an enthusiastic mountaineer and Dr John Blewett writes 'he once told me that he had taken the two sons into the hills above Braemar and let them loose in thick mist to find their own way home'. (They both got home and were later to emulate their father on the staff at ARI and as accomplished mountaineers.) The old man became President of the Cairngorm Club 1919–24 and

recorded 60 ascents to the summit of his favourite Lochnagar, one of which was for the construction and unveiling ceremony of the indicator stack. See *Aberdeen Press and Journal*, 12 July 1924.

10. Bell, Clifford T. (1870–1918), MB CM 1896 Aberdeen. A general practitioner in Aberdeen and also senior medical officer to Oldmill Poorhouse. Joined the RAMC (Territorial Forces) in 1914 and died at 1st (Scottish) General Hospital.

11. Connon, Middleton (1874–1942), MB CM 1896 Aberdeen. Initially a general practitioner at Montrose he returned to Aberdeen and was, in addition to a radiologist, an assistant in the department of anatomy.

12. Levack, David P. (1899–1978), MB ChB(Hons) 1924 Aberdeen. Son of John R. Levack. Honorary radiologist to ARI 1928–47. Commanding officer 154(H) Fd Amb RAMC(V) 1938–40; ADMS 51(H) Div when captured at St Valery. Prisoner of war 1940–4. ADMS W. Africa Command after repatriation 1945. A lively raconteur, he described how in 1939 he took his territorial unit for its annual two week camp near Aldershot, was mobilized for war on arrival and did not return to Aberdeen until after four years in captivity. CBE (mil) 1946. Became senior consultant in radiology to the NE Regional Board 1948–64. Followed his father as president of the Cairngorm Club 1935–38. His brother J.W. (Bill) was an anaesthetist at ARI 1937–66.

13. Annual Report of the Directors of the Infirmary, 1933.

14. At the time of writing Dr Blewett is living in Melbourne, Australia. Details of his sprightly and graphic account of the 1930s are incorporated into this history.

15. Griffith, Harry D. (see note 3 of Chapter 14).

16. Innes, John (1907–72), BSc 1928, MB ChB 1937 Aberdeen. In general practice NE Scotland 1938–9. Assistant radiologist ARI 1940–6. Senior consultant radiologist, Victoria Infirmary Glasgow 1946–1972.

17. Bain, Alexander A.N. (1911–66), MB ChB 1936 Aberdeen. In general practice Hull 1939. RAMC 1939–45. Clinical assistant radiologist Royal Infirmary of Edinburgh 1945 and Western Infirmary, Glasgow 1946. Senior assistant radiologist ARI 1949. Senior consultant radiologist to Northern Regional Board Inverness 1950–66. A member of a 'medical family' in the North-East, his brothers were an anaesthetist and a rheumatologist in the ARI.

18. Blewett and Griffith never published this noteworthy advance. See Spiegler, G. An improved method and film holder for personnel monitoring. *British Journal of Radiology* 1959; **32**: 464–7.

19. This anecdote is related by Professor L.A. Gillanders.

20. The room had been presided over by two redoubtable figures, William Cowie and Doreen Morrice, whom many consultants and other staff will remember as ensuring a strict discipline of entry into their premises.

21. McKail, Robert A. (1914–86), MB ChB 1937 Edinburgh. Trained initially in experimental physiology at the Wilkie Laboratory, Edinburgh before learning diagnostic radiology first in Edinburgh and then at Glasgow Royal Infirmary. He developed an interest in thoracic radiology and was a specialist at Hairmyres Hospital, East Kilbride. Consultant radiologist ARI 1950–74, during which time he was a member of the Phase I Professional Planning Committee. He returned to Edinburgh to become a part-time lecturer in anatomy 1974–82.

22. Stewart, Archibald (1915–86), MB ChB Edinburgh 1940. Served with RAMC during the war and was mentioned in dispatches. Trained thereafter in paediatric surgery and radiology. Consultant radiologist to the Aberdeen Teaching Hospitals 1954–79 with a special interest in paediatric and obstetric radiology both of which he developed within the Foresterhill complex. See *Aberdeen Postgraduate Medical Bulletin* 1986; **20**(3): 42.

23. Mavor, George (see note 58 of Chapter 7).

24. Palmer, James H. (1929–67), MB ChB 1953 Aberdeen. RAMC 1954–6 (19th Field Regt RA). Trained in Edinburgh and Barnet General Hospital before becoming senior registrar at ARI and consultant in 1964.

25. Known as 'Laser Line' the public appeal and their generosity is commemorated by a plaque in the entrance concourse of Phase I.
26. The first name recorded is W.N. Thomson who went on to become a consultant radiologist at the Eastern General Hospital in Edinburgh.
27. Harold Bennett – became consultant radiologist to the Royal Cornwall, Truro and Falmouth & District Hospitals.
28. Alan Bryce – Subsequently consultant radiologist to North Cambridgeshire Hospital, Wisbech.
29. Craigie Anton, who went on to become consultant radiologist at Stobhill Hospital, Glasgow from 1963–83.
30. The course owes its origin to Dr (later Professor) Lewis Gillanders and was steered through the administrative pathways by Professor George Smith (surgery), Professor John Mallard (bio-medical and bio-engineering), Dr Denys Beddard (chief administrative medical officer, see note 6 of Chapter 5) and Dr A.M. (Sandy) Michie (Group Medical Superintendent). It corrected staffing anomalies and what Lewis Gillanders refers to as 'too many generals and not enough soldiers'.
31. S.S. Amar and A.I. Simpson – subsequently consultants in radiodiagnosis at Nottingham and Elgin, respectively.
32. Frank Smith appointed in 1979 as consultant in nuclear medicine; Jeff Hussey (1981) with a special interest in interventional procedures; and Elizabeth Robertson (1982) who brought, to ultrasound and CT, skills acquired as a senior registrar in London. Heather Deans (1988) with a special interest in breast screening was joined in the following year by Fiona Gilbert and Gillian Needham and in 1991, Olive Robb succeeded MacDonald as neuro-radiologist.
33. John Calder (1977–1985). Now consultant in radiology, Victoria Hospital, Glasgow.
34. Gillanders, L.A. Personal communication, 1990.
35. Levack, John (see note 9 above).
36. Philip, Frederick (1872–1926), MB CM 1898 Aberdeen. Assistant medical electrician at ARI 1911–24. Also district medical officer, Aberdeen Parish Council 1899–1926.
37. Cairns, William (1882–1963). Radiographer to the ARI 1921–47. In his later years he was to develop a squamous carcinoma on one hand as a consequence of repeated exposure to X-rays.
38. Clark, Helen. The sister in law of Andrew Fowler, surgeon to the ARI, she married John Wilson of Carntyne Engineering, Glasgow.
39. Miss Dorothy Ducat (later Mrs G.P. Milne, dec. 1973), Miss Elma Robertson (daughter of James Robertson, assistant anesthetist ARI 1910–18 – killed near Bapaume during the German spring offensive in 1918; married Dr Donald Wilson, medical officer of health for Inverness, Highlands and Islands), and Miss Pat Sharkey (who went to the Middlesex Hospital, London after qualifying in Aberdeen).
40. Society of Radiographers. Founded in 1920.
41. Successive holders of this post were: Raymond Lawrence, James Aberdein, and John Abbot (see note 42).
42. John W. Abbot, MBE, appointed in 1954, held the additional post of tutor for 16 years for which he was paid the sum of £50 per annum, though it is recorded that in the later part of his tenure this rose to a bountiful £75. On relinquishing his role as tutor to the College in 1970 he was promoted to group superintendent radiographer.
43. The holders of this post have been: Margaret McKenzie (1970–3), Sandra Hall (1973–4) and Donald Graham (1974–).

Chapter 13

1. Beveridge, Robert (1836–87), MD 1847 Marischal. Lecturer in anatomy and botany, and later in pathology. Pathologist to ARI and finally physician in 1869. He was president

of the Medico-Chirurigical Society 1873–4 having been secretary and treasurer for the previous 10 years. See *British Medical Journal* 1887; **1**: 181.

2. Two local 'loons' (young lads in English), Pirrie and Wilson (though it was Wilson's father who came from Huntly and then moved to London) were long-standing friends.
   Pirrie, William (see note 18 of Chapter 7).
   For a vivid account of Wilson's career and how he became able to give £10,000 to endow the chair of pathology, see Lyell, A. Erasmus Wilson and the chair of pathology at Aberdeen. *British Journal of Dermatology* 1979; **100**: 343. Also Burnett, W. The department of pathology of the university of Aberdeen; evolution under the first three professors 1882–1936. *Aberdeen Postgraduate Medical Bulletin* 1973; May, 2–11; Scott, G.B. *Department of pathology centennial 1882–1982*. Aberdeen University Central Printing Service, 1982.

3. Hamilton, David J. (1849–1909), MB ChB Edinburgh 1870. Spent two years in Vienna, Munich, Strasbourg and Paris on the proceeds of the triennial Astley Cooper prize. Pathologist to the Royal Infirmary of Edinburgh 1876–82. Foundation Regius professor of pathology, Aberdeen 1882–1908. LLD 1907 Aberdeen. Ogston wrote 'He came to Aberdeen to raise pathology from the degrading position into which it had fallen. . . A strong man, a determined man, a brilliant man was needed and Hamilton was all this'. See *British Medical Journal* 1909; **1**: 631–3; *Dictionary of National Biography* (2nd supplement) 1912; **2**: 192–3.

4. Rodger, James (1841–1900), MA 1863, MB CM(Hons) 1865, MD Aberdeen. Succeeded Beveridge as pathologist to ARI in 1869. Assistant physician 1886. President of Aberdeen Medico-Chirurigical Society 1886–7 having been secretary and treasurer for the preceding 12 years. Married to Ella Hill Burton Rodger, author of *Aberdeen Doctors* (Blackwood and Sons, Edinburgh, 1893). See *Lancet* 1900; **2**: 353.

5. Duncan, George M. (1873–1931), MB CM 1896 Aberdeen. Assistant pathologist ARI 1898. Served with 1st Scottish General Hospital 1914–19. Clinical pathologist and bacteriologist ARI 1921-31. Fondly remembered by many as 'Daddy Duncan'. See *British Medical Journal* 1935; **1**: 1056.

6. Dean, George (1863–1914), MA 1885, MB CM (Hons) 1889 Aberdeen. The son of a railway contractor from the Chapel of Garioch. Studied in Vienna and Berlin under Robert Koch. Assistant pathologist ARI 1892–7. Bacteriologist in charge Lister Institute, London 1897–1908. Regius professor of pathology Aberdeen 1908–14. See *British Medical Journal* 1914; **1**: 1389; *Aberdeen University Review* 1914; **2**: 126.

7. Minute Book Aberdeen Royal Infirmary, November 1908.

8. Minute Book Aberdeen Royal Infirmary, January 1914.

9. Shennan, Theodore (1869–1948), MB CM 1890, MD Edinburgh. Pathologist to Leith Hospital 1896, Royal Edinburgh Hospital for Sick Children 1900 and Royal Infirmary of Edinburgh 1902–14. Regius professor Aberdeen 1914–36. LLD Aberdeen. See *British Medical Journal* 1948; **2**: 839, 1000.

10. Smith, John (1892–1976), MB ChB(Hons) 1915, MD, DSc 1927 Aberdeen. Though not properly part of the history of the ARI, Smith was such an important figure in the development of bacteriology and public health in Aberdeen that he is noted briefly here. RAMC 1915–19 and burnt by mustard gas. In charge, laboratory of public health 1920–48. Consultant bacteriologist to the laboratory 1948–58. LLD 1965 Aberdeen. 'contributed original work on source of infection in puerperal fever, infantile gastroenteritis, Weil's disease, undulant fever and new types of salmonellae'. See *Aberdeen Postgraduate Medical Bulletin* 1977: January, 54–6.

11. Cruickshank, John (1884–1966), MB ChB(Hons) 1909, MD Glasgow. Pathologist at Crichton Royal Institution, Dumfries 1912–20. Officer in charge, mobile bacteriological laboratory and assistant director in pathology, RAMC 1916–19. Georgina MacRobert research lecturer, department of pathology, University of Aberdeen 1920–3. Reader in bacteriology 1923–6. Foundation professor of bacteriology 1926–54. Originally trained in the department of Robert Muir in Glasgow, his first interests were in malignant disease. However his experience during the war had given him a large experience in

dysentery and meningococcal meningitis, and bacteriology became his full-time interest. Director of regional blood transfusion service 1940–56. CBE 1946. See *British Medical Journal* 1966; **2**: 1013.

12. Young, John S. (1894–1971), MA, BSc, MB ChB 1923, MD(all Hons) Glasgow. Combatant in World War I with Cameron Highlanders and after the Battle of Loos was commissioned in the Black Watch. '. . .took part in almost every battle of the western front till the end of the war . . .and was awarded the Military Cross.' Trained with Robert Muir in Glasgow and later became reader in Leeds. Professor of pathology Queen's University, Belfast 1932–7 and Regius professor Aberdeen 1937–62. LLD Aberdeen and Glasgow. See *Aberdeen Postgraduate Medical Bulletin* 1972; February, 34–6; *British Medical Journal* 1971; **4**: 53.

13. Stalker, Alexander L. (1920–87), MB ChB(Hons) 1942, MD Aberdeen. After graduating he joined the RAMC on active service with the Brigade of Guards as RMO. He was known to say that the moment of his greatest pride was when he was asked to wear below his RAMC flash, the shoulder flash of the Grenadier Guards. His military allegiance was borne out by his subsequent appointments as ADMS 51st(H) Division (TA), a Deputy Lieutenant of the County of Aberdeen and Honorary Surgeon to the Queen in Scotland. He was an ardent admirer of his mentor and predecessor, J.S. Young. Regius professor 1972–82. See *British Medical Journal* 1987; **2**: 557; *Aberdeen Postgraduate Medical Bulletin* 1988: January, 39–40.

14. Lyall, Alexander (see note 37 of Chapter 10).

15. Among these were: Iain Anderson, consultant in clinical biochemistry, Victoria Infirmary, Glasgow; John Green, consultant at St Mary's Hospital, London; Harry Auld, consultant chemical pathologist, Chelsea and Kingston Group; George P. Fraser, who after a varied career became a senior biochemist in Northampton; and Peter Mitchell, who went to Dundee as consultant clinical biochemist in 1966.

16. Stewart, Corbet P. (1897–1962), BSc 1920 Newcastle, PhD, DSc. Although strictly not part of this history, C.P. Stewart was so central to the growth of scientific medicine in Scotland as to deserve mention. In conjunction with W.C. Wilson he had been responsible for many clinical developments of biochemistry during the 1930s in Edinburgh and had inspired a number of clinicians such as Andrew Wilkinson (subsequently to become senior lecturer in surgery in Aberdeen) to take an interest in the biochemical aspects of disease. He was, legend states, a founder of the Scottish Society of Experimental Medicine which was conceived by him and Wilson in a car journey on their return from an abortive meeting of the Physiological Society in Aberdeen, where the members of that august society had decided that the distance between London and Aberdeen was twice that between Aberdeen and London.

17. His account of the 'link building' will be found in Chapter 5, and attests to his humour and detachment.

Chapter 14

1. Arnott, Neil (1788–1874), MA 1805, MD 1814 Marischal. Educated at Aberdeen Grammar School. FRS 1838. Made important contributions to the understanding of sanitation, ventilation and public education in physics. Author of numerous texts including *Elements of Physics* (1827) which ran to five editions. Although he lived most of his life in London he donated generously to both Aberdeen University and the Robert Gordon Institute of Technology (formerly known as Robert Gordon's Technical College) in which he is commemorated by an undergraduate prize in physics and an annual public lecture respectively. Physician extraordinary to Queen Victoria. See *Aberdeen Journal*, 4 March 1874; *Dictionary of National Biography* 1908; **1**: 593–4.

2. Thomson, George P. (1892–1975). A pupil of Rutherford at Cambridge, he was to go on to win the Nobel Prize in 1937 for the discovery of the wave nature of the electron.

Professor of natural philosophy (physics) Aberdeen 1922–30. Knighted 1943. Master of Corpus Christie College, Cambridge 1952–62. See *Dictionary of National Biography 1971–1980*, pp.842–3. Oxford University Press, 1986.

3. Griffith, Harry D. (1898–1964), BA Cantab 1923. Worked under Sir J.J. Thomson and Sir Ernest Rutherford at the Cavendish Laboratory before coming to Aberdeen. See *Nature* 1964: **203**; 20–1.
4. Swindell, Gerald E. (1917–88), BSc Belfast. Medical physics appointments in Aberdeen, Manchester, Belfast and Dallas, USA. From 1975–9 he was on the staff of the Atomic Energy Agency in Vienna.
5. The 'Lincolnshire bolus.' See Lindsay, D.D., Stern Babette, E. A new tissue-like material for use as a bolus. *Radiology* 1953; **60**: 355–61.
6. See Mallard J.R., Trott, N.C. Some aspects of the history of nuclear medicine in the United Kingdom. *Seminars in Nuclear Medicine* 1979; **9**(3): 203–17.
7. Macgregor, Alastair (see note 43 of Chapter 10 and note 59 of Chapter 9).
8. Additional staff included: Alistair McIntosh (1958), radiation and radioisotopes; Alistair Murray (1961), radiotherapy physics; Douglas Moore (1962), radiation protection.
9. The Woolmanhill workshop was staffed by Archie Low and latterly by William Hutcheon.
10. The first technicians in the electronic development laboratory were Douglas Simpson and Ken Ross.
11. Wright, Edward M. Professor of Mathematics. Principal and vice-chancellor University of Aberdeen 1962–76. Knighted 1977.
12. Baird, Lady May (see note 15 of Chapter 5).
13. Mallard, J.R. Medical Physics – what is it? Hybird Tea numerically scanning clockwise. *Aberdeen University Review* 1967: **42**; 12–29.
14. Nuclear Enterprises Ltd made a considerable impact on the field of radioactive measurement for over 30 years after World War II.
15. Mallard, J.R. Some call it laziness: I call it deep thought (with apologies to Garfield), Hevesy Memorial Lecture 1985. *Nuclear Medicine Communications* 1987; **8**: 691–710.
16. Built by a team co-ordinated by A.R. Bowley.
17. There are a number of explanations why the term nuclear was dropped from the clinical application. Some say that it was the result of a demarcation dispute between radiologists and nuclear medicine physicians in the United States which was rationalized by invoking the emotional and off-putting linkage with destructive devices such as atomic weapons and the perceived unpopularity of nuclear power. Others that it was the work of a particularly influential group in England.
18. By J.M.S. Hutchison.
19. Particularly F.W. Smith.

Chapter 15

1. Address to Aberdeen Rotary Club. See *Aberdeen Daily Journal*, 4 April 1919, p.4. Henry Gray (see note 36 of Chapter 7).
2. Terms and conditions of service for blood transfusion. *Aberdeen Evening Express*, 27 May 1929, p.5; *Aberdeen Press and Journal*, 28 May 1929, p.3.
3. When a medical registrar was appointed in 1937, the responsibility for blood transfusion was delegated to him. Gauld, W.R. Personal communication, 1991.
4. Aberdeen Royal Infirmary Annual Report, 1935.
5. The Scottish National Blood Transfusion Association was formally constituted on 5 March 1940.
6. Cruickshank, John (see note 11 of Chapter 13).
7. Campbell, John S. (1919–63), MRCS, LRCP. Trained at Westminster Hospital Medical

School and was deputy director of the Sheffield blood transfusion service. Appointed director of North-East Scotland regional service in 1956 in succession to John Cruickshank. In the words of Chairman Lady Baird his early death: '. . .will be a great loss to the region'. See *Aberdeen Press and Journal*, 5 January 1963. Campbell was succeeded by Brodie Lewis until 1983. Stanislaw Urbaniak is the current director.

Chapter 16

1. Anon (A citizen and burgess). *The Dioscope or Return for the 'Spectacles'*. J. Davidson and Co., Aberdeen, 1834.
2. Jack Fraser was dispenser to the ARI 1927–46; Neil Kinniburgh 1947–64 and Graham Calder 1965–71 were chief pharmacists. With the appointment of Kenneth Stewart, 1972–81, the title changed to chief administrative pharmaceutical officer and the current CAPO is Arthur Williams.

Chapter 17

1. Neil Pedelty who came to ARI from the Royal Hospital for Sick Children, Edinburgh.
2. Crooks, James (1920–83), MB ChB 1951, MD Glasgow. An NCO in the Royal Corps of Signals he went to Singapore in 1940 with the 18th Division. Prisoner of war for four years at Changi Prison and was forced to work on the Burma railway. Later, after graduating in medicine, he trained under Professor Sir Edward Payne at the Western Infirmary Glasgow before becoming senior lecturer in materia medica and therapeutics at Aberdeen 1960–9. Thereafter professor of pharmacology and therapeutics at Dundee. When in Aberdeen he initiated SAFUR – a computer based follow-up register for thyroid disease in Scotland – an indication of his early advocacy of computers in medicine. CBE 1983. See *Aberdeen Postgraduate Medical Bulletin* 1983; May, 38–9; *British Medical Journal* 1983; **1**: 312.
3. Roy Weir was professor of community medicine 1969–90. The department has endured a number of changes in title from social medicine to community medicine and is currently public health.
4. Scottish Home and Health Department. Standardization of Hospital Medical Records. HMSO, Edinburgh, 1973.
5. Wilson, L.A., Petrie, J.C., Dawson, A.A., Marron, A.C. The new Aberdeen medical record. *British Medical Journal* 1978; **2**: 414–5.
6. Designed by Ken Ewen, the current Records Manager.

Chapter 18

1. Helen I.J. Chalmers, BSc.
2. Minutes relating to the Institution of the Aberdeen Infirmary and Lunatic Asylum 1739–42. Copied from the original 'register' of the Infirmary.
3. At 10 p.m. on 6 July 1988 there was an explosion on oil platform *Piper Alpha*, situated in the North Sea about 100 miles east of Aberdeen with 226 persons on board. The initial combustion was from the ignition of natural gas resulting in further conflagration and total destruction of the oilrig. The biggest disaster in the history of offshore oil extraction, there were only 62 survivors of whom one later died in hospital – these were evacuated by the emergency rescue and medical services to the Accident and Emergency Department at ARI. In the aftermath, survivors were visited at

Foresterhill by the Prince and Princess of Wales and the Prime Minister. There was a public memorial service a week later in the City's 'mither kirk' the Church of St Nicholas – an occasion of public grief the magnitude of which touched not only the people of Aberdeen but the whole nation. See Department of Energy. The Public Enquiry into the Piper Alpha Disaster. The Hon Lord Cullen. C.M. 1310; vols 1 and 2. HMSO, Britain, 1991.

4. Sowens (see note 36 of Chapter 2).
5. A particular form of dark beer brewed from malt, often lightly charred, and rather bitter.
6. Nightingale, Florence. *Notes on Nursing – what it is and what it is not*. Harrison and Sons, London 1860.
7. Grant, Margaret, BSc. Dietitian to ARI 1932–5.
8. Thomson, Maisie (see note 42 of Chapter 10).
9. It was not to end before the early 1950s and caused the catering staff of ARI enormous difficulties. Miss Moira Anderson, MBE, a niece of Sir Alexander Anderson (see note 59 of Chapter 10) and appointed catering officer at ARI in 1946, recalls there were five dining rooms: doctors, sisters, nurses, maids and porters – all with different menus. For patients there were 12 insulated trolleys to convey meals from the kitchen to the wards – a slow process slightly improved when the number of trolleys was doubled. This allowed one trolley each for the male and female ends of the wards.
10. MacFarlane, Mary. Suffered from heart disease which limited her mobility. She supervised diabetic out-patient nutrition until her death in 1978.
11. Macgregor, Alastair (see note 43 of Chapter 10).
12. John Stowers was appointed to a personal clinical chair of diabetes and endocrinology in 1979. He retired in 1984.
13. Christine Adamson resigned after nine months and was followed in 1968 by Hazel Coubrough (now Witte) who is still in post.
14. The first speech therapist to be appointed to ARI was Miss Edna J. Jackson, MA, in 1946. This initiative was lost with the advent of the NHS.
15. Mrs Madeline Miller.

Chapter 19

1. Stephenson, W. Quoted in the *Daily Free Press*, 28 October 1880.
2. Millar, W.M. Early days of the Aberdeen Medical Society. In: Milne, G.P. (ed.) *Aberdeen Medico-Chirurgical Society: A Bicentennial History*. Aberdeen University Press, 1989, p.1–17. See also Douglas, A.S. The chair of medicine – past and future. *Aberdeen University Review* 1971; **44**: 121–36.
3. Both parishes are off the strath (valley) of the River Dee, east of Braemar. They were fertile and reasonably prosperous but are now, in their upper reaches, almost uninhabited. For an interesting account of Glengairn at the turn of the 19th century see Stewart-Fraser, Amy. *The Hills of Home*. Routledge and Kegan Paul, London, 1973.
4. Keith, A. *A Thousand Years of Aberdeen*. Aberdeen University Press, 1972 and 1980.
5. Marischal Chair of Medicine. Founded in 1700. The first occupant was Patrick Chalmers. See Mitchell, G.A.G. The medical history of Aberdeen and its universities. *Aberdeen University Review* 1958; **37**: 225–38.
6. McGrigor, James (see note 17 of Chapter 9).
7. Recommendations for admission of students. Minute Book Aberdeen Infirmary, 21 May 1751.
8. Rules for conduct. Minute Book Aberdeen Infirmary, 15 November 1754.
9. John Gregory and David Skene. For biographical details see: Comrie, J.D. The early medical school at Aberdeen. In: *History of Scottish Medicine*. Balliere Tindall and Cox, London, 1932; vol. 1, pp.365–95.

10. William Livingstone and George French (see Chapter 2, p.29).
11. Clinical lectures course. Minute Book Aberdeen Royal Infirmary, 18 September 1786. See also *Aberdeen Journal*, 23 October 1786.
12. Skene lectures in anatomy. See *Aberdeen Medico-Chirurgical Society: A Bicentennial History*. Milne, G.P. (ed.) Aberdeen University Press, 1989, pp.71–82.
13. Minute Book Aberdeen Royal Infirmary, 16 June and 8 July 1800.
14. Bulloch, J.M. *A History of the University of Aberdeen 1495–1895*. Hodder & Stoughton, London, 1895.
15. Graham, H.G. *Social Life in Scotland in the Eighteenth Century*. Adam and Charles Black, London, 1950, p.478.
16. See Mitchell, G.A.G. The medical history of Aberdeen and its universities. *Aberdeen University Review* 1958; **37**: 237.
17. Anon. A Letter to the Managers of the Aberdeen Infirmary on the Present State of that Institution and of the Medical School of Aberdeen. Printed by John Davidson and Co., Aberdeen, 1830.
18. Anon. A Pair of Spectacles for the Magistrates and Public wherewith to view the State of Our Infirmary with some account of the State of the Medical School (so called) of this City. Printed by John Davidson and Co., Aberdeen, 1833.
19. Anon (A citizen and Burgess). The Dioscope or Return for the 'Spectacles'. John Davidson and Co., Aberdeen, 1834.
20. *Regulations of the Royal Infirmary of Aberdeen 1838*. D. Chalmers and Co., Aberdeen, 1838.
21. Royal Commission on Medical Education. For a detailed account, see Hamilton, D. *The Healers: A history of medicine in Scotland*. Canongate, Edinburgh, 1981.
22. Kilgour, Alexander (see note 6 of Chapter 6).
23. Anon (A Citizen). A letter to Alexander Kilgour Esq, containing some strictures on his speech . . . on the subject of University Union. A. and R. Milne, Aberdeen, 1855.
24. Henderson, William (1793–1877), AM Marischal College 1809, MD 1813 Edinburgh. Lecturer in Materia Medica at Marischal College before the Union of King's and Marischal in 1860. Thereafter an examiner in medicine. Inherited the estate of Caskieben (lower Donside) in 1863 on the death of his brother but continued to reside at 49 Schoolhill. See Rodger, Ella H.B. *Aberdeen Doctors*. Blackwood and Sons, Edinburgh 1893: 289; *Aberdeen Daily Free Press*, 1 May 1877:4.
25. Infirmary Subcommittee on Medical Education. Report on clinical teaching in the hospital with letters from medical and surgical staff, 13 April 1864. George Cornwall and Sons, Printers, Aberdeen.
26. Minutes of the Court of the Hospital, 7 April 1864.
27. Biography of these individuals will be found as follows: Hay, Matthew (see note 1 of Chapter 4); Marnoch, John (see note 33 of Chapter 7); Mackintosh, Ashley (see note 10 of Chapter 6).
    Crombie, James E. (1861–1932), MA 1882, LLD 1907 Aberdeen. Son of John Crombie (Marischal College 1933–4) of the firm Messrs John J. Crombie, Grandholm. Aberdeen University Rector's assessor 1900–8. Chancellor's assessor 1913–32. Donor of the pavilion at King's College sports field and a generous benefactor of the Joint Hospital Scheme. Commemorated by the Crombie-Ross Hall in the Foresterhill Nurses' Home and a plaque in the original surgical pavilion. See *Aberdeen University Review* 1932; **20**: 37.
    Jaffrey, Thomas (1861–1953). Born Aberdeen. Entered the North of Scotland Bank (now part of the Clydesdale) aged 16 years. Later became Actuary of Aberdeen Savings Bank. Founded chair of political economy at Aberdeen University. Also donated generously to the building of Aberdeen Maternity Hospital. Rector's assessor on the University court 1924–37. Generous chairman of Aberdeen Art Gallery Committee 1928–51. Freeman of the City of Aberdeen. His portrait by Sir William Orpen is in Aberdeen Art Gallery. Knighted 1920. 1st Baronet 1931. LLD Aberdeen.
28. Dawson, Viscount of Penn. The Unity of the Medical Services. *Aberdeen University Review*, 1938; **26**: 4–9.

29. See *Aberdeen Bon Accord and Northern Pictorial*, 11 December 1936. The architects were Pite, Son and Fairweather (see note 3 of Chapter 5).
30. Davidson, Stanley (1904–81), MB ChB (Hons) Edinburgh 1919. Born at Huntly Lodge (now a hotel). His medical studies were interrupted by World War I when he served as a captain in the Gordon Highlanders. Severely wounded in 1915 he was discharged in 1917. Regius professor Aberdeen 1930–8. Professor of medicine Edinburgh 1938–59. Knighted 1955. '. . .a brilliant if flamboyant lecturer and an inspiring leader'.

    HAFD remembers him as a man for all seasons and a foil to his colleague from Aberdeen, James Learmonth. Davidson would stop the young in the quadrangle and ask for the latest update in the field – thus saving himself the need to read the literature. Well known for his textbook which evolved from his lecture notes in Aberdeen and Edinburgh and which persists to this day. See *Aberdeen Postgraduate Medical Bulletin* 1982; January, 41; *British Medical Journal* 1981; **283**: 993, 1131; *Lancet* 1981; **2**: 819.
31. Learmonth, James (see note 45 of Chapter 7).
32. Campbell, David (1889–1978), MB ChB (Hons) Glasgow 1916. Born in Patna (Ayr) and was a distinguished student at Ayr academy. After graduation served in France and was awarded the MC. Thereafter studied in Glasgow and at Johns Hopkins, and came to Aberdeen in 1930 as Regius professor, a post he held until his retirement in 1959. Dean of the Faculty 1932–59. President General Medical Council 1949–61 – an office he seemed to discharge without any reference to the bureaucracy which invests the post today and with a minimum of fuss. Knighted 1953. See *Aberdeen Postgraduate Medical Bulletin* 1979; January, 31; *Lancet* 1978; **1**: 1373; *British Medical Journal* 1979; **2**: 61; *Times* 15 June 1978.
33. University Grants Committee Review 1981. The role of this body was to make recommendations to the Treasury for individual university funding following regular inspections and reviews. It was superceded by the Universities' Funding Council in 1989.

Chapter 20

1. Shaw, G.B. *Man and Superman. Maxims for Revolutionists. Reason.* Constable and Co., London, 1934, Prefaces, p.193.
2. National Health Service Re-organisation Act. HMSO, Britain, 1973.
3. Griffiths Report. Sir Roy Griffiths, deputy chairman of Sainsburys, was invited by the government to become chairman of an enquiry into management within the NHS in 1983. A result of this was the publication of: *Community care: agenda for action*. HMSO, Britain, 1988.
4. NHS and Community Care Act. HMSO, Britain, 1990.
5. These terms embrace one of the current contentious issues following on the 1990 Act which gives the opportunity for a large hospital organization such as the Foresterhill complex to remain under the conventional structure from the SHHD and the Region (Grampian Health Board) as a directly managed unit (DMU) or to 'opt out' and become a Trust with a relatively independent management and possibly more flexible opportunities to exploit its special skills within a 'market economy'. In the closing days of 1991 Trust status was in fact granted by the Secretary of State for Scotland.

Index